american agriculture:

GEOGRAPHY,

RESOURCES,

CONSERVATION

New York · John Wiley & Sons, Inc.
London · Chapman & Hall, Ltd.

to Florence and Joan

companions on well-remembered journeys

preface

This book is a study of the agricultural regions of the United States and of selected farms which illustrate wise use and conservation of their resources. It is written for those who seek a systematic survey of American agriculture. I have in mind, particularly, students of the agricultural sciences, vocational agriculture, conservation, and geography.

The basic resources of agriculture are soils, plants, and water. As would be expected, there are remarkable regional differences in the quality and quantity of these essentials in a country as diverse in climate and surface relief as the United States. Such inexact terms as Wheat Belt and Cotton Belt express popular recognition of these differences and of the systems of farming developed to use them.

In the pages which follow we will be concerned with the reasons lying behind regional distinctions. We will also discover why farmers in various parts of the country specialize as they do and why the rules and practices of conservation change. The sharpest contrasts in our agricultural systems are those which distinguish practices of the humid East from those of the dry West. The text is divided accordingly.

The problems of western farmers are focused upon water; therefore it dominates the chapters dealing with the West. There is no such central theme for a discussion of farming in the humid East. Soils, surface relief, and climate combine in many ways to influence eastern farm organization and conservation. This is not to suggest that these same factors are insignificant in the West, but there they are overshadowed by the tyrant water.

The cartography which is so essential to the presentation in this book represents the combined efforts of many skillful persons. I am particularly grateful to Professor Guy H. Burnham under whose genial guidance it was performed. The majority of the original figures as well as the most intricate were drawn by Rebecca Alberg with evident finesse. She is a master of the art. Other illustrations were ably drawn by Robert Duffy, John Loughlin, Martin Gustavson, John Bley, Charles Lindberg, and Betty Vanderbilt.

Maps of individual farms and discussions of their management are an important feature of the book. I have visited all of them, walked across their fields, and observed the good management of their operators. These farms, as well as hundreds of others in all parts of the country which I have visited in recent years, have helped to formulate the judgments concerning the conservation problems and objectives that are discussed. In making a choice of field plans with which to illustrate the text I tried to be mindful of how well each farm reflects the character of its area.

In the preparation of the text I have benefited by the excellent suggestions and criticisms of Professors Richard J. Lougee, Clarence W. Olmstead, and Henry J. Warman. To the agencies of the United States Department of Agriculture and to the authors and publishers of quoted material I am grateful. Time and financial support, so essential to reflection and writing, were generously provided by the Graduate School of Geography of Clark University and by the Libby Fund.

EDWARD HIGBEE

University of Delaware
April 1958

contents

part one

land
resources
and
their
use

1

Against an inventory of the world's agricultural resources and of humanity's need for food, the abundance which we enjoy in the United States seems unbelievable. Britain produces more wheat per acre than we do, Egypt more cotton per acre, Japan more rice per acre. Yet the people of those countries are neither so well fed nor so well clothed as we are. This is partly because they have fewer tillable acres per capita than we do and because their costs of production in terms of manpower are higher than ours. Their agricultural production per capita and per farmer is lower. When it comes to labor efficiency, aided by mechanized equipment, we surpass all others. We have more tractors and self-propelled farm machines than there are in all other countries of the world. Economically, our primary concern is surplus production, whereas most of the world is hungry and poorly clothed.

Part of our good fortune is a geographical accident. Part is the remarkable amount of capital that we have invested in agricultural production for the individual consumer. Not all arable land is provided by nature; much is man made. We not only have an unusual supply of good land, but we have spent an enormous amount of money to develop it and to acquire the machines needed to work it efficiently. Also important is the fact that our human population is low compared with the wealth of our resources. The United States occupies only 6 per cent of the world's land surface, yet within our forty-eight states is 18 per cent of the arable acres of the earth. This advantage is even more significant when we consider that we are only about 7 per cent of the world's total population. With reference to the entire globe, we possess three times the average amount of tillable soil per capita. The major part of this endowment was nature's gift, but to it we have added much tillable land by irrigation, drainage, and application of modern soil technology. Because we have so much good land per citizen and can cultivate it so cheaply in terms of manpower we have a very high ratio of production per farmer and per consumer.

THE AMOUNT OF LAND

Wide differences distinguish the capacities of nations to produce food. Twenty-five per cent of the continental United States is arable land, capable of yielding fruits, grains, and vegetables. Thirty-eight per cent of France may thus be used, 30 per cent of India, 64 per cent of Denmark, 10 per cent of Russia. But Chile's endowment of arable earth falls to 5 per cent of her total expanse, Canada's to 4 per cent, Norway's to 3 per cent, and Iceland's to one half of one per cent. Obviously our worldly Eden is of unequal fruitfulness.

Calculation of how much land is suited to the plow sheds little light on a nation's well-being. More to the point is the amount of good land per citizen. How well does it yield? In terms of arable earth per capita only a few countries equal or surpass our figure of 3 acres. That is as much space for each of us as an average city block and the streets around it. Each inhabitant of Iceland has the equivalent of the street paving in front of a 60-foot house lot. Canada, despite a low proportion of good land, has 6.7 acres per capita because her population is small. Russia has about 2.8 acres of cropland for every person, France, 1.2, Denmark, 1.6. India has only 0.9 and Norway, 0.6.

THE QUALITY OF LAND

What makes land sterile or fertile, useful or useless? Not its area, but the nature of its land surface and the quality of its soils. The prevailing climate conditions land use. Beyond these physical controls are the controls of man's culture: his techniques, his economy, and the purposes of his agriculture. Is he a gardener raising his own subsistence while oblivious to hours of labor per acre, or is he a businessman farming for the channels of commerce, paying taxes, interest, wages, and rents? All these make a difference in appraising the suitability of space and the efficiency with which it is used. But what of the space itself?

Three quarters of the land of the United States is used in crop and animal husbandry. This includes 301 million acres of grazed woodland. The quality of this vast amount of land is highly variable. Some irrigated acres in the Southwest yield seven or eight tons of alfalfa hay annually. Some overgrazed range in the same area is practically worthless. But good or poor, by far the greater part of the land and most of our farm manpower is directly or indirectly devoted to animal husbandry. We are the largest population of heavy meat eaters and milk drinkers the world has ever known, and this is possible only because we have far more land than we need to support ourselves on a vegetarian diet. We are so richly endowed with productive soil that 66 million acres of our cropland are set aside for pasture. Even more significant, about 60 per cent of all our harvested cropland is used to supply feeds for domestic animals. In the use of space the United States is the realm not of man but of his domestic livestock. There is no prospect of human hunger in this nation for generations to come. We

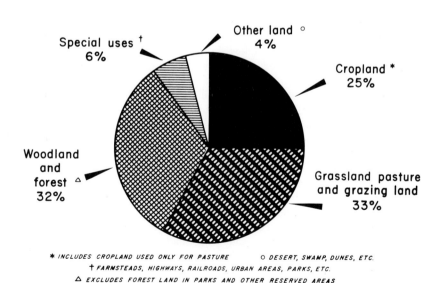

Figure 1:1. Major uses of land. (Source: U.S.D.A.)

Table 1:1. How Our Land is Used
(Source: Reference 4; p. 3)

Land use	Acreage Million acres	Percentage of total Per cent
Land used for crops, pasture, and forest		
Cropland used chiefly for crops		
Cropland harvested, failure, and fallow	380	20.0
Land in soil-improvement crops and idle cropland not harvested or pastured	19	1.0
Total[1]	399	21.0
Cropland used only for pasture	66	3.4
Total cropland available for crops	465	24.4
Pasture and grazing land, not cropland and not woodland	633	33.2
Woodland and forest[2]		
Pastured	301	15.8
Not pastured	314	16.5
Total	615	32.3
Special use[3]	110	5.8
Miscellaneous[4]	81	4.3
Grand total	1904	100.0

[1]Total cropland used chiefly for crops in 1954 includes cropland harvested (including crops, gardens, and orchards not otherwise reported and wild hay harvested); crop failure; summer fallow; cropland in soil-improvement and cover crops not harvested or pastured or used for another crop; and temporarily idle cropland.

[2]Woodland and forest, excluding 26 million acres withdrawn from primary forest use for parks and other special public-use areas, and duplications of 7 million acres with pasture (not woodland) reported by the 1954 Agricultural Census. The total woodland and forest area as of January 1, 1953, was approximately 648 million acres, according to the preliminary report of the U. S. Forest Service, Timber Resource Review, 1955.

[3]Urban and town areas, farmsteads and farm roads and lanes, highway and railroad rights-of-way, airports, parks, wildlife refuges, national-defense areas, flood-control areas, and other special-use areas.

[4]Includes miscellaneous unaccounted-for areas not among other uses, such as marshes, bare rock areas, deserts, sand dunes, and other lands which now generally have low value for agricultural purposes but which have social utility for wildlife and recreational use and potential value for minerals.

could support several times as many people as we do now if we ate no meat, eggs, or dairy products and used all our cropland to provide plant substances for direct human consumption.

If, however, future Americans are to have abundant quantities of animal products, some very important improvements must be made in our agriculture as time goes on. That is because the amount of cropland which we have today is not likely to increase very substantially. The United States Department of Agriculture has estimated that in 1975 we will have about 30 million more acres of cropland than we had in 1950. (Reference 3; p. 47.) Conversion of good pasture to cropland, new irrigation projects in the West, drainage and land-clearing projects in the East will create most of the new cropland. Meanwhile the Bureau of the Census has estimated that the human population of the United States may reach 210 millions by 1975. (Reference 5; p. 25.) While our population increases by two fifths, our cropland will increase by only one sixteenth. Since the area of our cropland cannot possibly keep pace with population growth, the productivity of our cropland will have to be increased or our diets will gradually become more vegetarian. As our population multiplies and the area of cropland per person is gradually reduced, a pressure against using cropland to support live-stock will develop, unless higher yields per acre keep pace with popula-tion growth. The United States Soil Conservation Service estimates that

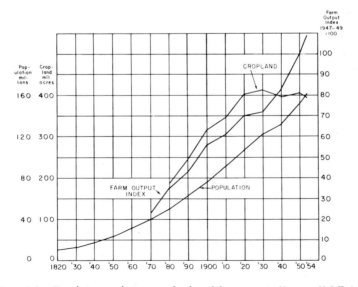

Figure 1:2. Trends in population, cropland, and farm output. (Source: U.S.D.A.)

Table 1:2. Major Uses of Cropland
(Source: Reference 4; pp. 15–16)

Item	1951–1953 Million acres	1954 Million acres	1955[1] Million acres
Food crops			
Food grains			
Wheat	66.7	54.3	47.2
Rice	2.0	2.5	1.8
Rye	1.5	1.7	2.1
Buckwheat	.2	.2	.1
Total food grains	70.4	58.7	51.2
Irish potatoes	1.4	1.4	1.4
Sweetpotatoes	.3	.3	.4
Dry beans	1.3	1.6	1.6
Dry peas	.3	.3	.3
Sugarcane for sugar and seed	.3	.3	.3
Sugar beets	.7	.9	.7
Sugarcane and sorgo sirup	.1	.1	.1
Peanuts for nuts	1.7	1.4	1.7
Soybeans for beans	14.2	17.0	18.6
Fruits and planted nuts[2]	4.8	4.5	4.5
Vegetables for fresh market and commercial processing	3.9	3.9	3.8
Farm gardens	2.6	2.4	2.4
Total food crops	102.0	92.8	87.0
Feed crops			
Feed grains			
Corn	80.8	80.3	80.0
Oats	38.1	42.3	40.9
Barley	8.8	13.2	14.3
Sorghums except sirup	12.3	18.1	20.9
Total feed grains	140.0	153.9	156.1
All hay			
Tame[3]	58.3	58.2	60.0
Wild	14.5	13.2	12.7
Total hay	72.8	71.4	72.7
Total feed crops	212.8	225.3	228.8
Other crops			
Cotton	25.6	19.2	16.9
Flaxseed	3.9	5.6	4.9
Tobacco	1.7	1.7	1.5
Minor crops[4]	1.1	1.0	1.2
Total other crops	32.3	27.5	24.5
Total 59 harvested crops[5]	339.7	338.7	333.3
Total 59 harvested crops, fruits, planted nuts, and farm gardens	347.1	345.6	340.3

[1] Preliminary.

[2] Includes tree fruits, small fruits, and planted nuts, as reported by the 1954 Census of Agriculture, and estimates of the Production Economics Research Branch of acreage in orchards having less than 20 fruit or nut trees.

[3] Excluding peanut-vine hay which is largely duplicated in peanuts picked or threshed.

[4] Broomcorn, cowpeas, sweetclover seed, and timothy seed.

[5] The acreage of the 59 principal crops excludes duplicated acreage in alfalfa, red clover, alsike clover, and lespedeza seeds, peanut-vine hay, and velvetbeans. Also not included are sweet corn for fresh market, some of the less important commercial vegetables (282,000 acres in 1952), hops, popcorn, cranberries, spelt, and various legumes and other crops harvested by livestock.

if all land which could be made suitable for continuous cropping were used for that purpose we would have only 604 million acres. (Reference 3; p. 101.)

Until about 1920 expansion of cropland acreage largely accounted for the increase in agricultural production needed to feed the growing population of our country. Since 1920 there has been very little increase in cropland. New land added by irrigation, drainage, and clearing has been offset by the retirement of old land because of soil erosion or other handicaps. Since 1920 increased productivity per acre of cropland has provided the food supply for our expanding population. It is this trend which must continue in the future.

Although there has been little net increase in the acreage of our cropland since 1915, the decline in the numbers of horses and mules since that time has had the same effect as the addition of 83 million acres of new cropland. (Reference 1; pp. 3–4.) This cropland once used to maintain horses and mules is producing food and fiber for human consumption. Our commodity surplus problem is very largely the result of the simultaneous release of these 83 million acres plus the improved productivity of most cropland which has occurred since 1920. In the future we cannot expect very large increases in cropland as the result of mechanization. Our horse and mule population is so small that only 10 million acres of cropland are used now to support it.

FOOD PRODUCTION AND DEMAND

If our human population had not been increasing at a rapid rate our surplus crop problem would be very much more serious than it is now. However, before the end of this century the people of the United States may look back upon this age of surplus as something of a freak. It is probable that by the year 2000 our population will have reached 300 millions. Because the amount of arable land is not likely to increase in proportion it is possible that within less than half a century there will be only 1.5 to 2 acres per capita, compared with 3 acres per capita.

For some years we have been able to ease the burden of surplus production by selling abroad, often at prices that are less than cost. We are exporting the produce from 40 to 50 million acres of cropland. There may come a time when we will need these commodities ourselves, and this cushion will be a comfortable one to fall back upon. However, our foreign shipments are sometimes an instrument of foreign policy, especially when we are able to relieve actual hunger or famine abroad. Not to have surpluses that might be used to our diplomatic advantage may prove even more troublesome than our efforts to dispose of foods

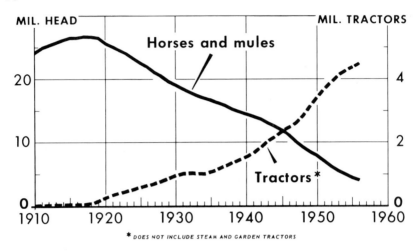

MIL. HEAD

Horses and mules

MIL. TRACTORS

20

4

10

2

Tractors*

0
1910   1920   1930   1940   1950   1960

0

*DOES NOT INCLUDE STEAM AND GARDEN TRACTORS

Figure 1:3. Horses and mules and tractors on farms. (Source: U.S.D.A.)

and fibers we do not need. The production of reasonable current surpluses and the stockpiling of moderate surpluses of past seasons is worth the price of federal purchase, storage, and disposal.

Never was there a time when it was not desirable to have more rather than less of the prerequisites for living. No man before or since the biblical seven years of plenty and seven years of famine has preferred scarcity to surplus. Modern techniques are not so refined that we can tailor farm production precisely to our needs. The vicissitudes of climate cannot be tamed any more successfully in our day than in the time of Joseph, although to some extent they can be counteracted. We have the choice of fostering a healthy, growing, and improving agriculture or of stifling it. Both for the nation and for the individual it is better and cheaper to be assured of too much rather than face the risk of too little. We need only recall the unsavory and costly nature of wartime black markets to realize what our predicament would be if our farmers could not meet our needs with food to spare. Cornering markets is still a pleasant game for the speculator. Nothing works more to his advantage than scarcity.

HOW OUR LAND IS USED

If we are to have a more productive agriculture as the means to maintain our present diet while our population increases, we should take a closer look at how our land is used. It is our program of land use which

Table 1:3. Classes of Grazing Lands
(Source: Reference 3; p. 25)

Region	Pasture in Farms				Grazing Land Not in Farms		
	Cropland Used for Pasture 1,000 Acres	Open Permanent Pasture 1,000 Acres	Woodland Pasture 1,000 Acres	Total 1,000 Acres	Open Grazing 1,000 Acres	Woodland Grazing 1,000 Acres	Total 1,000 Acres
Northeastern	3,697	6,550	4,123	14,370	—	2,650	2,650
North Central							
Corn Belt	14,939	16,563	13,014	44,516	—	5,300	5,300
Lake States	5,730	6,151	9,918	21,799	—	6,200	6,200
Northern Plains	4,672	71,326	2,267	78,265	5,729	800	6,529
Total	25,341	94,040	25,199	144,580	5,729	12,300	18,029
Southern							
Appalachian	11,725	9,493	7,670	28,888	—	11,950	11,950
Southeast	4,303	6,776	16,578	27,657	—	25,615	25,615
Mississippi Delta	5,880	5,017	9,532	20,429	1,000	27,120	28,120
Southern Plains	8,960	85,062	35,609	129,631	9,000	6,700	15,700
Total	30,868	106,348	69,389	206,605	10,000	71,385	81,385
Mountain	4,212	179,696	23,663	207,571	168,165	59,200	227,365
Pacific	5,214	29,015	12,341	46,570	31,535	39,200	70,735
United States	69,332	415,649	134,715	619,696	215,429	184,735	400,164

Note. There is a slight discrepancy between the figures in this table, published in 1955, and the figures in Table 1:1, published in 1957.

yields our abundant supplies of meat and dairy products. Approximately one quarter of the land area of the United States, 465 million acres, is cropland. One half of our country, 1000 million acres, is used as range and pasture. What are the actual values of cropland compared with the more extensive grazing areas? Cropland supplies not only grains, fruits, vegetables, and other crops needed for direct human consumption, but it also provides about 78 per cent of our livestock feeds. We have so much cropland that 66 million acres are used as pasture. These acres are also so productive that they supply half as much forage as 934 million acres of true grazing land. Despite their vast extent pastures and ranges supply only 22 per cent of our livestock feed. The possibilities of increasing the productivity of these grazing lands will one day be a matter of considerable concern. But we shall do well if we can increase the feed yield of these inferior acres at a rate equal to that of our population increase.

As the foregoing chart indicates, nearly 320 million acres of grazing land are wooded. Although there are some exceptions to the rule, the use of woodlands as grazing areas is normally considered neither good forestry nor good animal husbandry. Trees and grass are ecological rivals. Usually, situations which are best for one are not good for the other. Thus the use of woodlands as pasture, whether on private farms or in national forests, is something of an anachronism in an age well advanced in understanding the natural principles of land use. We cannot expect much increase in the forage value of woodlands. According to the Bureau of Land Management, the federal range, which constitutes the bulk of the 215 million acres of open grazing land listed in Table 1:3, has an average annual production of only 70 pounds of grass, dry weight, per acre. (Reference 2; p. 4.) One hundred acres of such land is required to maintain a single beef cow and her calf.

Federal range, national forests, and all other nonfarm lands which are used for grazing provide only 11.3 per cent of the feed value obtained from pastures in the United States. Since all pastures, including cropland used as pasture, yield only one third of the feeds consumed by domestic livestock, the 400 million acres of nonfarm grazing lands account for only 3.8 per cent of our livestock feed supply. Even the very best management of these lands would not greatly augment the nation's capacity to maintain livestock.

It is quite obvious that the major task of pasture improvement will fall upon the farmers who own the remaining 60 per cent of the nation's pasture and range. Less than half of these private lands are capable of substantial improvement, for most of them are either in the dry areas of the West, where precipitation is a limiting factor, or they are wood-

**Table 1:4. Feed Production on Pasture and
Grazing Land, 1949–1950**
(Source: Reference 3; p. 27)

Classes of Pasture	Acreage 1950	Yield per Acre in Feed Units[1]	Total Production in Feed Units[1]	Percentage of Feed by Classes of Pasture
	Thousand Acres	Pounds	Million Pounds	Per cent
Pasture in Farms				
Cropland used only for pasture	69,332	985	68,322	33.1
Open permanent pasture	415,649	199	82,634	40.0
Woodland pasture	134,715	115	15,462	7.5
Aftermath pasture	85,000	196	16,692	8.1
Land in farms used for pasture, excluding aftermath pasture	619,696	269	166,418	80.6
Grazing land not in farms	400,164	58	23,258	11.3
Total pasture and grazing land[2]	1,019,860	186	189,676	91.9
Total pasture feed production	1,104,860	187	206,368	100.0

[1] A feed unit is equivalent to 1 pound of corn in feeding value.
[2] Exclusive of 85,000 acres of aftermath pasture.

lands in the East. Some of the most suitable woodland tracts in humid areas may, of course, be cleared, limed, fertilized, and brought into a very productive condition. Such a trend is prominent in the southeastern states.

Upon analysis it becomes clear that our truly good grazing lands are not more than one quarter of the total. Funds expended upon improving them would seem to be wisely and safely invested. Every reasonable and economical effort should be made to improve the western range, but it is well to recognize the limitations of that dry region. Although there has been a trend toward permanent pasture improvement in the humid eastern states the western range, taken in its entirety, has continued to deteriorate. As matters stand, it would seem that we are relying upon our 3 acres of cropland per capita to supply not only the grains, fruits, vegetables, and other crops needed for direct human consumption but

Table 1:5.   How Cropland Was Used In 1954
(Source: Reference 4; p. 10)

Land Use	Acreage Million Acres	Percentage of Total Per Cent
Cropland used for crops		
Harvested	338	73
Crop failure	13	3
Summer fallow	29	6
Total	380	82
Cropland used for pasture	66	14
Other cropland [1]	19	4
Grand total	465	100

[1] Other cropland includes idle cropland and the acreage in cover and soil-improvement crops not harvested or pastured and not plowed under and used for another crop during the crop year.

also for about 78 per cent of our livestock products.   What are the details of cropland management?

In 1954 we had 465 million acres of cropland.   As we have previously noted, 66 million acres were used as pasture, chiefly in rotation with harvested crops.   Twenty-nine million acres, principally in the subhumid Great Plains, were fallowed in order to accumulate soil moisture for the succeeding season.   In other words, there are about 58 million acres which can be utilized only every other year, as the moisture of two seasons is required to produce one crop.   The amount of cropland fallowed in this manner will probably increase in future years, for this is an economical method of reducing losses caused by drought.   The United States is by no means immune to crop failure.   An average of 10 million acres is lost every year and never harvested.   During times of excessive drought these losses are substantially greater.   Approximately 30 million acres are left idle or are planted to soil-improvement crops which are plowed under. In the future, as the value of our agricultural produce increases with an increasing population, we will not let good land lie idle, and we will use methods of adding green-manure crops which will not deprive us of a season's harvest.

Since three quarters of the land area of the United States is employed agriculturally, what of the remaining quarter, or 505 million acres?   The largest portion, 314 million acres, is ungrazed woodland.   This is a small area when we consider that forests were once dominant over more than half of the land area of the nation.   We are still cutting virgin forests in the western states, particularly in the Pacific Northwest, but we harvest more sawtimber than we are growing. It is quite probable that as our population increases and as the demand for lumber rises accordingly the value of timber will augment greatly. We are aware of the substantial increase in the value of lumber during the past two decades. Tree farming has already become an attractive form of investment, particularly in the Southeast where land is cheap and pine grows rapidly. Although we may expect some woodland in use as pasture to be completely cleared of timber in order to establish good sod, we may also expect livestock to be entirely excluded from other substantial areas of woodland in order to increase the growth, quality, and numbers of trees.

Eighty-one million acres of this country are barren rock, open marsh, sand dunes, and desert. Some of these areas have great recreational value, and others, particularly the marshes, are the habitat of wildlife we wish to maintain. For the most part their best use is their present use. The remaining 110 million acres of the United States are chiefly devoted to human habitation, roads, and business sites. These are the urbanized areas and the roads which link them. The land employed for these purposes is increasing at the rate of approximately one million acres annually. This does not seem like much, but over a span of years it can be highly significant, especially as much of this land must be subtracted from crop production. Most of our cities are located in areas adjacent to agricultural land. Consequently, the explosion of the modern city into showers of suburban satellites is consuming some of our best farms. In most cases the farmer himself is glad to sell out to the encroaching city. Sufficient capital gain often provides lifetime retirement. The suburbanite is delighted to escape congestion. In parts of the heavily industrialized Northeast and in southern California this process of human glaciation is most advanced. Unlike the Pleistocene glaciers of nature, the human variety is not likely to retreat so long as man inhabits the earth. The time may come when urban encroachment upon productive cropland will be a general problem similar to that of accumulating cemetaries which have been considered a factor in China's inability to feed herself adequately.

REFERENCES

1. Anderson, James R., *Future Need for Agricultural Land Resources in the United States*, U.S. Department of Agriculture, Washington, D.C., December 1, 1956 (mimeographed).
2. Bureau of Land Management, *Rebuilding the Federal Range*, U.S. Department of the Interior, Government Printing Office, Washington, D.C., 1951.

3. Wooten, Hugh H., and James R. Anderson, *Agricultural Land Resources in the United States*, Agricultural Information Bulletin No. 140, Government Printing Office, Washington, D.C., 1955.

4. ———, *Major Uses of Land in the United States, Summary for 1954*, Agricultural Information Bulletin No. 168, Government Printing Office, Washington, D.C., 1957.

5. U.S. Bureau of the Census, *Revised Projections of the Population of the United States, by Age and Sex. 1960 to 1975*, Series No. 123, Government Printing Office, Washington, D.C., 1956.

climate
and
agriculture

2

Among natural influences upon an area's suitability for agriculture climate is primary. To a major extent man can improve the quality of soils if they are at all tillable. Against the impositions of climate and its daily variant, the weather, he is severely handicapped. He can, at considerable effort, assure himself of a dependable water supply by irrigation. But, generally, where rainfall is scant, water for irrigation is limited. The average length of the frost-free season of any particular place on the earth's surface is beyond modification by man, although with smudge pots and greenhouses he can insulate small acreages. One of the basic features of agriculture is the fact that it is conducted out-of-doors and thus is subject to all the vicissitudes of weather which may one year combine to produce a bumper harvest and the next year, by drought, flood, hail, or unseasonable frost, usher in calamity. Because it is impossible to predict what the weather will be during a coming season the planting of every crop is somewhat of a gamble. In addition to a direct influence upon crops, weather and climate also help to suppress or encourage beneficial or parasitic insects and microorganisms. Both the field work that the farmer must do and the time at which he does it are determined as much by the weather as by the crop itself.

Every farmer knows what the climate or average weather conditions in his region may be, but he also knows that those averages may be derived from the sums of slight or very wide deviations from the norm. The greater the deviation both above and below the norm, the more likely that the harvests will vary in quantity and in quality. There are parts of the United States in which the deviations are minimal and the possibilities are small of crop failure due to weather variations. The coastal valleys of the Pacific Northwest are fortunate in this regard. Other regions, such as the western portion of the Great Plains, experience wide annual fluctuations above and below long-time averages. Almost any very large area of the earth's surface has a number of climatic regions. If it is as large as the United States, spanning the full width of a continent, if it has mountain ranges interspersed with valleys and plains, if it is partially bounded by seas and extends over many degrees of latitude, then its climatic regions are many. Such multiplicity of climates can be a tremendous asset.

The southern tip of Florida is a truly subtropical zone. In northern Maine even the summers are cool—an excellent condition for potato culture. The variety of this country's crop production is a direct reflection of a rich climatic repertoire. Not only have we climates suitable for many types of crop and livestock husbandry, but the United States is so large that occasional crop losses in one section are generally compensated by normal production elsewhere. It is safe to predict that in any particular year essential demands will be fulfilled even though crops fail in some regions. If this were a small country in a location of considerable weather variability, it would be much more vulnerable. The costs of famine definitely exceed the costs of surplus production.

EVAPOTRANSPIRATION

All agricultural activity depends fundamentally upon plant growth. This growth requires a larger moisture supply in dry, hot regions than in those that are humid and cool. The additional moisture requirement is the result of greater moisture losses through transpiration. High temperatures, strong winds, and low relative humidity operate to increase transpiration losses. Not only do the water requirements of plants become greater with increasing atmospheric heat and aridity, but losses of soil moisture by evaporation at the surface of the ground also increase. Thus the supply of water available to a plant usually decreases under

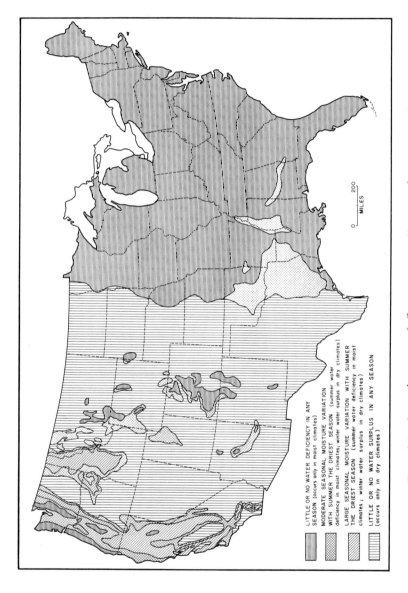

Figure 2:1. Seasonal variation of effective moisture. (Source: Reference 6; p. 94.)

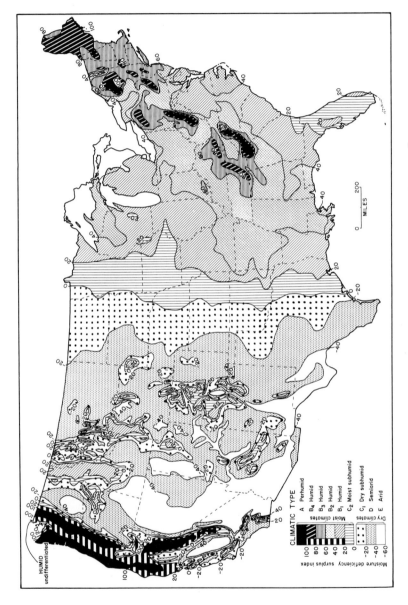

Figure 2·2.   Moisture regions in the United States. (Source: Reference 6; p. 94.)

the very conditions which increase the plant's need for water. To obtain equivalent yields of sugar beets more moisture must be supplied by irrigation in southwestern Arizona than is available by natural precipitation in southern Michigan.

When considering climatic factors in relation to agriculture it is impossible to ignore the combined effects of both transpiration and evaporation, or *evapotranspiration* as the combined processes may be called. By calculations which take into account mean monthly temperatures and day length (a function of latitude) it is possible to divide the land surfaces of the earth into regions characterized according to the approximate water requirements of plants. Thornthwaite, refers to the optimum water requirements of plants in a given region as its *potential evapotranspiration*, or P.E. (Reference 5; p. 633–655.) For instance, he has shown that in the United States the average water requirement, or PE, varies from 60 inches in sections of the southwestern desert to 18 inches in the higher altitudes of the Rocky Mountains and the Sierra Nevada.

Some places, of course, receive more precipitation than is needed, and other places receive less than the optimum. Because plants need water in greatest quantity during the summer growing season, it is possible for a region to have an adequate annual precipitation and yet be somewhat water-deficient in summer. The Willamette Valley in Oregon, the Alabama Black Belt, and the Mississippi "Delta" between Memphis and Natchez are examples.

In areas of deficient summer precipitation soil-moisture reserves, accumulated during the winter, may fully compensate for the temporary deficiency. Therefore, Thornthwaite has devised a formula for calculating a moisture index which considers precipitation as well as the ability of the soil to store water in periods of surplus precipitation for use by plants in periods of precipitation deficiency. A map based upon such moisture-index calculations divides the United States into nine climatic regions. Six of these regions have an average moisture surplus. Three regions have an average moisture deficiency. By the use of this map a farmer can determine moisture conditions for plant growth in his area for the *average* year. The map's zero lines divide areas of moist climate from those which have a perennial moisture deficiency. Where there is moisture deficiency, optimum yields are impossible without irrigation.

THE CLIMATE MAKERS

Regional climates and the daily weather are the product of many influences. Some, like mountains, seas, latitude, and polar ice, are fixed. Others, such as the movement of winds, atmospheric pressure, ocean currents, and the angles of the sun's rays, are variable. The earth's inclination toward the sun is in constant change as it follows regularly its daily and seasonal rhythms. With all of these influences exerting themselves, it is for good reason that climate varies from place to place and that weather varies from day to day. To the farmer the length of the growing season and the quantities of moisture available to his crops are of most concern. These are likely to be more variable where the land lies distant from the sea and where drought, hail, and unseasonable frosts may be the by-product of shifting air-mass movements.

Sources of Moisture. Essentially, all water cast upon the land comes originally from the sea. The interiors of continents are commonly dry or subject to drought, for they are so distant from the oceans that moisture-bearing air bodies may not reach them regularly. Yet proximity to the sea is not in itself assurance of adequate rainfall, as southern Californians in the path of subsiding and diverging air currents are aware.

In the middle latitudes cool ocean currents flow along the western shores of all the continents. On-shore winds blowing across these currents in summer are cool, relative to the temperatures of the continent. Thus in their landward passage these winds are warmed and so absorb moisture rather than discharge it. In winter the conditions are somewhat reversed.

The relationship of sea to land in the eastern United States is somewhat different. Warm ocean currents from the equatorial zone flow along the Atlantic and Gulf coasts. This is the rule in the lower and middle latitudes on the eastern margins of all the continents. Moisture-laden, landward winds passing from the warm seas over the eastern states precipitate considerable moisture upon the coastal areas and in the higher portions of the Appalachian Mountains. As a general rule, the farther these tropical, marine air masses progress toward the interior of the United States, the less moisture remains to be released. Then, too, as they pass northward their course veers generally to the east under the influence of westerly winds. Under these circumstances prolonged droughts are much less frequent along the eastern gulf and ocean seaboard than in the interior regions. Heavier rains are more likely to occur in the south-central states than in the north-central states.

The mid-continental plains, stretching between the Appalachians and the Rockies and from the Rio Grande to the Canadian border, are divided into a drier western section and a more humid eastern section. In the average year not enough moisture-bearing winds pass northwestward from the Gulf of Mexico to make cultivation without fallowing or irrigation a safe practice in the Texas panhandle or in the western portions of Oklahoma, Kansas, Nebraska, and the Dakotas. On the

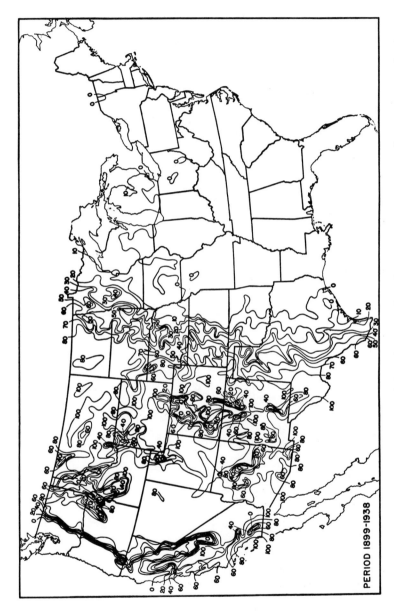

PERIOD 1899-1938

Figure 2:3. Per cent of years with less than 20 inches of precipitation. (Source: Reference 8; p. 721.)

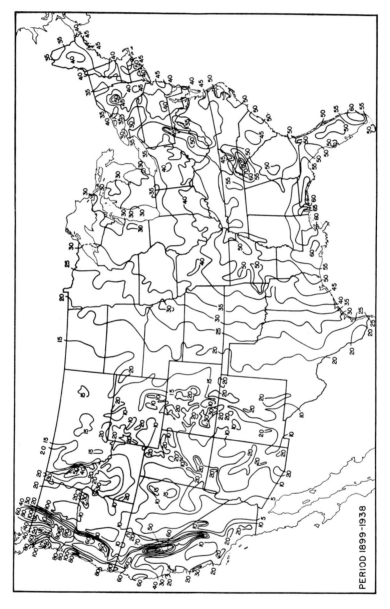

PERIOD 1899-1938

Figure 2·4.   Average annual precipitation. (Source: Reference 8; p. 711.)

High Plains there is generally more precipitation in summer than in winter, for in the latter season cold, dry air masses from over the frozen Canadian mid-continent move southeastward, effectively deflecting the northern passage of moist, tropical air from the Gulf of Mexico.

Between the western High Plains and the interior valleys of the Pacific states lies our vast intermontane country bounded by the Rocky Mountains on the east and by the Sierra Nevada-Cascades on the west. It is a region of great climatic complexity. As far as moisture supply is concerned, there is a close correlation between altitude and precipitation. Most of the moisture-bearing winds which enter this vast domain pass landward from the Pacific. Some penetrate from the Gulf of Mexico but less regularly. In either case by the time the marine air masses have scaled imposing mountain barriers they have cooled considerably at those higher altitudes and have lost most of their moisture. Only the most elevated interior ranges are well watered, for only they are high enough to force the winds to rise and cool and thus bring about condensation of remaining moisture.

The high ranges of the intermontane western states are rain and snow catchers. If it were not for their great altitude there would be less precipitation than there is and much less water for irrigation purposes. Most cultivated land in those states is located in the valleys below the mountains. Valleys immediately to the west of the high ranges often enjoy 15 to 16 inches of rainfall, sufficient for wheat if the land is fallowed every other year. This precipitation results when air masses are forced to rise as they approach the mountains from the west.

The most productive agriculture in the Intermontane Region is achieved on irrigated lands. On these lands the meager rainfall is supplemented by waters flowing into the valleys from the forested mountain crests. Much of this water is the result of winter snow accumulation and subsequent melting in the spring and early summer. The agricultural districts about Salt Lake City, Twin Falls, Boise, Phoenix, Tuscon, Yuma, and Albuquerque are all oases owing their fruitful condition to the high forested mountains and more elevated plateau districts—the sources of their water.

Length of Growing Seasons. As in the matter of moisture supply, the lengths of frost-free growing seasons are also influenced by latitude, altitude, and proximity to sea coasts. In addition, even slight variations in surface relief may be significant. Inland lakes, particularly the Great Lakes, exert important local influences.

At sea level on the equator there is never frost, for the earth and the atmosphere above it are always warmed at least twelve hours daily by the absorption of solar heat. The sun's noon rays are never more than

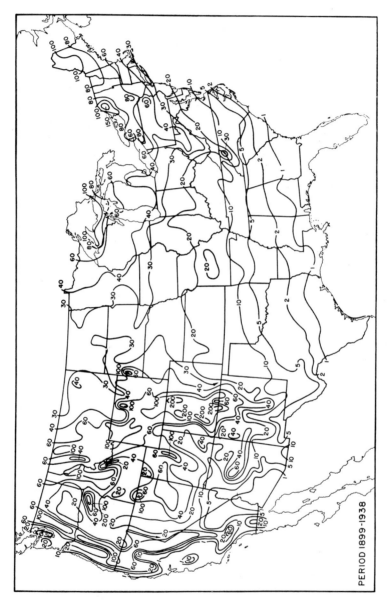

PERIOD 1899-1938

Figure 2·5.   Average annual snowfall. (Source: Reference 8; p. 727.)

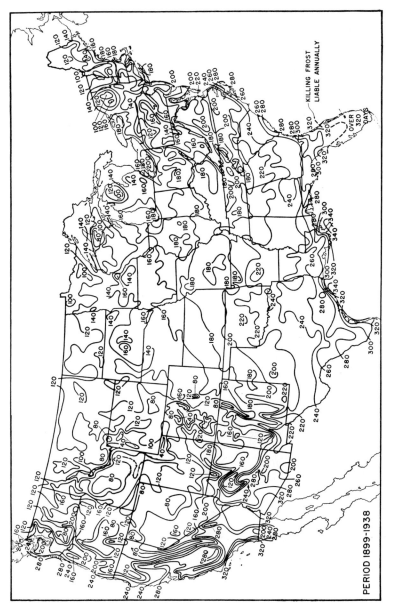

Figure 2:6.   Average length of frost-free period. (Source: Reference 8; p. 746.)

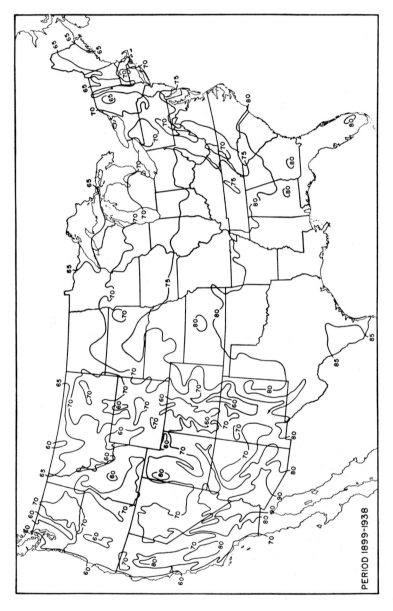

Figure 2:7. Average July temperature. (Source: Reference 8; p. 705.)

23.5 degrees from the vertical. At high elevations on the equator the atmosphere is so thin that radiation of heat from the earth's surface is rapid. Thus on the highest peaks of the Ecuadorian Andes there exist perpetual ice fields. In the United States the Colorado Plateau is cooler than the High Plains of Kansas because it is several thousand feet higher.

Since cold air is denser than warm air, and thus heavier per unit of volume, there is a tendency for cold air currents to descend along the slopes of mountains, particularly at night when insolation ceases. In early fall and late spring there is occasional danger of frost in the lowest valleys at the bases of hills and mountains. It is this phenomenon of cold "air drainage" which so greatly complicates the climatic description of areas of marked differences in surface relief. Of course, there are temperature differences in hill and mountain country which are caused by differences in altitude alone. On a summer day one might note a greater temperature variation between the forested Kaibab Plateau at the rim of the Grand Canyon and the desert valley floor, 6000 feet below, than could be observed between northern Maine and southern Florida.

Proximity to the sea and to large inland water bodies is of greatest importance to those portions of the land lying in the path of air currents which have passed over the waters. When the water is warm the air immediately above it is also warmed. When the water is cold or frozen the air is likewise chilled. In the path of the prevailing westerlies the western portions of Washington and Oregon enjoy winter temperatures as mild as those in eastern Virginia and North Carolina, which are located many degrees of latitude to the south. The westerly winds blowing inland from across the Pacific are relatively warmer than the land in winter; thus the temperature of the northwest coast is moderated. On the east coast, particularly from the Carolinas northward, the principal drift of air masses comes from the cold continental interior; thus the moderating influence of the warmer Atlantic is seldom noted westward beyond the Piedmont. Wherever there is snow it affects the temperatures of air masses near the ground. Cold air tends to remain cold and warm air is cooled as it passes over snow-covered ground.

The concentration of vineyards and deciduous fruit orchards on the eastern shores of Lake Michigan and on the southern shores of lakes Erie and Ontario reflect the slightly milder winter temperatures of those locations. They benefit by the tempering influence of the lakes upon frigid air flowing southeastward from the frozen mid-continent. The trees and vines, while winter dormant, are nevertheless subject to injury both by excessive winter cold and by spring frosts after growth has begun. In early spring the air blowing across the lakes is chilled; thus the growth and flowering of orchards is retarded, often until danger of frost is past. To some degree the numerous small lakes of central Florida seem to effect a moderating influence upon occasional frost-bearing "northers."

Latitude is a prime determinant of the length of frost-free seasons. The earth in its annual orbit about the sun is constantly shifting its inclination to the sun's rays. Those portions of our globe receiving solar radiation most directly are more effectively warmed in a given unit of time than those portions which receive oblique insolation. Never does the sun shine directly upon the earth at latitudes above the tropic lines of 23.5 degrees. However, during the spring and summer seasons the day length increases with increasing latitutde.

The increasing length of day with increase in latitude causes some summer days in southern Wisconsin to be hotter than the warmest ever experienced in the Amazon Valley. It is only the briefness of the season which distinguishes summertime Washington, D.C., from low-altitude sections of the humid equatorial zone. In the highest latitudes, just as at the highest altitudes, the rate of heat radiation from the earth is almost equal to the rate of insolation; thus perpetual glaciers exist. The gradual diminishment of the sun's warming influence, the result of the increased obliqueness of its rays striking the earth, accounts for the cool summers in northern Maine. Because the southern states are closer to the equator and receive less oblique insolation, their warm season begins sooner and ends later than in the northern states. Cotton, which requires a frost-free growing season of about 200 days, appears no farther north than southern Illinois and southeastern Virginia. Corn, which requires a minimum frost-free period of 140 days for maximum yields, is not a popular grain crop in the more northerly sections of the Middle-west or in New England. In North Dakota spring-sown wheat is commoner than fall-sown wheat because the winter season is longer and severer than in Kansas. In Kansas fall-sown "winter" wheats are favored. Winter frost-killing is unlikely, and the grain matures and is harvested before unfavorable hot weather arrives in early summer.

The great variety in length of growing seasons in the United States, together with the fact that in the southernmost portions of the country they begin early in the year when the North is still frozen, lessens inter-regional competition and the chances of seasonal market gluts. The advantage of staggered growing seasons is well illustrated in the case of market-vegetable production along the Atlantic seaboard. There the first harvests of the year are made in southern Florida. As the warm season advances northward, these harvests are followed successively by others in northern Florida, coastal Georgia, the coastal Carolinas, the

Delmarva Peninsula, New Jersey, Long Island, the Connecticut Valley, and Maine. After the northern growing season is ended by frosts southern production begins again in Florida. An army of itinerant workers who pick these successive crops follows the harvest seasons from south to north and back again as regularly as migratory waterfowl and the swallows of Capistrano. There are some growers, too, who have operations both in the South and North.

In the Great Plains wheat country the harvests begin in northwest Texas in June and continue into the Dakotas and Canada in July and August. Thousands of self-propelled combines, singly or in contractors' units, travel the full breadth of the Great Plains doing custom harvesting along the way. Truck caravans hauling them constitute the major local highway traffic during the period of their migration. The harvest, transport, and storage of the nation's annual wheat crop is a task which tests our ingenuity and sometimes even staggers the most elaborate railroad system in the world. If the harvest seasons did not range from June to August, the job would be much more complicated and expensive.

REFERENCES

1. Brooks, C. E., *Climate Through the Ages* (revised), McGraw-Hill Book Co., New York, 1949
2. Geiger, Rudolf, *The Climate Near the Ground*, Harvard University Press, Cambridge, 1950.
3. Hare, F. K., *The Restless Atmosphere*, Hutchinson's University Library, London, 1953.
4. Kimble, G. H. T., *Our American Weather*, McGraw-Hill Book Co., New York, 1955.
5. Thornthwaite, C. Warren, The Climates of North America According to a New Classification, *The Geographical Review*, New York, October 1931.
6. Thornthwaite, C. W., An Approach Toward a Rational Classification of Climate, *The Geographical Review*, New York, January 1948.
7. Trewartha, Glenn Thomas, *An Introduction to Weather and Climate*, McGraw-Hill Book Co., New York, 1943.
8. U.S. Department of Agriculture, *Climate and Man—1941 Yearbook of Agriculture*, Government Printing Office, Washington, D.C., 1941.

soils
and
land
capability

3

Soils differ widely in their ability to hold water and nutrient elements and to make the nutrient elements and water available to the roots of growing plants. These differences are of fundamental importance to farmers. Some differences in soils are apparent to the eye and others can be felt. Some characteristics of soils can be determined only by chemical and physical analyses. Soil scientists have standards and methods by which they measure soil characteristics. To observe the nature of any soil properly it is essential to examine its profile.

THE SOIL PROFILE

The soil profile is a vertical cross section from the surface down to the underlying parent material from which the soil has been formed. A profile may be a few inches to many feet in depth. The depth of the profile in itself is of importance. If it is but a few inches over bed rock, the seriousness of even slight erosion is self-evident. Some annual

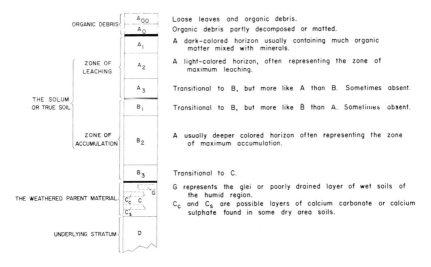

Figure 3:1.   Diagram of a soil profile. (Source: Reference 11; p. 1169.)

plants, such as wheat and corn, may develop roots to the depth of five or six feet. Alfalfa may develop roots which descend more than fifteen feet, if the soil itself is that deep and if moisture and nutrients are available. Obviously, for maximum yields a deep soil is desirable.

The technique used in the classification of soils is somewhat analogous to the methods of plant and animal taxonomy which are based upon type specimens and their visible characteristics. Soil taxonomy is based upon the morphological characteristics of soil profiles. It is primarily a field science. Differences between soils, therefore, must be observable in the field where detailed maps are made. Generalized maps of soils, such as those of Great Soil Groups, are compiled from more detailed field maps.

Figure 3:1 is a general soil profile which is horizontally layered. These layers are known as horizons, and the presence or absence of various horizons is one of the means by which individual soils are classified. Differences in the color of horizons are vital in classification. Color differences reflect modifications created by climate, vegetative cover, and topography, all acting on a particular parent material over a period of time. For instance, a fresh alluvial deposit does not show such profile development because it has not been in place long enough. However, tall grass, having grown for centuries in North Dakota, has produced humus accumulations which have blackened the surface of minerals in the A horizons of well-drained soils.

Soil Aggregation.   There are differences and similarities between the ways in which individual particles of soil aggregate in the various horizons, although sometimes the soil particles do not aggregate at all. Sandy soils, for instance, are frequently nonaggregated.   The aggregation of a soil reflects the influence of parent materials, climate, vegetation, and topography.   For example, columnar and prismatic structures are common in the B horizons of soils which have developed in arid and semiarid regions; crumb and granular structures are common in soils which have developed under the heavy vegetative cover of grass or forest in subhumid and humid regions.   The kinds of aggregates which develop in various horizons help to distinguish one soil from another, and these differences are usually of importance to the farmer.   The way a soil drains or holds water during and after rain is influenced by the character of its aggregates.

Sizes of Soil Particles.   The size of the individual mineral particles which are the building-blocks of soil aggregates definitely influence the quality of a soil.   According to the International System of Soil Particle Classification, clays are particles less than 0.002 millimeters in diameter. It is no wonder that they cannot be seen singly by the eye. Silt particles are 0.002 to 0.02 millimeters in diameter.   Various sand particles range between 0.02 and 2.0 millimeters in diameter, and the larger ones can be detected individually by the unaided eye.   A separation of the sand, silt, and clay fractions of a soil can be made in a laboratory, although the experienced soil surveyor can quite accurately estimate the relative amounts of sand, silt, and clay in a soil sample by wetting it and rubbing it between his fingers.

Figure 3:2 is a simple triangular diagram which illustrates the approximate composition in percentages of sand, silt, and clay in various soil classes.   When a soil survey refers to a silt loam, it is referring to a specific soil class—the *silt loam.*   The proportions of sand, silt, and clay in a silt loam soil must be within the prescribed ranges.   Using the triangular chart Figure 3:2, note the percentage ranges of sand, silt, and clay in sandy clay loams.   Also determine the soil class of a soil which has 18 per cent clay, 36 per cent silt, and 46 per cent sand.   Is it a loam? Yes, it is.

It makes a great deal of difference to a farmer whether most of his soils are sands, silt loams, clays, or something else.   Sands have poor water-holding capacity and thus are easily subject to drought.   Clays are often, but not always, sticky when wet and cloddy when dry. Tropical latosols, for instance, often have water-stable clay aggregates which do not swell when wet; thus they do not become very sticky. Generally speaking, a good soil has enough sand to promote good drain-

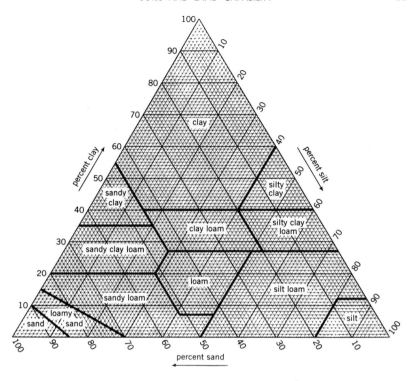

Figure 3:2.   Guide for textural classification. (Source: U.S.D.A.)

age, enough clay to promote aggregation and reasonable water-holding capacity, and sufficient silt to give body without promoting either excessive drainage or imperviousness.

We have noted that differences between one soil and another are evident in their profiles. Color, type of aggregation, and textural composition can be observed in the field. More exact measurements of these differences may be made by laboratory tests. There are many other vital characteristics of soils which can be determined only in a laboratory. We are not concerned here with these important laboratory diagnoses. The interested student will study them in Soil Science.

SOIL CLASSIFICATION

Table 3:1 is a system of soil classification which is based upon profile characteristics observable in the field. Category VI soils are distinguished as *zonal, intrazonal,* and *azonal.*

Table 3:1. System of Soil Classification
(Source: Reference 11; pp. 993–5)

Category VI Order	Category V Suborder	Category IV Great Soil Groups	Category III Family[1]	Category II Series[1]	Category I Type[1]
	Soils of the cold zone	1. Tundra soils			
Pedocals	1. Light-colored soils of arid regions	2. Desert soils	Mesa	Mesa	Mesa gravelly loam.
				Chipeta	Chipeta silty clay loam.
			Mohave	Mohave	Mohave loam.
				Reeves	Reeves fine sandy loam.
		3. Red Desert soils	Portneuf	Portneuf	Portneuf silt loam.
		4. Sierozem	Joplin	Joplin	Joplin loam.
		5. Brown soils		Weld	Weld loam.
		6. Reddish Brown soils	Springer	Springer	Springer fine sandy loam.
				White House	White House coarse sandy loam.
	2. Dark-colored soils of the semi-arid, subhumid, and humid grasslands.	7. Chestnut soils	Rosebud	Rosebud	Rosebud fine sandy loam.
		8. Reddish Chestnut soils		Keith	Keith silt loam.
		9. Chernozem soils	Amarillo	Amarillo	Amarillo fine sandy loam.
		10. Prairie soils		Abilene	Abilene clay.
		11. Reddish Prairie soils	Barnes	Barnes	Barnes very fine sandy loam.
			Carrington	Carrington	Carrington loam.
				Tama	Tama silt loam.
Zonal soils	3. Soils of the forest-grassland transition.	12. Degraded Chernozem soils	Zaneis	Zaneis	Zaneis very fine sandy loam.
		13. Noncalcic Brown or Shantung Brown soils.		Renfrow	Renfrow silt loam.
			Holland	Holland	Holland sandy loam.
				Vista	Vista sandy loam.
			Placentia	Fallbrook	Fallbrook fine sandy loam.
				Sierra	Sierra coarse sandy loam.
				Placentia	Placentia fine sandy loam.
				Ramona	Ramona sandy loam.
			Weihaiwei	Weihaiwei	Weihaiwei loam.
				Tinghsien	Tinghsien fine sandy loam.
Pedalfers	4. Light-colored podzolized soils of the timbered regions.	14. Podzol soils	Kalkaska	Kalkaska	Kalkaska loamy sand.
				Au Train	Au Train loamy sand.
			Rubicon	Rubicon	Rubicon sand.
				Roselawn	Roselawn sand.
			Hermon	Hermon	Hermon loam.
				Colton	Colton loamy sand.
				Becket	Becket loam.
		15. Brown Podzolic soils	Gloucester	Gloucester	Gloucester loam.
					Gloucester sandy loam
				Merrimac	Merrimac sandy loam.
					Merrimac loamy sand.
		16. Gray-Brown Podzolic soils	Miami	Miami	Miami silt loam.
				Fox	Fox silt loam.
				Bellefontaine	Bellefontaine loam.
			Plainfield	Plainfield	Plainfield loamy sand.
				Coloma	Coloma loamy sand.
			Chester	Chester	Chester loam.
				Frederick	Frederick silt loam.
		17. Yellow Podzolic soils	Porters	Porters	Porters loam.
		18. Red Podzolic soils (and Terra Rossa).	Norfolk	Norfolk	Norfolk sandy loam.
			Orangeburg	Orangeburg	Orangeburg sandy loam.
				Greenville	Greenville sandy loam.
	5. Latosolic soils of forested warm-temperate and tropical regions.	19. Yellowish-Brown soils		Magnolia	Magnolia sandy loam.
		20. Reddish-Brown soils		Cecil	Cecil sandy loam.
		21. Latosols	Coto	Coto	Coto clay.
			Bayamón (ferruginous).	Bayamón	Bayamón clay.
			Nipe (ferruginous).	Nipe	Nipe clay.
				Rosario	Rosario clay.

Category VI Order	Category V Suborder	Category IV Great Soil Groups	Category III Family[1]	Category II Series[1]	Category I Type[1]
Intrazonal soils	1. Halomorphic (saline and alkali soils of imperfectly drained arid regions and littoral deposits.)	1. Solonchak or saline soils	Sage	Sage	Sage clay.
			Lahontan	Lahontan	Lahontan clay loam.
		2. Solonetz soils	Phillips	Fresno	Fresno clay loam.
				Phillips	Phillips loam.
			Beadle	Rhoades	Rhoades loam.
				Beadle	Beadle silt loam.
		3. Soloth soils	Arvada	Arvada	Arvada clay loam.
	2. Hydromorphic soils of marshes, swamps, seep areas, and flats.	4. Wiesenböden (Meadow soils)	Clyde	Beckton	Beckton silty clay loam.
				Clyde	Clyde silty clay loam.
				Webster	Webster silty clay loam.
		5. Alpine Meadow soils	Duncom	Duncom	Duncom silt loam.
		6. Bog soils	Edwards	Edwards	Edwards muck.
			Carlisle	Carlisle	Carlisle muck.
				Pamlico	Pamlico muck.
			Greenwood	Greenwood	Greenwood peat.
				Spaulding	Spaulding peat.
		7. Half Bog soils	Maumee	Maumee	Maumee loam.
		8. Planosols	Grundy	Bergland	Bergland loam.
				Grundy	Grundy silt loam.
				Oswego	Oswego silt loam.
			Clermont	Clermont	Clermont silt loam.
				Vigo	Vigo silt loam.
			Crete	Crete	Crete silt loam.
				Idana	Idana silty clay loam.
		9. Ground-Water Podzol soils	Saugatuck	Saugatuck	Saugatuck loamy sand.
				Allendale	Allendale sandy loam
			Leon	Leon	Leon sand.
				St. Johns	St. Johns loamy sand.
		10. Ground-Water Laterite soils	Tifton	Tifton	Tifton fine sandy loam.
		11. Brown Forest soils (Braunerde)	Brooke	Caguas	Caguas clay.
				Brooke	Brooke clay loam.
			Burton	Burton	Burton loam.
	3. Calomorphic	12. Rendzina soils	Houston	Houston	Houston clay.
				Soller	Soller clay loam.
				Bell	Bell clay.
			Aguilita	Aguilita	Aguilita clay.
				Diablo	Diablo clay.
Azonal soils		1. Lithosols	Underwood	Underwood	Underwood stony loam.
				McCammon	McCammon loam.
			Muskingum	Muskingum	Muskingum stony silt loam.
			Dekalb	Dekalb	Dekalb stony loam.
		2. Alluvial soils	Wabash	Wabash	Wabash clay loam.
				Cass	Cass loam.
			Laurel	Laurel	Laurel fine sandy loam.
				Sarpy	Sarpy very fine sandy loam.
			Sharkey	Sharkey	Sharkey clay.
			Genesee	Genesee	Genesee silt loam.
					Huntington silt loam.
			Gila	Gila	Gila very fine sandy loam.
					Pima silty clay loam.
			Hanford	Hanford	Hanford loam.
				Yolo	Yolo loam.
		3. Sands (dry)			

[1] Families, series, and types listed are intended only as examples to illustrate the system of classification.

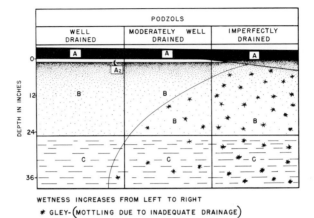

Figure 3:3.   Effect of drainage on the development of podzol soils. (Source: Reference 3; p. 3.)

Zonal Soils.   If the profile of a soil reflects definite climatic influences in a developed profile on well-drained land, it is a *zonal* soil.   It is noted that the zonal soils are further subdivided into *pedocals* and *pedalfers*.   A pedocal is a soil characterized by a calcium accumulation.

Since calcium carbonate is slowly soluble in water, it is apparent that little water leaches through the profile of the pedocals—otherwise the calcium carbonate would be removed.   Therefore the pedocals are typical of arid and semiarid regions.

The pedalfers, on the other hand, have no visible calcium carbonate depositions in their profiles.   Instead the B horizon is characterized by iron and aluminum oxide discolorations.   These discolorations in well-drained soils range from light yellow to deep red and purple rusts.   A pedalfer is a soil characterized by accumulations of the oxides of aluminum (Al) and iron (Fe).   The soils of the humid mid-latitude and tropical regions are pedalfers.   In the United States the pedocals begin on the western fringe of the prairie-grassed central plains and extend westward wherever the rainfall is low.   Figure 4:1 shows the approximate line of separation between pedocals and pedalfers in the central United States.

Intrazonal and Azonal Soils.   The *intrazonal* soils in Category VI are those which have a profile development that has been impeded by poor drainage or that has been unusually influenced by parent material. The reader will note in Figure 3:3 how drainage or lack of it influences profile development.

The *azonal* soils are those which show no development of horizons in their profiles because not enough time has elapsed since the parent materials were deposited in their present location.

Suborders. Category V in Table 3:1 includes the suborders of the
soil-classification scheme. The principal determinants of these suborders
are temperature and rainfall. Except where the subsoil is saturated or
permanently frozen, vegetative cover generally changes from grass to
timber as the climate changes from subhumid to humid. These vegetative influences also play a part in determining the suborders. Figure 3:4
is a simple diagram which illustrates the principle of the suborder classification of zonal soils in the United States.

The intrazonal soils in Category V are divided into three suborders.
The calomorphic soils are those in which the influences of a highly calcareous parent material persist in the solum despite a humid climate.
The hydromorphic soils are those with poor drainage but without alkali
salt accumulations. The halomorphic soils are poorly drained and show
alkali salt accumulation.

Great Soil Groups. It is upon the Great Soil Groups, or Category
IV, that some soil taxonomists and most geographers place great emphasis. They are interested not so much in the use which is made of
soils but in the environmental conditions which have influenced the
development of certain general profile characteristics. For example, the
profiles of all Brown Podzolic soils, regardless of their parent materials,
have some visual color similarities in their profiles which come from
development upon well-drained topography under mixed coniferous-

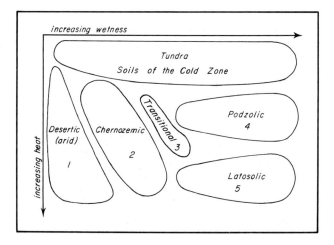

Figure 3:4.   Geographic relationships among the six major groups of zonal soils.

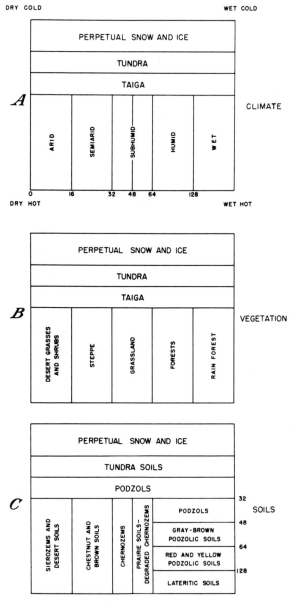

Figure 3:5. Correlations of Great Soil Groups with climate and vegetation. (Source: U.S.D.A.)

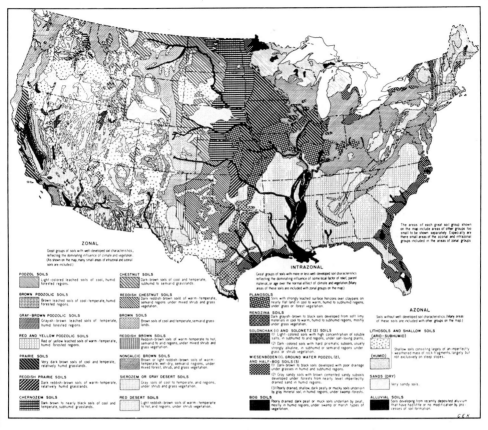

Figure 3:6. Map of Great Soil Groups. (Source: U.S.D.A.)

deciduous forest. The relationship between Great Soil Groups and native vegetation is illustrated in Figure 3:5.

Soil Types, Series, and Families. The soil chemist, agronomist, and farmer are generally most interested in the specific characteristics of specific soils. There is too much variation between soils within the broad Great Soil Groups for the results of agronomic experiments and certain laboratory analyses to have any practical meaning to a farmer unless they can be indentified with precise soil *types*. Some representative soil types are listed under Category I of Table 3:1. The farmer is specifically interested in soil types in contrast to Great Soil Groups for just about the same reasons that he is specifically interested in hogs or wheat rather than in the broad categories of vertebrate animals and flowering plants. He is directly involved with the particular.

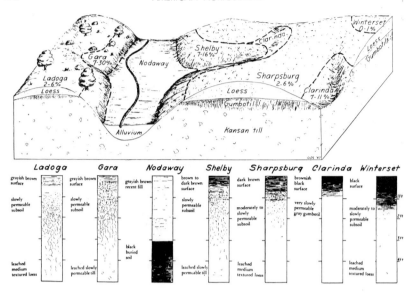

Figure 3:7. A block diagram of soil series, Taylor County, Iowa. (Source: Reference 6; p. 8.)

A soil type is a distinct individual. It is usually found distributed over a limited area and is derived from a specific parent material which has weathered on a definite kind of surface relief, under a specific association of plants, such as a beech-hickory forest or a bluestem prairie. The range of climatic variation under which a soil type develops is much more restricted than that which may influence the development of an entire Great Soil Group. And, very important, the composition of sand, silt, and clay in the A horizon of the profile is positively specific. *Thus the soil type is the basic unit of detailed soil mapping and land-use planning.* It is so specific that its profile has certain characteristics which are possessed by no other soil. These characteristics are observed in the field by the soil surveyor when he maps soil types.

Soil types which are alike in every profile characteristic except the proportions of sand, silt, and clay in the A horizon are considered close relatives, and they are said to belong to the same *series*. When there are only slight differences between the profiles of two or more series they are said to belong to a *family*. The relationships between type, series, and family are intimate and might be compared with the relationships between the individual, brothers, and cousins. Soil families, series, and types usually derive their names from the locality in which they were first discovered by a soil surveyor. To find, describe, and name a new soil series is to a soil surveyor a satisfaction akin to that experienced by the biologist who discovers a new species of animal or plant.

The soil surveyor knows which of the Great Soil Groups he is dealing with whenever he surveys a particular farm, but if his map were to show only the Great Soil Groups it would have little practical value. In many areas the surveyor would not make a map at all because he would have the soils of only one Great Soil Group to work with. Figure 3:7 is a block-diagram presentation of a number of soil series found in Taylor County, Iowa. Their relationships to parent materials, topography, and indigenous vegetation are indicated. Climatic influences are similar throughout the area. A map based upon such a detailed survey, with additional subdivisions into types, is of great value in farm management.

Some Characteristics of Soils. In a sense, soil is a living medium. It is unlike stone or its pulverized remains. Its solid framework, although usually constructed of mineral particles, is so completely modified by biological activity that it is definitely different. If a soil were not distinct from its inert mineral parent materials, erosion would be of lesser consequence. Of course, when the pulverized mineral mantle itself is thin, erosion destroys not only the soil but the very possibilities for its reconstruction from these unweathered biologically inert materials.

True soil has a remarkable capacity not shared by the unaltered primary minerals of pulverized stone which lie beneath it. Over the long period of time required for soil formation, chemical and biological modifications produce secondary clay minerals and humic complexes which have special properties. They can adsorb positively charged ions, such as calcium (Ca^{++}), potassium (K^+), and magnesium (Mg^{++}), from the soil solution when they are abundant, e.g., after the farmer applies fertilizer, lime, or manure to a field. These secondary clay minerals and humic complexes can also release the adsorbed nutrient ions into the soil solution when that solution is lacking in them. This behavior is known as cation exchange capacity.° Plant roots obtain essential elements by absorbing them from the enriched soil solution. Of all cation exchange materials in soil, humus is by far the most active and most important. The development of secondary clay minerals and humic complexes requires long periods of time. When erosion removes top soil it removes the product of a long period of evolution and, more important, it removes the most dynamic portion of the profile. It is for this reason that every effort should be made to prevent soil erosion. This can be done by using each piece of land according to its ability to resist erosion.

°A cation is a positively charged ion.

Figure 3:8.   Picture of soil-survey map being drawn. (Source: Reference 8; cover.)

THE SOIL SURVEY—ITS SYMBOLS

When a soil surveyor makes a soil map he usually uses an aerial photograph as a base.   He determines the boundaries of soil types by examining their profiles with an auger.   Each soil type is given a number which is written inside the boundary of the area that the soil type occupies on the photograph.   Figure 3:8 shows the drawing of a soil map.   It should be noted that inside each soil-type boundary three numbers are written in sequence, such as 26–5–4.   This order is standard.   The first number refers to the soil type; the second indicates the slope of the surface of the land.   For instance the number 5 in the above code means that there is a general vertical rise or fall of 5 feet over a horizontal distance of 100 feet. A slope of this magnitude is called a 5 per cent slope.   The third number of the trinomial code refers to the degree of erosion which has occurred. Zero would indicate no erosion, a plus sign would indicate deposition, and number 1 would indicate slight erosion.   Each successively higher number would indicate that a greater degree of erosion has occurred.

The symbol (7) after the third number would indicate that gullies have developed in the field.

USE-CAPABILITY CLASSES AND LAND-CAPABILITY MAPS

Some soil types can stand more intensive tillage than others on identical slopes. For instance, under cultivation a sandy soil on a 10 per cent slope would be more likely to wash or blow than a well-aggregated silt loam on a 10 per cent slope. A well-aggregated soil will erode less easily than one which is structureless. On the basis of many observations soil conservationists have been able to group all soils on all kinds

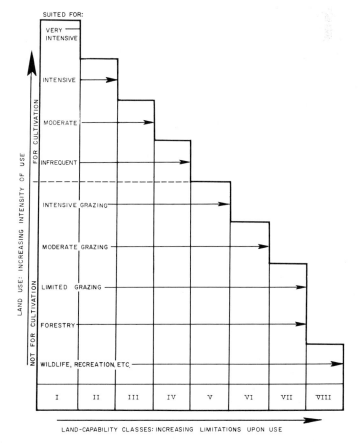

Figure 3;9. Relation of land-capability classes to safe land use. (Source: Reference 8; p. 10.)

Figure 3:10.   Picture illustrating land-capability classes.   (Source: Reference 8; p. 5.)

of terrain into eight land-capability classes.   By such simplification the
diverse and sometimes complicated data of the basic soil-survey map can
be presented to the farmer in the easily understandable form of a *land-
capability map*.   Such a map will never have more than eight land-use
categories represented, and usually not more than four or five land-
capability classes are represented on a single farm.

Experienced soil conservationists are able to recommend the most
practical ways to use the land in each capability class so as to be most
profitable to the farmer and yet protect the soil against erosion.

A chart of the eight land-capability classes is presented in Figure 3:9.
Class 1 lands may be used for everything from intensive cultivation
under good management to a woodlot or wildlife area.   Class 1 lands are
generally almost level, with deep, well-aggregated soils of a loamy
texture and well drained.   However, Class 8 lands are made up of such
poor soil or such steep terrain that they are not suitable for any other
use than as wildlife habitats or recreation areas.   Any removal of vegetative cover, even temporarily, would probably result in erosion.   A
pictorial illustration of land-capability classification is shown in Figure
3:10.

A land-capability map is not made directly in the field and it is not
to be confused with a soil map.   It is really a technical appraisal of
how the land described and delineated on a soil map should be used.   A

land-capability map can be properly constructed only from the basic soil-survey map which is the true inventory of a farm's soil assets. The construction of a land-capability map requires an understanding of the behavior of soil types under different kinds of management and is prepared by experienced soil conservationists in consultation with other agricultural scientists.

Figure 23:4 shows a land-capability map which served as a guide in the preparation of the companion *landuse map*. There are a number of possible ways in which a farm with specific land capabilities could be used; so it is necessary for the conservationist and farmer to confer about the crops and animals to be raised. With both the farmer's preferences and the land's capability in mind, the soil conservationist prepares a plan of land use to guide the farmer.

To be practical every farm must be studied in detail, not only as to soil resources but also with regard for the economic and labor resources of the farmer. Figure 23:4 shows a plan for land use which is based upon proper consideration of land capabilities and of the needs of the farmer who operates it. A number of land-use maps are used in subsequent chapters to illustrate management practices in various parts of the United States. All of these are based upon soil surveys and the subsequent preparation of land-capability maps. They are, therefore, good examples of wise land management.

REFERENCES

1. Kellogg, Charles E., Potentialities and Problems of Arid Soils, Preprint from *Proceedings, International Symposium On Desert Research*, Research Council of Israel in Cooperation with United National Educational, Scientific and Cultural Organization, Jerusalem.
2. Kellogg, Charles E., *The Soils That Support Us*, The Macmillan Co., New York, 1941.
3. Knox, Ellis G., *Jefferson County Soils and Soil Map*, New York State College of Agriculture at Cornell University, Ithaca, 1952.
4. Lyon, T. Lyttleton, Harry O. Buckman, and C. Nyle Brady, *The Nature and Properties of Soils*, The Macmillan Co., New York, 1952.
5. Marbut, C. F., Soils of the United States, *Atlas of American Agriculture*, Part III, Government Printing Office, Washington, D.C., 1935.
6. Scholtes, W. H., Guy D. Smith, and F. F. Riecken, *Taylor County, Iowa, Soils*, Government Printing Office, Washington, D.C., 1954. This is a U.S. Department of Agriculture and Iowa Agriculture Experiment Station soil survey. Its organization and presentation differs in a number of respects from the usual county soil survey. It is a model of usefulness and readability. Excellent as an introduction to soil surveys in general.
7. Simonson, Roy, W., The Soil Under Natural and Cultural Environments, *Journal of Soil and Water Conservation*, Vol. 6, No. 2, April 1951.

8. Steele, J. G., *The Measure of Our Land*, Soil Conservation Service, Government Printing Office, Washington, D.C., 1951.

9. U.S. Department of Agriculture, *Soil, The Yearbook of Agriculture, 1957*, Government Printing Office, Washington, D.C.

10. U.S. Department of Agriculture, *Soil Survey Reports*, Government Printing Office, Washington, D.C. These reports, which generally discuss the soils of a single county, are based upon field surveys and upon data generally obtained through the cooperation of State Agriculture Experiment Stations. A map of the soils surveyed is a part of each report.

11. U.S. Department of Agriculture, *Soils and Men, The Yearbook of Agriculture*, 1938, Government Printing Office, Washington, D.C.

12. U.S. Department of Agriculture, *Sound Land Classification Rests on Soil Surveys*, Beltsville, Md., 1951.

part two

the
dry
West

4

Considering the varieties of climate, topography, soil, and natural vegetation that are found in various parts of the United States, it is logical that the character of the nation's agriculture should differ from place to place. The contrasts between farming in the North and in the South are notable, whether one considers the East, West, or Middle West. Such disparity in the lengths of growing seasons as one finds between northern Maine (90 days) and the southern tip of Florida (365 days) is bound to result in differences in crop specialization and ways of farming. But the greatest contrast of all is between the agriculture of the dry West and that of the humid East. A dairyman in New York would scarcely understand the vocabulary of a pump-irrigation cotton grower in Arizona. A Pennsylvania farmer who applies lime to correct soil acidity might be puzzled by the difficulties a farmer in western Kansas may have with alkaline soils caused by too much calcium carbonate.

In between the very dry desert and oasis portion of the West and the humid corn and cotton belts of the East is the transition area of the Great Plains. However, the frequency of recurring drought on the Great Plains is such that the farmers of that area have more in common with those of the dry West than with those of the humid East. In the early days of pioneer settlement the Great Plains were known as "The Great American Desert," and so they are called on some nineteenth-century maps. Because there is a unity in the basic principles of land use in dry regions and a more complicated diversity in the land-use problems of the humid eastern United States the systematic treatment of agricultural regions in this book is divided into two sections. One deals with the dry West, the other with the humid East.

The 100th meridian, which bisects the Dakotas and forms the eastern boundary of the panhandles of Oklahoma and Texas, is occasionally considered the line which divides the United States into a humid East and a dry West. Sometimes the boundary that separates the Great Plains from other physiographic provinces to the east is used to partition the nation into dry and humid halves. Since census statistics are summarized by states, it is often convenient to consider the seventeen western states as being the "dry West."

As mentioned in Chapter 3, soil scientists recognize a basic cleavage between soils with visible depositions of calcium carbonate in their profiles and those which are leached of all visible traces of lime. Thus the line between pedocal soils with lime depositions and the pedalfer soils which are without them is sometimes recognized as a boundary between the humid and arid areas of the nation. The most appropriate line of demarcation is that based on evapotranspiration (Figure 2:1).

Not all the West is dry or semiarid, although the largest part of it is: a corner in the Northwest along the Pacific Ocean from San Francisco northward is humid in winter, and mountain heights in general receive considerable snow and some rain. There are other areas with subhumid climates, such as the Palouse of Washington and the Judith Basin of Montana. The eastern border of the plains states is subhumid to humid. In general, it may be said that limited precipitation is the dominant agricultural handicap of the West. However, as we consider statistics for the seventeen western states, it would be well to keep in mind that certain data may be biased by the more favorable rainfall which occurs in some districts, particularly in the eastern portions of the plains states.

Although climate is the arbiter of western land use and western agriculture, topography creates and accents much of the character of individual places within the broader region. The largest area of fairly level terrain and deep soils is the Great Plains. Yet even this region is much dissected by the dendritic patterns of rivers, creeks, and washes.

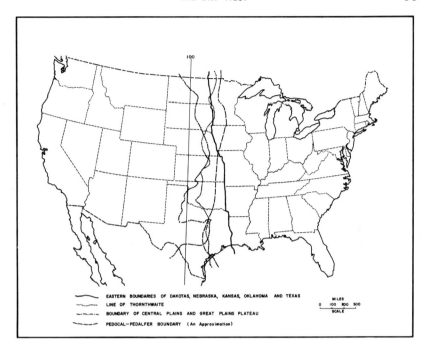

EASTERN BOUNDARIES OF DAKOTAS, NEBRASKA, KANSAS, OKLAHOMA AND TEXAS
LINE OF THORNTHWAITE
BOUNDARY OF CENTRAL PLAINS AND GREAT PLAINS PLATEAU
PEDOCAL—PEDALFER BOUNDARY (An Approximation)

MILES
0   100   200   300
SCALE

Figure 4:1. Boundaries between the humid East and the dry West.

From the Rocky Mountains to the Pacific Ocean the cultivation of crops is generally limited to valley and basin districts. The uplands of mountains and plateaus are often too rough and the soils too thin for agriculture. Sometimes cultivation in the highlands is limited by the shortness of the summer growing period. Much of the water brought as snow or rain to the hilly uplands is eventually concentrated at lower altitudes in streams and as ground-water accumulations in valleys and basins. Wherever there is river water or a subsurface ground-water table in a valley or basin the possibilities of irrigation exist if the topography and soils are satisfactory. Western irrigation agriculture is generally this type of valley-oasis cultivation.

Even though the irrigated lands of the West are the most productive, there are many more acres that are "dry farmed." Dry farming is agriculture dependent upon rain and snow. It often differs considerably in techniques from ordinary tillage practices in the humid eastern United States, but in its dependence upon natural precipitation it is the same. The name dry farming is used in the West to distinguish that kind of agriculture from tillage under irrigation. There are dry-farming districts in Oregon's Willamette Valley which receive 40 inches of precipitation. Summers, however, are dry. Eighteen to 20 inches of rain are common in Washington's Palouse, before the foothills of the northern Rocky Mountains, and 20 to 35 inches are normal along the eastern borders of the Great Plains. The term dry farming generally implies farming carried on under the handicap of low rainfall. It is usually impossible with less than 14 to 16 inches of annual precipitation, for yields are substantially less than those obtained where precipitation comes chiefly in summer and exceeds 30 inches annually and far below those obtained where full irrigation is practiced. The extent of dry farming in the West is greatly limited by rough terrain, thin soils, and, most of all, unfavorable climate, principally drought.

GENERALIZED TYPES OF FARMING IN THE WEST

The broad general pattern of western agriculture is uncomplicated and is based upon a few fundamental facts.

As noted in Figure 4:2, the largest area is devoted to range livestock. The map is an oversimplification because there is regional variety in the character of the range and in the ways it is used. Figure 4:2 also does not show the truly forested areas, particularly in the more mountainous sections where grazing is not practiced. However, in the very extensive area designated as grazing that is the predominate form of land use.

Dry climate, rough topography, thin soils, and a short growing season at high altitudes are the principal factors which preclude crop cultivation in the range country. As for the distribution pattern of the limited cultivated lands, there are a few features of special significance. Irrigation agriculture, confined to scattered river valleys, is characteristic from the Rocky Mountains to the Sierra Nevada-Cascades and in California. As far as crop cultivation on the Great Plains is concerned, irrigation is important in the valleys of the westernmost sections. Newer irrigation projects, particularly along the Missouri River and its tributaries, will eventually bring this pattern of irrigated-oasis agriculture into greater prominence in the eastern Great Plains.

The Great Plains stand out as the transition belt between the western irrigated-valley type of agriculture and the eastern types of extensive cultivation which spread out over wide areas wherever the terrain and soils are suitable. However, with the exception of southeastern Kansas and the easternmost borders of Oklahoma and Texas, it is correct to say that lack of rain and snow is the primary handicap to the agriculture of the plains states. Much of the uncertainty and difficulty of crop production on the Great Plains is due to the fact that a system of extensive

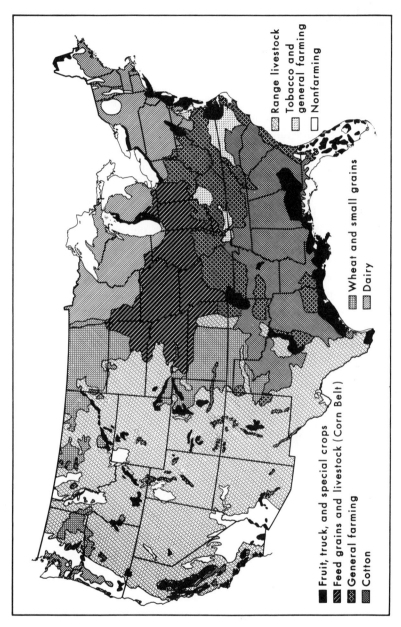

Figure 4:2. Major types of farming in the United States. (Source: U.S.D.A.)

Range livestock

Tobacco and general farming

Nonfarming

Wheat and small grains

Dairy

Fruit, truck, and special crops

Feed grains and livestock (Corn Belt)

General farming

Cotton

tillage developed in the humid eastern states is the basic pattern of land use in this sporadically arid area rather than the restricted irrigated-valley type of oasis agriculture which is typical of the dry West.

Figure 4:2 shows considerable variety in the cropping systems of the plains states. Since a lack of optimum rainfall is characteristic of all of them, these differences in cropping systems are closely related to the length of the growing season. Consider both the maps of annual thermal efficiency and climatic type (Figures 2:1 and 2:2). Cotton is most prominent from central Oklahoma, southward, where the growing season exceeds 200 frost-free days. Kansas is the heart of the winter-wheat belt where the grain is sown in the fall and harvested the following year before hot summer weather sets in. Winters are generally mild; thus the danger of frost-killing is low. Corn is the most important crop in eastern Nebraska where summers are hot. Corn is a tropical plant but it is not tolerant of drought; consequently there is risk of low yields in planting it. The Nebraska state average is 28 bushels per acre, compared with that of Illinois which is 50 bushels per acre. Corn is a minor crop in North Dakota where the growing season is short. Spring-sown wheat dominates the northern and northeastern plains because it develops well during cool spring weather, yet is quite tolerant of moderately low precipitation.

Table 4:1.　Land Use in Seventeen Western States*
(Source: Reference 2; pp. 53, 60, 63)

Region	Area	Grazing Lands Nonwooded	Forest and Wooded Areas	Cultivated Land Irrigated	Cultivated Land Dry-Farmed
Northern plains states	195,432	78,402	5,428	1,939	93,879
Southern plains states	212,828	104,353	43,099	4,815	36,488
Mountain and Pacific states	753,368	390,742	220,060	20,525	36,636
Total, West	1,161,628	573,497	268,587	27,279	167,003
U.S. Total	1,903,825	632,417	615,384	399,257	

*Figures are thousands of acres—1954 data.

Grazing Lands in the Dry West. The seventeen western states cover 61 per cent, or 1,161 million acres, of the land area of the United States. Of this total more than half, or 573 million acres, is grass and shrub grazing lands. The total area of such nonwooded range and pasture in the entire country is 632 million acres. It is amply evident that grazing dominates western agriculture insofar as area of land is con-

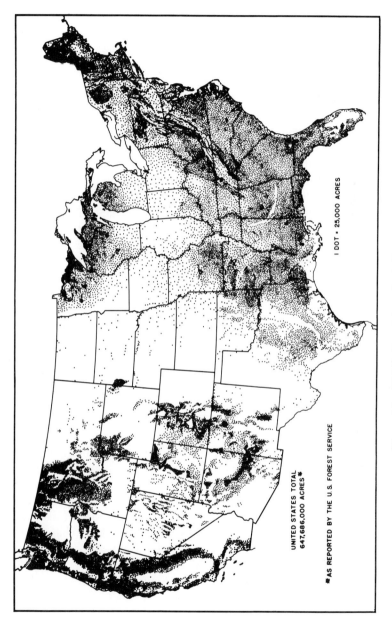

UNITED STATES TOTAL
647,686,000 ACRES*

*AS REPORTED BY THE U.S. FOREST SERVICE

1 DOT = 25,000 ACRES

Figure 4·3.   Distribution of forest land. (Source: U.S.F.S.)

cerned. It is noted in a later chapter, however, that the average production of these grazing lands is exceedingly low

Forest and Wooded Areas. The forests of the western states are of great value. Those of the Pacific states which constitute the finest reserve of high-grade coniferous trees in the nation are our principal source of softwood lumber. Western forests are also vitally important as protective cover for the upper watersheds from which flow the streams to irrigate the desert valleys.

Considering the climatic character of the West, which, except at high altitudes and along the Pacific coast, favors grass and shrubs rather than trees, it is remarkable that there is as much forest and woodland as there is—some 268 million acres, or 44 per cent of the U.S. total. Two hundred thirty-five million acres are in national forests. Except for the Black Hills of South Dakota, the northern plains are practically devoid of woodlands. The quality of southern plains woodlands is poor, and a large portion of what are called woodlands in the intermontane West are low-grade piñon pine and juniper growth of little commercial value but important for helping to stabilize thin soils on hilly lands.

Cropland. Both the character and distribution of cropland in the western states sharply reflect the influence of climate and topography. The plains states, which comprise 35 per cent of the area of the entire West, have 70 per cent of the total cropland. Higher rainfall which permits very extensive dry farming is the primary reason for this preponderance. Of course, as has already been indicated, the eastern margin of the plains states is humid in the south and moist subhumid in the north. The statistics given are heavily weighted by the intensity of crop agriculture in those areas of higher rainfall. The major wheat regions are in the plains states, and Texas is the leading producer of cotton. Both of these crops have considerable drought tolerance. However, if it were not for much level to gently sloping terrain in the plains states in contrast to the rougher topography of the mountain and pacific areas, crop agriculture would probably not be such a prominent type of land use.

It is significant that more land is devoted to crops in North Dakota and Kansas than is used for grazing. As considered in a later chapter, this may be one of the underlying reasons for hardship during periods of severe drought. In Nebraska crop and grazing lands are about equal in area; range and pasture in Oklahoma and South Dakota slightly exceed the area of cropland; and Texas has almost three times more grazing land than tilled fields.

Only 57 million acres are cultivated in the Mountain and Pacific states. This is 8 per cent of the area. Twenty million acres are irrigated, and it is the production of these irrigated lands that is chiefly responsible for the agricultural wealth of these states. The effect of the dry climate is reflected in the statistics. In total area these eleven western states are almost 40 per cent of the United States, yet they have only 14 per cent of the cropland. The exceptional yields and the premium values of crops grown under irrigation compensate heavily for limited acreage. The value of California's agricultural produce exceeds that of any other state in the Union. California has only 13 million of our 399 million acres of cropland, but 7 million of these acres are irrigated.

Although emphasis has been placed upon the differences between cropland and range in the discussion of these elementary statistics, it should be noted that in many parts of the West, particularly in the irrigated areas, there is a close integration of range and tillage operations. Many ranchers are also farmers, for without irrigated cropland much of the range could not be used efficiently. In the Great Plains there is a strong trend toward the integration of ranching and cash-crop farming. A farm which is part range in an area of recurring drought is more likely to weather a crisis than a farm which is entirely devoted to cropping.

REFERENCES

1. Wooten, Hugh H., and James R. Anderson, *Agricultural Land Resources in the United States*, U.S. Department of Agriculture, Washington, D.C., 1955.
2. ———, *Major Uses of Land in the United States*, U.S. Department of Agriculture, Washington, D.C., 1957.
3. U.S. Bureau of the Census, *U.S. Census of Agriculture, 1950—Land Utilization— A Graphic Summary*, Washington, D.C., 1952.
4. U.S. Department of Agriculture, *Agriculture's Capacity to Produce*, Bureau of Agricultural Economics, Washington, D.C., 1952.
5. U.S. Department of Agriculture, *Farm Production Practices, Costs, and Returns*, Bureau of Agricultural Economics, Washington, D.C., 1949.
6. U.S. Department of Agriculture, *Irrigation Agriculture in the West*, Office of the Secretary, Washington, D.C., 1948.

forests
and
waters
in the
West

5

Precipitation required to maintain good woodland is approximately the same as that required to support agriculture, unless irrigation or dry-farming methods are used. Eighty years ago John Wesley Powell, then geologist in charge of the U.S. Geological Survey in the Rocky Mountain region, noted this fact. He wrote,

> The amount of mean annual rainfall necessary to the growth of forests if protected from fire is probably about the same as the amount necessary for agriculture without irrigation; at any rate, it is somewhere from 20 to 24 inches. All timber growth below that amount is of a character so stunted as to be of little value, and the growth is so slow that, when once the timber has been taken from the country, the time necessary for a new forest growth is so great that no practical purpose is subserved. (Reference 2; p. 15)

Generally, the western agriculturist avoided land clearing in the forest areas. He preferred the arid to semiarid valleys where he took up irrigation. He could have chosen to plant certain crops where rainfall is sufficient for their needs, but for good reasons he elected the deserts—

60

when supplied with water! If you were a farmer in the West, why would you make the same decision? Would you recognize that most forested areas are on slopes where soils are thin and easily eroded once the forest vegetation is removed? Would you observe that the growing season is shorter at high altitudes than on the lower valley plains? Would you note that transportation charges to market are high almost everywhere in the mountainous West; that to bear these costs it is necessary to produce crops having special values or serving as supplements to the livestock industry which utilizes the dry grasslands? Would you note that these crops could best be raised in the desert valleys by irrigation agriculture? Would you recognize, as stockmen do, that grazing animals have to retreat to the warmer but drier lowlands in the winter and that they need the supplement of irrigated pasture and field-grown hay to tide them over? Surely you would discover, if you were to consider irrigation at all, that the easiest terrain upon which to distribute water is level valley land rather than hillsides, even though the latter are closer to the headwaters of streams. For reasons such as these the western farmer does not generally operate where rainfall is adequate but rather in the desert lowlands where he must irrigate or in locations where dry farming is feasible.

It should be clear from the foregoing that the major sources of western irrigation water are the forested regions. Only in the wooded zones does enough rain fall consistently to support perennial streams. Botanists have observed through studies of plants and environments that forests occur primarily in those areas in which there is sufficient precipitation to permit the percolation of some water through the soil profile. It is this percolation water which ultimately maintains springs and perennial streams. The native shortgrasses, bunchgrasses, and desert shrubs characteristic of the greater part of the western landscape are an indication that not·enough rain falls to wet the entire soil profile regularly and consistently. Their root systems and their growth habits are adjusted to seasonal or superficial soil wetting. The shortgrass and bunchgrass areas of the West, like the deserts, seldom contribute to that subterranean water flow which maintains perennial streams.

RAINFALL, VEGETATIVE COVER, AND RUNOFF

One should not overlook the fact, however, that some irrigation water does come from lands covered with grass and desert shrub. Occasionally, this may be subsurface seepage, but more frequently it is surface run-off which reaches drainage ways by flowing downhill faster than it infiltrates and percolates through the soil. Rains in the low-altitude grass

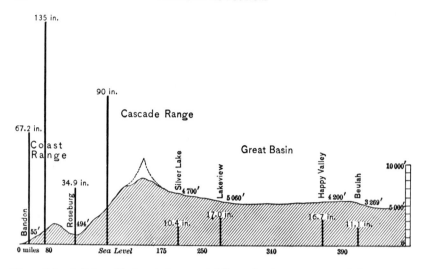

Figure 5:1. Relief profile in relation to rainfall on the Coast Ranges and the Cascades of Oregon. (Source: Reference 1; p. 163.)

and desert-shrub areas are frequently of a convectional type that fall in sudden gusty showers. Because of the infrequency of these rains perennial stream flow cannot be maintained by their runoff. Rainfall in the forest zones on the high mountain flanks is usually of the orographic type which develops as air masses bearing some moisture vapor are forced to rise on the windward slopes of the mountains. As the air rises, it cools to the condensation point of the moisture vapor, and precipitation takes place. Orographic rains are usually less tempestuous than convectional showers, so that infiltration and percolation generally exceed runoff when the vegetative cover is of good quality.

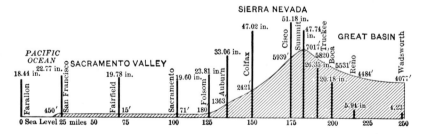

Figure 5:2. Relation of relief to rainfall in the Sierra Nevada. (Source: Reference 1; p. 173.)

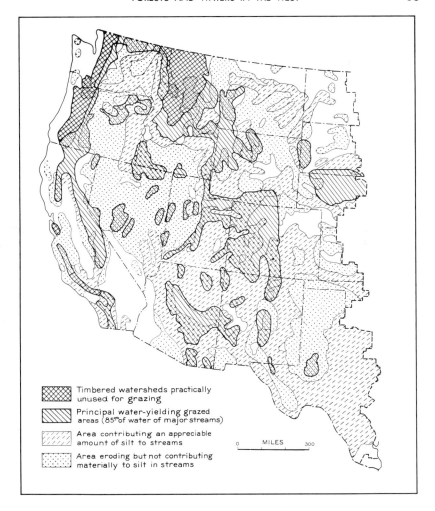

Timbered watersheds practically
unused for grazing

Principal water-yielding grazed
areas (85% of water of major streams)

Area contributing an appreciable
amount of silt to streams

Area eroding but not contributing
materially to silt in streams

0   MILES   300

Figure 5:3.   Source areas of western waters. (Source: U.S.F.S.)

Against the erosive impact of falling rain, good forest cover offers
better protection to the soil than either bunchgrasses or desert shrubs,
which seldom provide sufficient canopy, especially when grazed, to shield
the soil.   When the soil is well protected from the direct impact of rain
it is in a more absorptive condition than when it is exposed to direct
pounding.   Studies have shown that at least 65 per cent of the soil must
be protected by a vegetative canopy to resist pulverization and erosion.
At high altitudes orographic rains come with sufficient regularity to

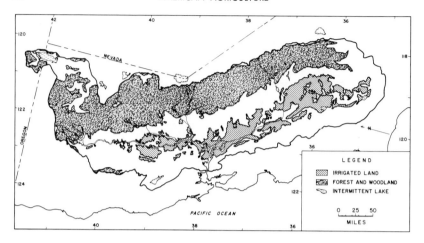

Figure 5:4. Forest watershed and irrigated land, Central Valley Basin, California. (Source: Reference 3; p. 155.)

maintain heavy vegetation. Forest cover protects the soil, so that most of the water is absorbed into the profile. Nevertheless, there is almost always some surface runoff in the forested zones, particularly during the period of rapid snow melt in the spring. The influence upon rainfall of land elevation and position with respect to prevailing winds is well illustrated in examples cited by Bowman (Figures 5:1 and 5:2).

The drainage pattern of any river basin is necessarily determined by the relief and slopes of that basin. The stream flow begins in trickles at many diverse points on the rim of the drainage area. Eventually, these rivulets consolidate into a river. In the West, as a rule, rivulets and streams receive their heaviest and most constant charge of water from springs and runoff in the forest belts. The heavier the annual rainfall, the heavier the forest growth and the flow of underground waters into springs which feed the streams.

The student of western agriculture should be aware of the significant relationship between forested lands and the perennial streams utilized for irrigation. It is not an accident that our finest national forests and such national parks as Yellowstone, Yosemite, Sequoia, Rocky Mountain, and the Grand Tetons dominate the headwaters of great western rivers. The continental divide is the most important physical influence upon the course of rivers flowing through the dry West. Figure 5:3 illustrates how water used for irrigation begins its flow from forested lands. National parks and national forests are prominent sources of water.

As citizens interested in the development of agriculture in the West, what opinions do you hold with respect to the management policy of national parks and national forests? Consider the map showing forests and irrigated land in the Central Valley of California (Figure 5:4). Are you surprised that this valley is the largest, most valuable area of irrigation agriculture in the nation, and that chiefly because of its harvests California leads- all the states in the value of agricultural commodities?

The Significance of National Forests. Within the intermontane region of Nevada, Idaho, Utah, and Wyoming are nineteen national forests which cover nearly 29 million acres. In that vast area 80 per cent of the water used by homes, industries, and irrigators flows from national forests existing above altitudes of 7000 feet. In some sections as much as 94 per cent of the water used for irrigation, domestic purposes, business, power, and industry comes from public watershed lands. These forested, high-mountain areas supply the bulk of water for 315 cities and communities in the Intermontane Region. Water yields from national forests vary from year to year, as the total precipitation itself varies, but it is estimated that almost 29 million acre-feet is the average annual production. These waters supply 4 million acres of irrigated land in addition to meeting most urban requirements. (Reference 6.)

Every year each acre of national forest in the intermontane area of the four states contributes about 1 acre-foot of water to stream flow—a reliable source for 190 storage reservoirs and 69 power plants. Each person in the area uses about 175 gallons of water per day for home use. This is one fifth acre-foot annually.° Certainly the future growth of populations, both rural and urban, as well as the expansion of cities and farms will depend heavily upon how well the national forests are managed so as to maintain maximum water yield. As far as the whole arid West is concerned its forests are more important as sources of water than as anything else. In addition, they are, of course, valuable as sources of lumber and as hunting, grazing, and recreation grounds.

In view of the preceding discussions Figure 5:5 is of interest, for it shows the relationship between altitude, precipitation, and types of tree growth. The example is from the southern portion of California's Central Valley. There, where the growing season is longer than at more northerly latitudes, the 25-inch line of annual precipitation marks the boundary (as well as any single figure can) between grass and woodland. The principal area, which contributes percolation and runoff, begins in the ponderosa pine zone and extends into the particularly rainy province of the giant sequoia and red fir. Because of winter snowfall, followed by spring and summer snow melt, the crests of the Sierra Nevada above

°An acre-foot is sufficient water to cover one acre to the depth of one foot.

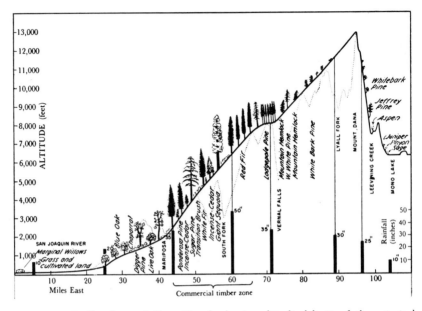

Figure 5:5. Profile of central Sierra Nevada showing altitudinal limits of the principal forest types. (Source: Reference 4; p. 353.)

the timber line are also significant contributors to total water yield. It will be noted that heaviest precipitation occurs at an elevation of about 6000 feet. It is apparent that moisture vapor in the majority of the air masses blowing in from the Pacific Ocean and across the warm California deserts must reach this altitude on the flanks of the Sierra Nevada before orographic cooling induces condensation and heavy precipitation. The fog, rain, and drizzle conditions which impress the visitor to the Sequoia National Forest are caused by orographic cooling. One may leave Fresno in the San Joaquin Valley on a sunny afternoon and within a few hours drive into a belt of fog and drizzle higher up the mountain slopes. For the student of ecology the first journey from desert to fog forest and on to alpine meadow remains unforgettable, and every repetition stimulates his thought as to all the influences and consequences involved.

The Limitations of Forests. Forests alone are incapable of stabilizing the flow of surface and underground waters so that stream flow can be equalized the year around. The seasons of maximum precipitation or snow melt are too distinct in the West to permit forests to function in this manner. That forests could accomplish such a task has never been the contention of any serious conservationist. It is, however, the observation of hydrologists that flood peaks are minimized to the extent that rain and snow melt are induced to pass into streams as ground water rather than as surface runoff. It is the forests' ability to reduce flash floods, soil erosion, and reservoir siltation that evokes the desert farmer's interest in forest management. He knows that dams are necessary to even out the annual flow of streams which is particularly variable in the West. However, dams without reservoirs are useless for flood control or for the storage of irrigation water. Uncontrolled runoff and erosion can fill reservoirs with silt and render them useless as storage basins. This type of damage is discussed in a subsequent chapter.

Forest Management. The way in which forests are managed when on private lands is up to their owners. Public agencies are responsible when the forests are public property. Rarely is the desert agriculturist in a position to exert his personal influence upon the management of the forests from which his water flows. In the Basin and Range Province of Nevada streams carrying irrigation water sometimes originate in forests owned at least partially by the individual or corporation using the water. In such cases the water user has direct influence upon forest management. In the Central Valley of California the irrigating farmer knows that the forests behind the clouds on nearby mountainsides contribute to his water supply, but he has little to say about how they should be managed. If they are public lands, he can exercise some influence through his vote and by lobbying. At least he can keep informed because the forests are close, and he can visit them at his leisure.

The situation is quite different for the irrigator of Yuma, Arizona, who uses Colorado River water which has come from the high Rockies as far away as Colorado and Utah. With great difficulty, almost to the point of impossibility, could he exert influence upon the management of wooded lands many hundreds of miles away. It is one thing to know that good forest management is essential to a prosperous irrigation agriculture; it is quite another for most farmers to exercise any influence upon that management, either on private or public lands. Yet their very solvency and the continuation of irrigation agriculture is involved.

REFERENCES

1. Bowman, Isaiah, *Forest Physiography*, John Wiley and Sons, New York, 1911.
2. Powell, J. W., *Report on the Lands of the Arid Region* (second edition), Government Printing Office, Washington, D.C., 1879.
3. President's Water Resources Policy Commission, *Ten Rivers in America's Future*, Government Printing Office, Washington, D.C., 1950.

4. U.S. Department of Agriculture, *Trees—Yearbook of Agriculture, 1949*, Government Printing Office, Washington, D.C., 1949.

5. U.S. Department of Agriculture, *Water—Yearbook of Agriculture, 1955*, Government Printing Office, Washington, D.C., 1955.

6. U.S. Forest Service. *National Forests of the Intermountain Region* (a folder), Ogden, Utah, 1954.

multiple
uses
of
western
forests

6

LUMBERING

Vitally interested as he is in forests as the major source of irrigation water, the farmer is only one among many with a stake in the management of these forests. Today, the woodlands of the western states provide approximately 46 per cent of the nation's saw timber.

More trees are felled in the southeastern states than in the West, but they are almost entirely second-growth stock of smaller average dimensions. Large portions are suited only for pulpwood. As virgin woodlands in the eastern United States became almost completely cut over by the middle of this century, the western forests remained the last source of large coniferous trees. In 1951 the West produced 18,826 million board feet. Of this total the Pacific Northwest of Washington and Oregon yielded 62 per cent, followed by California with 26 per cent, and the Rocky Mountain areas with only 12 per cent.

Although a map (Figure 4:3) would indicate that the Rocky Mountain forests, together with those of the upper Colorado Plateau, are the most extensive in the West, it is shown in Table 6:1 that their timber yield is not in proportion to their area. This is partially due to the lower annual precipitation of the Rocky Mountain zone and, consequently, to sparser growth. To a lesser extent it is due to the difficulty of logging in the very rough terrain of the Rockies and upper Colorado Plateau.

Table 6:1.   U.S. Timber Cut—1944–1952
(Source: Reference 8; p. 33)

		Total in Billion Board Feet	Softwood in Billion Board Feet	Hardwood in Billion Board Feet
North	1944	8.3	2.8	5.5
	1952	6.7	2.4	4.3
South	1944	22.6	14.1	8.5
	1952	19.6	11.7	7.9
West	1944	18.8	18.7	0.1
	1952	22.5	22.4	0.1
United States	1944	49.7	35.6	14.1
	1952	48.8	36.5	12.3

GRAZING

The grazing of forest land, particularly where tree growth is thin, is a significant practice in the West. This is a custom early established by white settlers, who used the lands on which the forest undergrowth had been burned by Indian huntsmen. The deliberate burning by Indians thinned the woodlands of the drier regions and commonly eliminated them in some parts. J. W. Powell in 1878 reported from personal observation that

The timber regions are only in part *areas of standing timber.* (Powell's italics) This limitation is caused by fire. Where the rainfall is great and extreme droughts are infrequent, forests grow without much interruption from fires; but between that degree of humidity necessary for their protection, and that smaller degree necessary to growth, all lands are swept bare by fire to an extent which steadily increases from the more humid to the more arid districts, until at last all forests are destroyed, though the humidity is still sufficient for their growth if immunity from fire were secured . . . . In the main these fires are set by Indians . . . . On their hunting excursions they systematically set fire to forests for the purpose of driving the game. This is a fact well known to all mountaineers. Only the white hunters of the region properly understand why these fires are set, it being usually attributed to a wanton desire on the part of the Indians to destroy that which is of value to the white man. (Reference 2; pp. 15–18.)

Table 6:2. Sheep and Goats Permitted to Graze on National Forests in Eleven Western States (in thousands)*

(Source: Reference 4; pp. 94–95)

Year	Ariz.	Calif.	Colo.	Idaho	Mont.	Nev.	N. Mex.	Ore.	Utah	Wash.	Wyo.	Total 11 Western States
1918	434	582	1106	1960	810	468	523	784	842	222	779	8510
1923	281	469	904	1525	628	329	304	650	771	178	665	6704
1928	265	435	1033	1322	598	316	234	648	759	162	624	6396
1933	291	369	946	1316	588	308	205	612	739	145	619	6138
1938	226	306	861	1182	423	263	176	497	655	112	587	5288
1943	137	251	773	895	391	248	154	320	662	108	582	4521
1948	89	147	656	675	273	141	110	175	526	49	466	3307
1949	86	128	623	623	270	139	108	165	490	40	408	3080

Cattle and Horses Permitted to Graze on National Forests in Eleven Western States (in thousands)†

Year	Ariz.	Calif.	Colo.	Idaho	Mont.	Nev.	N. Mex.	Ore.	Utah	Wash.	Wyo.	Total 11 Western States
1918	341	223	411	204	193	90	193	167	190	31	137	2180
1923	262	200	348	169	164	73	133	136	164	27	130	1806
1928	196	158	289	135	133	55	94	91	120	13	114	1398
1933	203	147	290	139	138	55	101	88	117	15	115	1408
1938	197	132	250	128	94	56	94	79	109	16	106	1261
1943	171	136	196	114	109	57	99	71	117	21	115	1206
1948	139	118	178	117	117	60	84	73	114	20	109	1129
1949	139	115	169	113	116	55	82	72	111	21	108	1101

*Excludes lambs and kids under 6 months of age which are not listed on grazing permits.
†Excludes calves and colts under 6 months of age which are not listed on grazing permits.

Table 6:3. **Significance of Grazing Districts and National Forests in Feed Supply of Western Livestock—1949**

State	Animals on Farms in 1000's of AUM°	Grazing Districts 1000's of AUM	National Forests 1000's of AUM	Total AUM in 1000's	Percentage of AUM from Grazing Districts	Percentage of AUM from National Forests
Arizona	12,046	578	1,288	1,866	4.8	10.7
California	38,378	485	563	1,048	1.3	1.5
Colorado	26,076	960	1,034	1,994	3.7	4.0
Idaho	14,947	1,453	869	2,322	9.7	5.8
Montana	29,220	955	616	1,571	3.3	2.1
Nevada	8,047	2,316	339	2,655	28.8	4.2
New Mexico	18,653	2,258	784	3,042	12.1	4.2
Oregon	16,248	1,150	443	1,593	7.1	2.7
Utah	10,654	2,462	791	3,253	23.1	7.4
Washington	11,962	–	119	119	–	1.0
Wyoming	17,904	1,856	582	2,438	10.4	3.3

°AUM is Animal Unit Month, which means 1 head of cattle, or 1 horse, 1 mule, or 5 sheep or goats grazed for 1 month.

When we consider that this was observed only eighty years ago and that grazing by herds of domestic sheep and cattle has since then favored grass and shrubs rather than trees, we more easily understand why much land in the Rocky Mountains which might have had timber is not wooded at all. Even where trees stand, the woodlands are commonly pocked with open glades of grass and browse. The Forest Service reports, "Every year, about 4,500,000 sheep and goats and 1,325,000 cattle, horses, and swine, belonging to some 34,000 permittees, graze in our national forests." (Reference 7; p. 11.) This activity is almost entirely in the West.

As noted later, there is evidence that grass and brush, in an area sufficiently humid to support forest, will allow more runoff water than if trees were permitted to grow. From the standpoint of the irrigation farmer and the livestock herdsman it might be thought that the wisest policy to practice would be a system of land management which would favor grass, sheep, and cattle. Of course, there arises the question of competing interests. What of the lumbermen who want timber; of the tourist who goes to the mountains because they are forested; of the various businessmen who cater to those tourists who otherwise would go elsewhere; of the millions of sportsmen who want national forests stocked with wild game they can hunt rather than with someone else's domestic animals? In the eleven western states in which most of the national forests are concentrated there has been, because of these competing pressures, a marked decline in the numbers of sheep and cattle which are permitted to graze.

The principal reasons for the declines shown in Table 6:2 are

1. A decrease in the forage quality of the national forests resulting from overgrazing.

2. A reduction in grazing allotments in the national forests as a consequence of previous overgrazing.

3. The difficulty, according to stockmen, of obtaining competent hired help at reasonable wages as the older sheep herders die or retire and the resulting lack of adequate protection against dogs and coyotes. (Reference 4; p. 100.)

Of all domestic livestock grazing in the eleven western states only a small percentage of the total occurs in the national forests.

Although 53.9 per cent of the land area of these states is federal property, it is obvious that the public domain is not the most important grazing territory. The best range is already in private hands, particularly where irrigation is possible. Scarcely more than 1 per cent of the nation's cattle and only 11 per cent of its sheep graze in the national forests. This is surprising when one considers the severe damage to vegetative cover caused by these relatively few animals.

WILDLIFE RESERVATIONS

With the rapid increase in the human population and a corresponding decline in wilderness areas where good hunting with gun or camera is possible, there has been a growing demand on the part of the public that more of the federal forests be reserved for wildlife. The grass and browse of the national forests, now utilized by domestic livestock, could support an equivalent wildlife population which would afford sport to a large number of citizens who want that recreational opportunity and cannot find it elsewhere. The gradually increasing influence of this point of view is reflected in larger reservations for big-game animals. The harvest of wildlife is regulated to assure both good hunting and an opportunity for the animals to reproduce and increase. The trend has been most emphatic in Colorado and California.

WATERSHED MANAGEMENT

Although we have noted the specific and sometimes competing interests of irrigation farmers, urban water users, ranchers, lumbermen,

Table 6:4. Big Game Grazed on National Forests in Eleven Western States
(Source: Reference 4; p. 97)

Year	Animal Unit Months Grazed By			Percentage of AUM Grazing By		Change From 1921	
	Big Game° 1,000 AUM	Livestock 1,000 AUM	Total 1,000 AUM	Big Game Per Cent	Livestock Per Cent	Big Game 1,000 AUM	Livestock 1,000 AUM
1921	1,606	16,450	18,056	8.9	91.1		
1926	2,314	12,483	14,797	15.6	84.4	+ 708	−3,967
1931	3,142	12,406	15,548	20.2	79.8	+1,535	−4,044
1936	3,778	11,547	15,325	24.7	75.3	+2,172	−4,903
1941	5,100	9,786	14,886	34.3	65.7	+3,494	−6,664
1946	5,359	8,422	13,781	38.9	61.1	+3,753	−8,028
1949	5,481	7,428	12,909	42.5	57.5	+3,875	−9,022

°Big game: antelope, deer, elk only.

and sportsmen, we have neglected to consider one of the most important aspects of all: the part that these national forests play in total watershed behavior. If national policy were to be decided solely on the basis of the interests of the majority, or according to proportional representation, the decision would ignore fundamental biological facts. The whole sum and character of watershed resources and performance would deteriorate unless vegetative cover were maintained in accordance with natural principles. This does not mean that there is only one best method of management, but it does mean that proper watershed management must consider biologic and hydrologic facts. What are the basic facts regarding water runoff, soil erosion, and vegetative cover in any watershed?

As stated in a publication of the Department of Agriculture,

A basic premise of watershed management is that the amount and rate of stream flow expresses the natural and cultural characteristics and conditions of the watershed which produces it. (Reference 1; pp. 4–7).

In other words, as one's body temperature, is an indication of physical health so is the character of stream flow in any watershed a reflection of the condition of the whole watershed: how it is vegetated and how it is being used. Stream flow can be measured and charted on hydrographs. For instance, a stream gaging station fitted with automatic devices can record the rate and amount of flow leaving a watershed.

Figure 6:1 shows a composite hydrograph representing typical stream discharge resulting from a high-intensity storm.

The composite hydrograph, represented by the solid line, is drawn by the pen of the stream-flow recorder. The broken lines in the figure are not recorded by the pen on a chart. Rather, they are derived by established techniques of hydrograph analysis to represent the several sources of flow which combine to make up the total actual flow past the gage.

How forest and range use affects stream flow can be visualized by analyzing the relation between each component on the hydrograph and the soil. Soil condition, of course, changes according to the nature, condition, and use of the vegetation. To help show these relations reference is made to both Figure 6:1 and the illustration of rainfall disposal shown in Figure 6:2.

The uppermost solid line in Figure 6:1 shows total discharge past the stream-flow gage. This discharge comes from three sources: (1) base flow; (2) surface runoff; (3) subsurface flow. Note that at any one instant the sum of base flow, subsurface flow, and surface runoff equals total discharge—Line K–L–O.

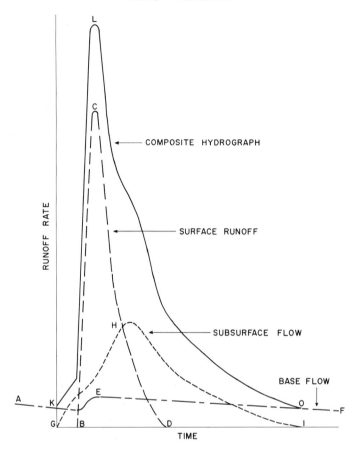

Figure 6:1.   A stream-flow hydrograph. (Source: Reference 1; p. 5.)

The base-flow line in Figure 6:2 corresponds to line A–E–F in Figure 6:1.   It represents the drainage of deep ground waters, and it fluctuates only slightly with the precipitation cycle.   This is the effluent of the ground-water table and is the flow which normally supports springs and maintains rivers in dry weather.   A second source of discharge is surface runoff which is represented by line B–C–D in Figure 6:1 and is also illustrated in Figure 6:2.   This surface runoff water does not enter the soil but rather runs over its surface.   For this reason surface runoff rates reflect the intensity and amount of rainfall.   They are also influenced by the infiltration and percolation capacities of the soil, which in turn are modified by vegetative cover.   The peak of surface runoff discharge (C on the hydrograph, Figure 6:1) coincides in time and can closely approximate the peak rate of total watershed discharge. The rate usually rises rapidly to the peak during or shortly after the intense part of a storm. Subsequent decline is somewhat less rapid.

The third component labeled subsurface flow in Figure 6:2 is illustrated by line G–H–I in Figure 6:1. It originates from water stored temporarily in the soil at shallow depths (usually less than 24 inches) over a more or less compact soil zone. As water accumulates over this layer it moves down the slope through the soil towards the stream channel. Surbsurface flow is not as sensitive to rainfall intensity as surface runoff. Even for equal volumes of outflow its peak rate will be considerably lower than that of surface runoff because the outflow is more prolonged.

The shape of the hydrograph of each component of stream flow reflects the time required for the water to reach the open channel. Thus surface runoff, as shown in Figure 6:2, takes the quickest way to the channels, often through existing or newly created rills and gullies on the surface. Subsurface flow moves more slowly on its way to the stream. Often, however, this type of runoff is intercepted by gullies before it reaches the channel and is then quickly transferred to surface flow. Base flow moves

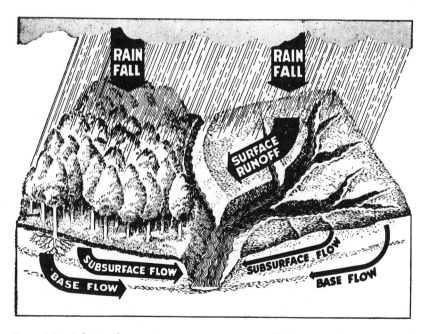

Figure 6:2. Relation of vegetative cover to water removal. (Source: Reference 1; p. 6.)

most slowly. Once in the channel, the water from all sources moves down stream relatively fast. Any practices which change the nature of the vegetation will in turn cause changes in the physical characteristics of the soil and therefore influence the amounts of water which will become surface, subsurface, and base discharge.

The physical state of the soil determines the following hydrologic developments:

1. *Infiltration,* or the rate at which water moves into the soil.
2. *Percolation,* or the rate at which water moves downward through the soil.
3. *Storage capacity,* or the ability of the soil to retain water.

These factors in turn determine the proportions of the three stream-discharge components. When infiltration rates, percolation rates, and water-storage capacities are high then immediate runoff from a given storm will be low. Under these conditions much of the storm's precipitation will move into the soil. There part of it may be stored, a part may go to surbsurface flow, and still another part may move on downward to base flow. These are the slow routes to a stream channel. Soil erosion is not caused by these waters unless landslides develop as the result of excessive storage and subsurface flow. Conversely, at the opposite extreme, when there is a low infiltration rate with little storage then most of the precipitation leaves the area as surface runoff. There is, consequently, a marked increase in peak rates of stream flow, possible flood conditions, and, very likely, soil erosion.

The Coweeta Experiment. An example of the effects of land management on stream flow is shown in Figure 6:3. The hydrographs from two of the several experimental watersheds at the Coweeta Hydrologic Laboratory in western North Carolina illustrate the changes brought about by removing forest vegetation and using the land for farming in a mountainous district.

The altered and unaltered watersheds cover 23 and 39 acres, respectively. Stream flow on the altered watershed was measured for six years prior to its alteration in order to determine its runoff characteristics while timber occupied the land. The timber was clear-cut in 1939–1940. Six acres were planted to corn and cultivated according to local practices. Twelve of the remaining 17 acres were grazed. Five acres were found to be too rough for either cropping or grazing. The effects of changed vegetation on stream flow are shown by a comparison of two storms of about the same size. One of these storms occurred before timber cutting in 1934; the other, after treatment in 1946. The hydrograph of the unaltered watershed shows little difference in stream flow

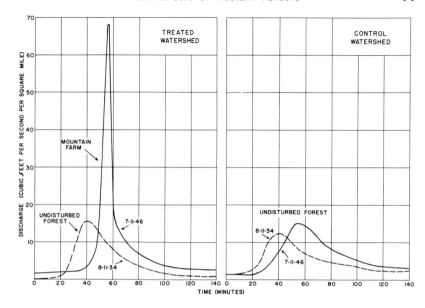

Figure 6:3. Effects of land use on stream flow. (Source: Reference 1.)

resulting from the same two storms. On the unaltered watershed the peak discharges were 12 and 15 cubic feet per second per square mile (c.s.m.).

Hydrographs of the altered watershed tell quite a different story. Whereas the 1934 storm produced a peak discharge of only 16 c.s.m., the 1946 storm produced about 69 c.s.m. The difference was due almost entirely to an increase in surface runoff, as shown by an analysis of the hydrograph. As previously indicated, this increase in runoff resulted from changes in vegetative cover ,and soil condition caused by removing timber and using the land for cultivation and grazing.

Consequences of Mismanagement. When areas in the national forests are overgrazed several results besides the depleted vegetation are observed. The soil is compacted by the animals' hoofs to the extent that water infiltration rates are reduced. This promotes surface runoff, and soil erosion results. Excessive removal of vegetative protection exposes the soil to the direct impact of falling rain. This, too, facilitates erosion by dispersing soil aggregates into fine particles that are more easily carried away. With loss of soil, the subsequent vegetative growth is less vigorous. Sometimes it never recovers fully.

Another consequence of erosion is that the silt carried by runoff waters is eventually brought to reservoirs behind dams storing water for irrigation, power, and urban consumption. In 1937 the National Research Council observed that on the basis of sedimentation surveys made by government agencies 83 per cent of all existing reservoirs in the United States are threatened with extinction by siltation within less than 200 years. At that time 38 per cent of the reservoirs had a life expectancy of only 1 to 50 years; 24 per cent, 50 to 100 years; 21 per cent, 100 to 200 years; and only 17 per cent, more than 200 years. We have done little to reduce siltation since those surveys were reported, but we are spending millions for new dams which within predictable time will become desert shrines like the Pyramids—imposing to view but robbed of function.

The 1950 report of the President's Water Resources Policy Commission considers grazing practices in the national forests. The following are a few excerpts.

The national forests of the Pacific Northwest now supply summer forage for 270,000 cattle and horses and over a million sheep. However, 7 million of the 22 million acres of national forest ranges are evergrazed, with attendant damage to the water resources. To overcome this a reduction in the grazing intensity has been under way for some time. Concurrently, a range-improvement program has been going forward. Some range-reseeding work is being done. (Reference 10; p. 13.)

Sediment is a major problem in the upper Rio Grande and Pecos River sub-basins. The McMillan Reservoir, on the Pecos River, has already lost 90 per cent of its usefulness as a storage reservoir for the Carlsbad Project. Based on a 1944 survey, Alamogordo Reservoir, constructed in 1937 to replace McMillan, is losing about 2.3 per cent of its original capacity annually. . . . Soil erosion is moderate or severe on many areas. . . .

The Forest Service of the Department of Agriculture administers the national forests, which include much of the high mountain area and furnish most of the water supply. These forests are not now high sediment producers, but numerous local areas are eroding because of fire or range misuse. These conditions are slowly being improved by adjusting livestock use to forage production, better logging methods, and more efficient forest-fire control. Much greater progress is necessary in obtaining better watershed conditions and in preventing the production of sediments. Most national forests contain a high percentage of intermingled private lands. Although the Forest Service attempts to obtain as good practices on these lands as on the Federal lands, many owners follow methods which result in land damage. By a program of land purchase and of exchanging timber for land, the Service has been able to consolidate some of its holdings. (Reference 10; pp. 297–299.)

WATER FOR IRRIGATION

In the dry West the water yield of a watershed is the prime concern of the irrigator. Maximum yield will result from removing vegetative cover by heavy grazing or by injudicious timber removal. Such maximum yields could promote soil erosion and the discharge of silt into reservoirs which would minimize their value as storage basins. The wise management of any watershed calls for many considerations.

Numerous experiments have been made to test the effect of timber cutting on total water yield. One of considerable interest was reported in 1948 by the Department of Agriculture. The results of this experiment conducted in Colorado are shown in Table 6:5:

Table 6:5. Disposition of Precipitation as Affected by Timber Cutting
(Source: Reference 9; p. 33)

In Inches	Merchantable reserve stand per acre in board feet°				
	11,900 (uncut)	6000	4000	2000	0
Precipitation reaching the ground	16.77	19.04	19.89	20.33	21.78
Losses aside from interception	6.43	7.66	7.57	7.89	8.26
Water available for stream flow	10.34	11.38	12.32	12.44	13.52

°Timber cutting left both merchantable and smaller trees at least 3.6 inches in diameter as follows:

Reserve stand in board feet	Number of trees per acre
0	147
2000	206
4000	181
6000	223

The complete removal of all merchantable timber resulted in a net gain of 3.18 inches of water per acre per year. It was learned that standing trees intercepted and prevented some snow and rain from reaching the ground. This is reflected in the differences in the figures of precipitation reaching the ground. Less moisture was lost, however, from the uncut areas during the summer months than from the cut areas because less rain reached the ground in the uncut areas. Evapotranspiration during the warm months was calculated by the experimenters to have been equal to summer precipitation reaching the ground; but more snow was lost through evaporation from the ground on cut-over land because it was not protected from the sun and wind by a tree canopy. Although no noticable soil erosion was observed on the cut plots, the researchers mention in their report that soil and slope conditions differ greatly in the

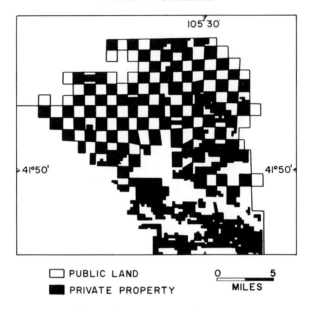

Figure 6:4.   Land ownership in a portion of Roosevelt National Forest.

West, and therefore they could not generalize about other than the experimental area.   They stated,

It is strongly emphasized that the results of these experiments by no means justify or even suggest destructive exploitation of forests in the guise of watershed management; but they do show that the amount of water available for stream flow may be substantially increased by carefully managed timber cutting. In any area that is sensitive to erosion or susceptible to floods, increases in water supply resulting from timber cutting may be more than offset by sedimentation and flood damage to both the watershed and water-using land.   In such areas, water production must be subordinated to watershed protection; and on any watershed the dictates of wise land management require that timber cutting be done only with adequate precautions to conserve all watershed resources. (Reference 9; p. 37.)

In view of the multiple-use value of western national forests to lumbermen, irrigation farmers, ranchers, sportsmen, power generators, and every urban citizen it is obvious that the special interests of no one group should be allowed to dictate management policy.   Although economic and cultural factors are important in formulating decisions, it should not be overlooked that a watershed is a natural feature of the physical landscape and its flora and fauna, either wild or domestic, are living organisms.   The soil is not static but changes rapidly in composition and structure, depending upon how both fauna and flora are managed. Unless the natural principles of land use are understood and abided by in the management of each watershed there are likely to be costly and unhappy consequences.

The ownership pattern of western forest areas somewhat complicates the task. The interests of the nation which are staked in the public domain must be resolved with those of private landowners who possess lands in almost every watershed. This calls for diplomatic and wise counsel. How complicated the situation sometimes becomes is illustrated by Figure 6:4.

Many millions of acres in the West are similar checkerboards of public and private lands. In most cases this pattern was derived from the railroad grants of the late nineteenth century when the government gave the railroads every other section of land for several miles in width along projected rights-of-way. The sale of these lands helped to finance railway construction.

REFERENCES

1. Lassen, Leon, et al., *Some Plant-Soil-Water Relations in Watershed Management*, U.S. Department of Agriculture, Washington, D.C., 1952.
2. Powell, J. W., *Report on the Lands of the Arid Region of the United States* (second edition), Government Printing Office, Washington, D.C., 1879.
3. Randall, C. E. and M. F. Heisley, *Our Forests: What They Are and What They Mean to Us*, U.S. Department of Agriculture, Misc. Pub. No. 162 (revised), Government Printing Office, Washington, D.C., 1950.
4. U.S. Department of Agriculture, *Domestic Wool Requirements and Sources of Supply*, Government Printing Office, Washington, D.C., 1950.
5. U.S. Department of Agriculture, *Water—Year Book of Agriculture, 1955*, Government Printing Office, Washington, D.C., 1955.
6. U.S. Forest Service, *Some Plain Facts About the Forests*, Misc. Pub. No. 543 (revised), Government Printing Office, Washington, D.C., 1949.
7. U.S. Forest Service, *The Work of the Forest Service*, Misc. Pub. No. 290 (revised), Government Printing Office, Washington, D.C., 1945.
8. U.S. Forest Service, *Timber Resource Review*, Chapter III, Government Printing Office, Washington, D.C., 1955.
9. Wilm, H. G. and E. G. Dunford, *Effect of Timber Cutting on Water Available for Stream Flow from a Lodgepole Pine Forest*, U.S. Department of Agriculture Tech. Bull. No. 968, Government Printing Office, Washington, D.C., 1948.
10. President's Water Resources Policy Commission, *Ten Rivers in America's Future*, Washington, D.C.
11. Graham, Edward H., *The National Principles of Land Use*, Oxford University Press, New York, 1944.

the
wise
use
of
water

7

Water in the arid West is wasted in many ways. The greatest losses occur for these reasons:

1. Because we have not constructed the dams necessary to hold back all flood waters that escape to the sea, especially during springtime when snow melts rapidly in the high mountains (Figures 7:1 and 7:2).

2. Because sufficient measures have not been taken to check seepage losses through porous earth-bottom canals.

3. Because many farmers have not undertaken the land-leveling and drainage operations on their properties which would result in the most economical application and recovery of water.

THE CENTRAL VALLEY PROJECT

The Central Valley of California is the most important single area of irrigation farming in the United States, yet its potential is only half realized (Figure 7:3). Annual stream flow is erratic and unevenly dis-

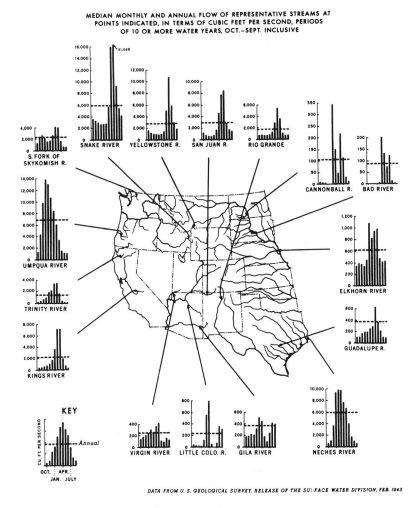

MEDIAN MONTHLY AND ANNUAL FLOW OF REPRESENTATIVE STREAMS AT
POINTS INDICATED, IN TERMS OF CUBIC FEET PER SECOND, PERIODS
OF 10 OR MORE WATER YEARS, OCT.–SEPT. INCLUSIVE

DATA FROM U. S. GEOLOGICAL SURVEY, RELEASE OF THE SURFACE WATER DIVISION, FEB. 1943

Figure 7:1.   Normal seasonal flow of western streams.

tributed. Annual runoff into the valley since 1904 has varied from
an estimated maximum of more than 60 million acre-feet in 1906–1907 to
a recorded minimum of less than 8.5 million acre-feet in 1924. A forty-
year average of 33 million acre-feet has been estimated for the period
1903–1904 to 1942–1943. (Reference 2; p. 99.)

The net irrigable acreage of the Central Valley is estimated by the
Bureau of Reclamation at over 8 million acres. Some lands cannot be
irrigated every year because fallowing may be essential to maintain soil

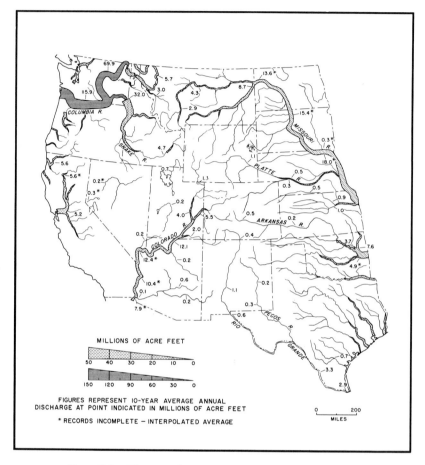

Figure 7:2. Water supply in western rivers. (Source: U.S.D.A.)

structure and fertility. It is therefore assumed that the maximum irrigable area in any one year will ultimately be about 6.5 million acres. The net water requirement for 6.5 million acres is believed to be 16.6 million acre-feet, or about one half the average annual discharge of valley streams. Several million acre-feet are utilized by metropolitan areas and to maintain stream levels in the delta district so that salt water from San Francisco Bay will not push inland. The net annual requirement for all future purposes is estimated at approximately 20 million acre-feet. Thus, properly harnessed and distributed, there is sufficient water in the valley for all essential needs.

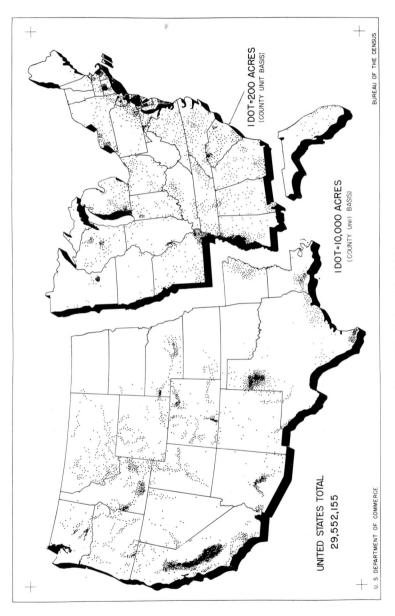

Figure 7:3.   Irrigated land in farms.

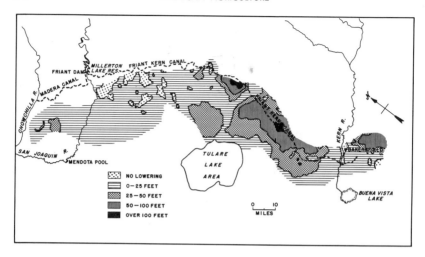

Figure 7:4. Ground-water table drop; lower Central Valley, California. (Source: Reference 2; p. 104.)

Water surplus in the Central Valley is concentrated in the upper Sacramento River area, whereas a perennial deficit exists in the arid upper San Joaquin River and Tulare Lake basins. Ground water has long been pumped in the latter districts with a consequent lowering of the water table (Figure 10:1).

The primary objective of engineers who plan for an equitable distribution of water in the Central Valley is to transfer surplus waters from the Sacramento River into the water-deficit districts that are several hundred miles southward. Major portions of this goal are already achieved. By the construction of Friant Dam and reservoir, the upper San Joaquin has been decapitated. The intercepted waters are now transferred by way of the 153-mile Friant-Kern Canal as far south as the Bakersfield district.

To compensate for the diversion of water from the upper San Joaquin surplus waters from the Sacramento are made available to the San Joaquin below Friant Dam by an ingenious series of engineering devices. The keystone is Shasta Dam and its reservoir with an average annual discharge capacity of 5 million acre-feet. Shasta Dam withholds spring runoff on the upper Sacramento, and this water is released downstream during the drier summer months to maintain a higher than normal flow. As this surplus approaches the lower Sacramento it is transferred by the Delta Cross Channel Canal to the lower San Joaquin near the town of Tracy. At Tracy a gigantic pumping operation lifts the water 197

feet into the cement-lined Delta-Mendota Canal, which conveys it by
gravity at a maximum initial rate of 4600 cubic feet per second to
Mendota Pool on the upper San Joaquin—a distance of 120 miles.
Mendota Pool lies a few miles from the point at which Friant Dam

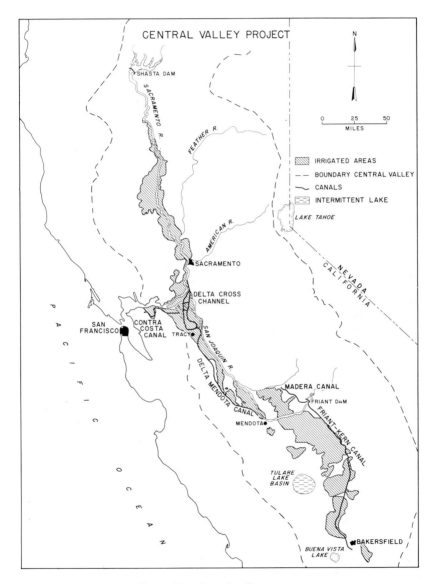

Figure 7:5.   Central Valley Project.

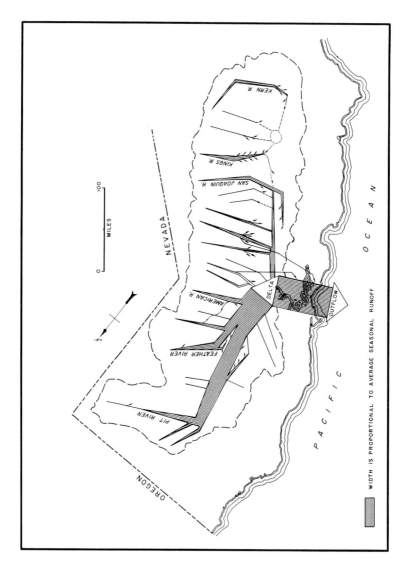

Figure 7·6.   Stream flow of Central Valley. (Source: Reference 2; p. 117.)

cuts off the normal flow of the upper San Joaquin River. Thus the water borrowed from the San Joaquin is repaid with water from the Sacramento.

Additional dams, reservoirs, and canals are needed to capture other surplus waters and convey them into deficit areas. Some have already been constructed; many more are planned, and in time all irrigable land in the Central Valley will be supplied. In this respect California is extremely fortunate, for in most other arid districts of the West there is not sufficient sweet water to satisfy the needs of all irrigable lands.

THE COLORADO-BIG THOMPSON PROJECT

The Colorado-Big Thompson Project in the state of Colorado illustrates how surplus water in an area of limited soil resources can be conveyed across a mountain barrier into an area of rich soils but insufficient water. The continental divide bisects the state of Colorado. Westward of this ridge the Colorado River originates in the forests of Rocky Mountain National Park.

Sources of Colorado River Water
(Source: Reference 1; p. 7)

	Average Annual Acre-Feet
Wyoming	1,840,000
Colorado	11,470,000
Utah	2,748,000
New Mexico	577,000
Arizona	3,054,000
Nevada	60,000
California	20,000
Total Production	19,769,000
Channel Losses	−2,037,000
Total Available	17,732,000

The Colorado River rapidly gains volume as many tributaries join it in the high Rockies, but its course is marked by deep and narrow canyons. Areas of level soils suitable for irrigation are very limited. However, so much water flows from the mountains and high plateaus of Colorado that the state quite reasonably claims an important share of it. In 1922 a compact was signed between all the states of the Colorado River basin. By the terms of this compact, 7.5 million acres-feet of the river's annual flow are reserved for the upper-basin states of Colorado,

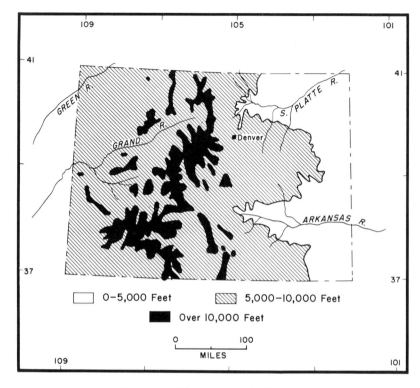

Figure 7:7.   Elevation zones in Colorado.

New Mexico, Utah, and Wyoming.   Colorado was a pioneer in the development of western irrigation, but the growth of its agricultural economy is even now vitally dependent upon further irrigation engineering.

When one refers to a detailed topographic map it is apparent that the areas most suited to irrigation in Colorado lie east of the continental divide, particularly beyond Denver on the South Platte.   The further development of this area is impeded by a limited water supply.   Construction of the Colorado-Big Thompson Project has made possible the annual transfer of nearly one third of a million acre-feet of Colorado River water across the continental divide into the Big Thompson River, which is a tributary of the South Platte.   This is a vitally important supplement to the water supply of about 600,000 acres of irrigated land.

Figure 7:8 shows some of the details of the Colorado-Big Thompson water transfer:

1. Green Mountain Reservoir on the Blue River is designed to stabilize the flow of the Upper Colorado River.   It holds back snow-melt flood

waters for release into the Colorado during the summer. This is necessary to compensate for the decapitation of the Colorado itself by Granby
and Willow Creek dams and reservoirs.

2. The intercepted headwaters of the Colorado are pumped from
Willow Creek to Granby and to Shadow Mountain reservoir.

3. Thence the water descends by the 13-mile Alva B. Adams tunnel
through the continental divide into the headwaters of the Big Thompson
River on the eastern slopes of the Rockies.

4. A series of distribution canals, tunnels, and reservoirs on the eastern
slopes control the release and flow of the transferred water to the irrigated districts of the South Platte River system to which the Big
Thompson and several other rivers belong.

The Colorado River Basin.   As mentioned, the Colorado-Big
Thompson Project utilizes about one third of a million acre-feet of
Colorado River water.   The average annual virgin flow of the Colorado
River across the Mexican boundary before irrigation was undertaken is
estimated to have totaled 17,732,000 acre-feet annually.   Even now
an annual average of approximately 9 million acre-feet pass unused into
the Gulf of California.   There is a wide fluctuation in the flow of the
Colorado from year to year.   It is believed that in its virgin condi-

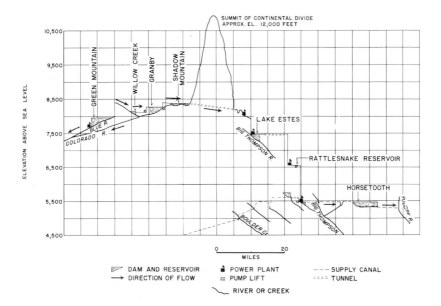

Figure 7:8.   The Colorado-Big Thompson Project.

SELECTED WESTERN RIVERS, WATER YEARS ENDING SEPTEMBER 30, 1920-47

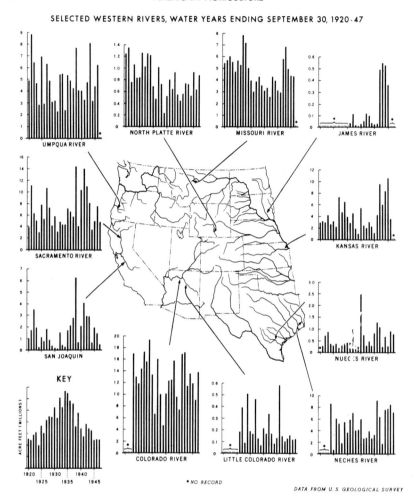

Figure 7:9. Annual variation in stream flow.

tion the extreme discharges were as low as 5 million acre-feet in drought
years and as high as 25 million acre-feet in years of peak runoff (Figure
7:9). (Reference 3; p. 13.) The reason for water wastage in this area
is that not enough dams have been built to hold back the peak spring
flows. There is far more land in the lower Colorado River basin capable
of irrigation than there will ever be water to take care of it, unless
desalted sea water is brought from the Gulf of California.

The demand for Colorado River water illustrates how keenly individual states compete with one another for shares in the flow of a great

interstate river.   The means required both to stabilize the flow and to apportion the water equitably are among our most important engineering projects.   Some are already fact.   Some are only on the drafting boards. The Colorado River basin includes almost all of Arizona, roughly half of Utah and Colorado, as well as sections of New Mexico, Wyoming, Nevada, and California.   It is on the whole a sparsely settled region containing the largest portion of the driest land in the United States. Within its boundaries are a great number of small oases and a few very important irrigated districts.   The extent of economic development would be far greater than it is if all the water of the river were put to use.   It is this prospect of future growth which creates such intense interest in how the water will be apportioned, for the extent of economic development will be almost in direct proportion to the amount of water received.

By treaty with Mexico that country is guaranteed a flow of 1.5 million acre-feet annually.   Thus somewhat more than 16 million acre-feet are usable in the United States.   In 1922 the four upper basin states of Colorado, Wyoming, New Mexico, and Utah agreed under the Colorado River Compact never to withdraw more than an average 7.5 million acre-feet annually.   The balance of almost 8.5 million acre-feet was left to the three lower-basin states.   According to the Department of the Interior "There is no final agreement among the States of the Colorado River basin as to the amount of Colorado River water to be allocated to individual states nor have all of the states made final allocations of water among projects within their boundaries." (Reference 3; p. 13.)   The reasons for this indecision are many, but among the foremost is the fact that there is not enough water to satisfy all interested parties in all the states.   In view of the intense rivalry between some states and groups within states, decisions are not arrived at easily or quickly.   Also, the cost of dams, distribution canals, and tunnels is beyond local means to finance and must await federal appropriations.   Meanwhile, water in the river is wasted, for it cannot be used until reservoirs are created to hold it back for dependable distribution in the growing season.   More has been done on the lower Colorado than in the upper basin.

The key development on the lower river is Hoover Dam and the Lake Mead reservoir behind it.   Hoover Dam, together with Davis, Parker, and Imperial dams, exercises effective control of the stream from the Nevada-Arizona line southward.   Thus the Los Angeles metropolitan district, which lies far outside the basin, is assured by aqueduct of a firm supply of sweet water.   The irrigated areas of California's Imperial Valley and extreme southwestern Arizona are well provided for; but a long series of projected structures will have to be built on the upper

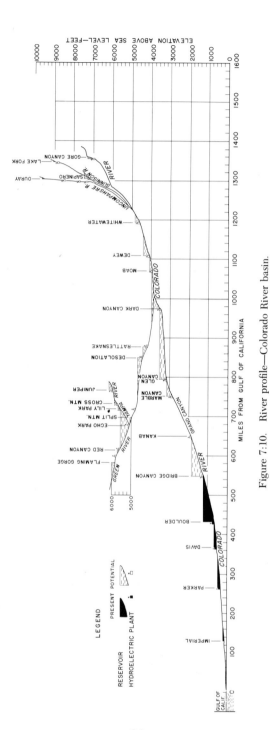

Figure 7:10.   River profile—Colorado River basin.

Colorado and its principal tributaries before it is possible to hold back the millions of acre-feet which could assure the same type of firm water supply in the upper basin states, in Nevada, and in central Arizona.

One of the most highly developed irrigated areas in the Southwest is in central Arizona. Phoenix is the principal city of that oasis in which approximately 725,000 acres are irrigated. The water comes from the Salt and Gila rivers and from the ground water table which is recharged chiefly by seepage through the river channels. The first great reclamation structure built in the United States was Roosevelt Dam on the upper Salt River. Several other important dams have since been erected to regulate the flow of surface waters. Nevertheless, the need for additional water is so great that there is an annual overdraft of ground water amounting to nearly one million acre-feet. Consequently the ground-water table is dropping at an alarming rate; in some areas as much as 10 feet annually. Unless supplementary water from the Colorado River is brought into Central Arizona by an elaborate engineering program, several hundred thousand acres of irrigated land will revert to desert when the ground-water levels drop so low that reserves are exhausted or pumping charges become so great that farmers cannot afford them. Thus one of our earliest centers of irrigation agriculture already faces the prospect of decline if additional water is not "imported."

The Central Arizona Project, as it is described in its present blue-print stage, envisages the diversion of over a million acre-feet of Colorado River water into the Salt-Gila Valley. There are several suggestions as to how this stupendous task could be accomplished. One proposes a dam 740 feet in height at Bridge Canyon on the Colorado between the Grand Canyon and Lake Mead. From Bridge Canyon reservoir the water would pass by gravity through 92 miles of tunnels and 235 miles of canals and aqueducts to the nominal head of irrigation at Granite Reef Reservoir. (Reference 3, p. 180.) Another proposal suggests that power generated at Bridge Canyon Dam be used to operate a multiple-stage water lift at Parker Dam; thus water stored behind Parker Dam would be pumped up to a level from which it could flow by gravity to Granite Reef Reservoir.

The magnitude of the engineering efforts required to distribute western river waters to areas best suited for irrigation is illustrated in the foregoing examples. Even in a country as rich as the United States it is understandable that such projects take time. As long as work remains to be done there exists the prospect of economic growth and progress in many oasis communities. A more serious condition will face these communities when all the waters are harnessed and appropriated. Then they will be confronted with a physical limitation to progress, unless by that time

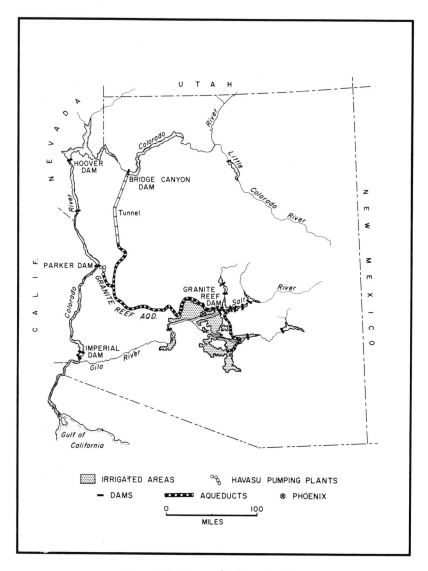

Figure 7:11. Central Arizona Project.

economical means are developed for desalting sea water and delivering it to places capable of further expansion because they have good soil resources.

WASTEFUL WATER LOSSES

In discussing water supplies the problem of wasteful water losses is often overlooked. Figure 7:12 illustrates the manner in which irrigation water withdrawn from reservoirs, streams, and wells was disposed of in one western state in 1949.

If one considers that the 0.7 foot of rainfall was received directly on the land, it would appear that 10.2 feet of man-delivered water were required to supply 0.9 foot to growing crops. That is not efficient. Was all the lost water an unavoidable waste? A very large proportion of the losses in conveyance and regulation (4.9 feet) resulted from sheer neglect. Large main canals as well as individual farm ditches are all too often cut through porous ground, and no measures are taken to make their bottoms and sides impervious to water. There is comparatively little seepage from cement-lined canals, such as the Friant-Kern Canal, yet only the most modern projects and the most alert farmers are undertaking this kind of construction. One canal company near Denver, Colorado, loses 70 to 80 per cent of its water between a reservoir and the farms it serves. Eight New Mexico farmers more than doubled water delivery to their irrigated plots by laying a cement paving over just 700 feet of a sandy section of their main canal.

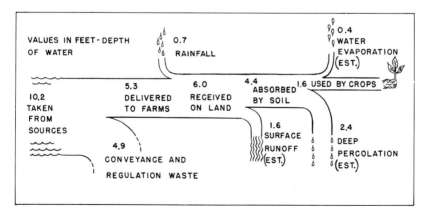

Figure 7:12. Disposal of water diverted and pumped for irrigation in one western state in 1949. (Source: Reference 5; p. 120.)

The 1.6 feet of surface runoff shown in Figure 7:12 not only indicates a waste of water but suggests that soil erosion probably occurs as well. Most land is not so truly level in a natural state that it can be irrigated without surface runoff. However, by using the proper machinery to cut, fill, and plane the land, the natural slope and undulation of irrigable fields can be evened so that both water losses and soil erosion may be reduced to a minimum. The percolation losses of 2.4 feet could very likely be reduced, although some percolation is an essential feature of irrigation agriculture in arid regions. Without some percolation to carry excess soil salts into subterranean channels, there would be an accumulation of these salts on the surface of the fields, where they would eventually prove toxic to cultivated plants.

Under the best management, tile and ditch drains are constructed to withdraw excessive percolation water. If the percolation waters are not too saline, they may be diluted with sweet water and reused, and in this way the same water may serve several irrigators. In the Imperial Valley of California a farmer is not permitted to irrigate until he has made provision for drainage. The Imperial District furnishes each farm within its development with a water intake canal and a drainage outlet canal (Figure 9:1).

Some specialists with a lifetime experience in irrigation agriculture believe that the irrigated acreage of the West could be doubled without building another dam if only the water now available were delivered in cement-lined canals and if the fields themselves were properly leveled so as to accept water most efficiently. The proper recovery, dilution, and reuse of percolation waters is already a factor in the extension of several progressive irrigation districts.

REFERENCES

1. Central Arizona Project Association, *The Central Arizona Project*, Phoenix (mimeographed).
2. United States Bureau of Reclamation, *Central Valley Basin*, Government Printing Office, Washington, D.C., 1949.
3. United States Bureau of Reclamation, *The Colorado River*, Government Printing Office, Washington, D.C., 1946.
4. United States Bureau of Reclamation, *Reclamation Project Data*, Government Printing Office; Washington, D.C., 1948.
5. United States Department of Agriculture, *Water—The Yearbook of Agriculture, 1955*, Washington, D.C., 1955.
6. United States Department of the Interior, *Missouri River Basin Progress Report*, Billings, Montana, 1950.

the
growth
of oases

8

In the truly arid West, where rainfall is too scant for dry farming, the expansion of all field agriculture and much of the grazing industry is dependent upon the extension of irrigation systems. Although the nation as a whole may not now require more farm land and more agricultural production, nevertheless individual states and communities are not inclined to check their own growth just because other places are already in business and might be hurt by the competition. For instance, practically all of southern Idaho would be a sparsely inhabited desert were it not for a chain of thriving oasis communities which have developed parallel with irrigation farming along the margins of the Snake River and its tributaries.

These are some of our newest, most prosperous, and stable agricultural communities, the foundation of the remarkable economic strength which characterizes the large but as yet underpopulated state of Idaho. These growing oasis districts exhibit a vitality and enthusiasm which is commonly lacking in many older agricultural regions; thus it is under-

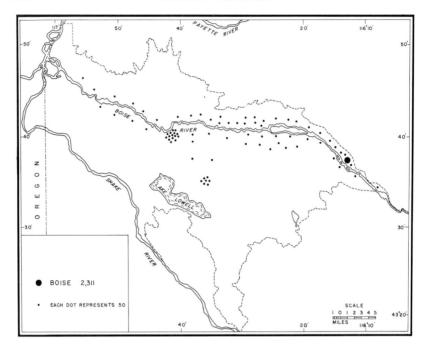

Figure 8:1.   Boise Valley—population 1890. (Source: Reference 1; p. 74.)

standable that wherever there is a possibility of extending irrigation in the arid West the local pressure to do so is intense. As one Idaho farmer was heard to remark, "It's a good thing everyone doesn't like Idaho the way I do. There wouldn't be enough room for all the poor disappointed people."

The development of the Boise Valley is a case in point. In 1862 when gold was discovered in the gravels of Boise River only a few hunters and trappers lived in the entire region. Then followed an invasion of thousands of gold seekers. A few years of frantic mining ended in exhaustion of the gold deposits and in the abandonment of the territory except by those who meanwhile found a more stable means of sustenance. Some say as many as 30,000 people were in Idaho City around 1865. By 1869 only 1000 remained. The influx of prospectors paid well for whatever food could be produced by a smaller, more conservative group of individuals who began irrigation farming.

When the gold rush was over the agricultural economy did not collapse, for by that time railroads had connected the region with more distant and permanent markets. In 1880 there were fewer than 5000 persons in Boise Valley but there were already 19,943 acres of irrigated land. By 1950 there were more than 300,000 acres in cultivation and the valley had a population of 120,000. This was one fifth of all the people in the entire state.

In 1890 nearly all the people in Boise Valley were concentrated in the lowlands bordering the river where water was easily diverted from the stream and spread over the adjacent farms. By 1940 there was a much wider scattering of people made possible by a more elaborate canal system which carried water far beyond the immediate river bottoms. The system of water capture and delivery in 1890 was crude compared with that of 1940. The modernization which has occurred is representative of the way most irrigation districts have evolved in the West. The Boise Valley in its irrigated section is typical of the irrigated areas adjacent to many western streams (Figure 8:3).

Close to the river channel is the bottom land of a former flood plain. Because of dams and reservoirs in the upper watershed there is now little danger of overflow. Most of this land is, or has been, intensively farmed. The water used is diverted at points upstream and conveyed to the farms

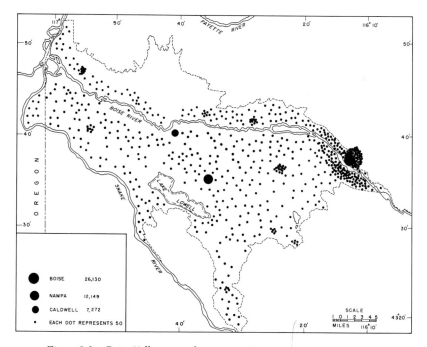

Figure 8:2. Boise Valley—population 1940. (Source: Reference 1; p. 77.)

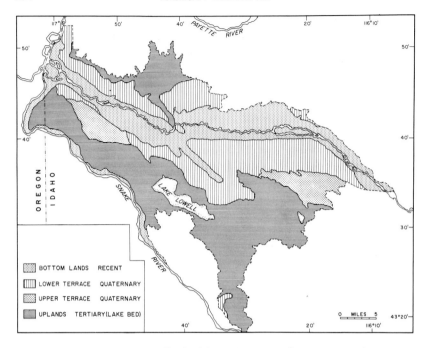

Figure 8:3.   Boise Valley land forms. (Source: Reference 1; p. 24.)

by gravity through canals. Wider and wider areas flanking the bottoms have come into production as more and more water has been diverted farther and farther upstream through the building of dams and canals.

IRRIGATION ON THE RIVER TERRACES
AND LACUSTRINE PLAIN

The upper and lower terrace areas in Figure 8:3 represent geologically earlier flood-plain levels of the Boise River. The lacustrine plain which flanks both the bottom lands and terraces was established in Tertiary time when all the area now irrigated was a great lake. This lacustrine plain, exposed at the end of the Tertiary period, is at present about 300 feet above the channel of Boise River. To irrigate this lacustrine plain with water by gravity it has been necessary to divert the water from Boise River at points far upstream where reservoirs created by dams are at elevations greater than the land ultimately irrigated.

This is the way many irrigation districts in the West have expanded— first along the bottoms where water diversion was easy, later at eleva-

tions on the valley flanks.   To bring the water to the valley flanks costly
dams and longer canal systems are essential.   Almost all new land which
will come into use in the future will require even more elaborate structures.   Occasionally pump installations will be necessary to lift water
where gravity feeding is impractical or where there is to be a transfer
of water from one watershed to another.   In 1950 there were 468 miles of
main-line canals in Boise Valley having a combined flow capacity of
13,564 second-feet and capable of serving 300,000 acres.   Branching off
the main-line canals were 1474 miles of lateral canals which conveyed
water to the individual farms.   Thus there was an average of one mile of
canal for every 150 acres under cultivation.

Waterlogging and Salt Accumulation.   In regard to the drainage
of surplus irrigation water Boise Valley is also typical of many western
irrigated districts.   As new lands on the valley flanks have been brought
into cultivation, the ground-water table has risen in sections of the low-
lying bottoms.   Percolation waters have flowed underground from the
new lands into the subsoils of the old lands, which are at lower elevations.   In some places these percolation waters have risen under hydro-

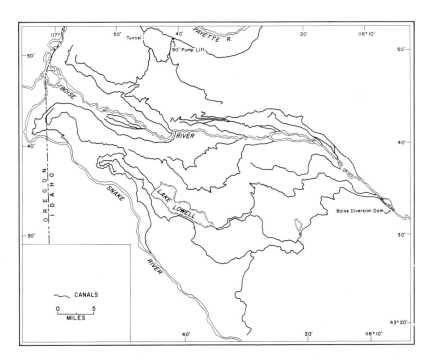

Figure 8:4.   Boise Valley main-line canal system. (Source: Reference 1; p. 104.)

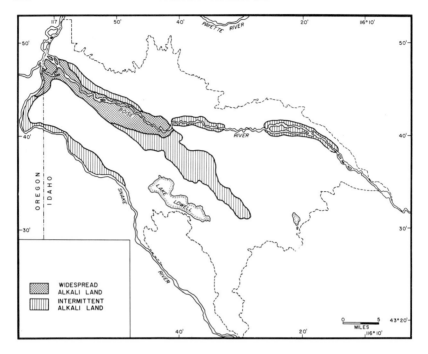

Figure 8:5.   Boise Valley alkali lands. (Source: Reference 1; p. 184.)

static pressure to the surface of fields in the bottoms.   There, by evaporation, they have deposited alkaline salts brought with them in solution.   After a time the concentration of salts may become such that the soil is rendered unfit for tillage.   The waterlogging itself also destroys the usefulness of land.   Figure 8:5 shows districts in the Boise Valley in which soil salinity is encountered in varying degrees.

To counteract waterlogging better drainage facilities are essential and more conservative water application methods should be practiced, particularly on the uplands.   As yet the underground drainage system of Boise Valley, both natural and artificial, is inadequate to the task.   Its main features are illustrated in Figure 8:6.   Until there is a more thorough development of drainageways, the extent of salinity damage and waterlogging is likely to increase as more land comes into cultivation on the periphery of the present oasis.   The rate of salt poisoning, however, will be reduced if better methods of water application are introduced.

Better Methods of Water Application.   Aside from preventing soil deterioration by seepage and by alkali accumulation, better methods of water application help to reduce soil erosion and to conserve water itself. Because the surface of land in its natural state is rarely level it is commonly advisable to level the fields with special machinery. If too much cut and fill should be required or if an undesired bench terrace system would result, the next best thing is to even the grade of slope to make it uniform. Irrigation waters can be more easily controlled on slopes of uniform grade than on those slopes where the grade changes and the surface undulates. In almost every locality in which there is irrigation farming there are some operators who have employed land-leveling machinery. When a farm is improved in this way a more rational system of water delivery and application can be employed. As an example, two figures illustrate a farm near Twin Falls, Idaho. Figure 8:7 shows the farm before the land was leveled and before the water-delivery system was reconstructed according to engineer's specifications. Figure 8:8 is the result of both improvements.

Field-contour lines in Figure 8:7 show a variation in slope of 1 to 4 per cent (vertical drops of 1 to 4 feet per 100 feet of horizontal distance). The old-style earthern irrigation ditches had no drop structures; conse-

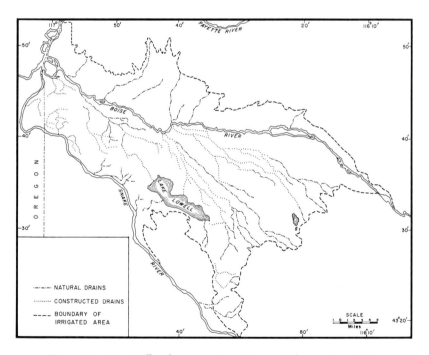

Figure 8:6. Boise Valley drainage system. (Source: Reference 1; p. 187.)

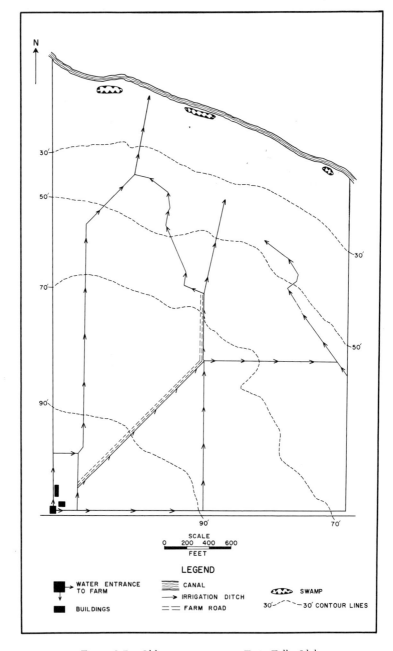

Figure 8:7.   Old irrigation system—Twin Falls, Idaho.

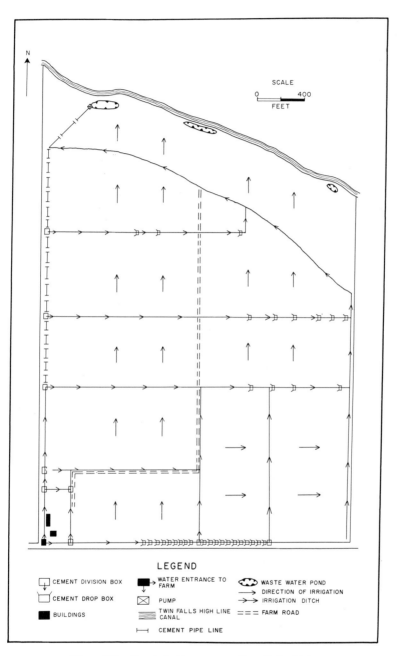

Figure 8:8. New irrigation system—Twin Falls, Idaho.

quently water flowed through them at greater speed on the 4 per cent slopes than on the 1 per cent slopes. Also the pattern of ditch distribution was poorly executed, so that some portions of the farm were at some distance from an irrigation ditch. They often received either too much or too little water. Because of the uneven slopes soil erosion and loss of water were frequent on this farm before the changes shown in Figure 8:8 were made.

The distribution canals in Figure 8:8 are designed with concrete lining. There are also cement drop structures along the lines to let the water flow down grade. Where the slope is greatest, to the north along the west line, the water is carried in cement pipes and its flow is controlled at division boxes. The new water-distribution system divides the farm in such a way that areas of different slope and pitch are well segregated. Consequently, water can be applied more equitably, especially since the fields themselves have been leveled to uniform grades of slope. An additional feature of the new plan shown in Figure 8:8 is the arrangement made to pump seepage waters into the cement-pipe main for use in the fields. Formerly this seepage, an accumulation of percolation water from the main canal, was wasted. The switch from a trial-and-error water-distribution system to one laid out on the basis of a detailed topographic survey is costly and cannot be accomplished quickly by the average farmer. The achievement of such a task on a large property might occupy the best years of a lifetime, but it is now recognized as the wisest kind of investment if done gradually so as not to dry up the farmer's immediate assets and credit. When one reads the tables of values of irrigated farm land it is such costly improvements which make them stand out by comparison with the values of land in humid regions. Unimproved land in arid areas is worth very little.

Well and Pump Irrigation. In the Salinas Valley of California, where all the good bottom land has long been in cultivation, new fields coming into production are on upper terraces. There has been such a strong draft upon the surface waters of the Salinas River that the stream is exhausted before it reaches the lower basin. Pumping from the ground-water table is now the main source of supply for lower-basin farms. This is a condition which has developed in many older irrigated areas of the arid West.

Figure 8:9 is the map of a pump-irrigated farm consisting of both bottom and terrace land. Almost the entire water-distribution system is constructed of concrete pipes with valves at frequent intervals for the attachment of gated pipe laterals. These laterals, made of aluminum, are easily moved from place to place, as needed. Slots or gates in

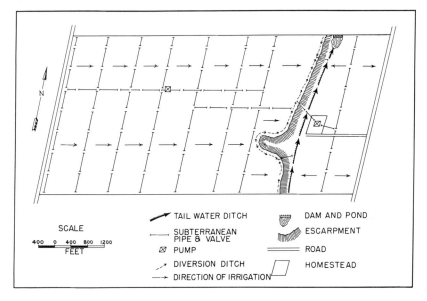

Figure 8:9.   Pump-and-pipe irrigated ranch—Salinas Valley, California.

the aluminum pipes are adjustable for accurate control of water flow. By land-leveling and land-planing, the slopes of the terrace fields have been evened to reduce erosion and to make possible the equitable spread of water.

One well is located near the center of the terrace section of the farm, another near the center of the bottom land.   Tail water recovered from the terrace land is trapped by a diversion ditch and is transferred by gravity through pipes to a tail-water ditch on the bottom lands.   It may be stored in the pond indicated on the map.   The diversion ditch, which is cement lined, serves another purpose.   It intercepts runoff water resulting from winter rains and prevents that water from cutting gullies into the terrace escarpment.

Sprinkler Irrigation.   In some irrigated districts where water is plentiful but where level or slightly pitched land is already in cultivation a sprinkler-type system can be used to bring water to land too steep or rough for gravity-flow distribution.   The water itself may be drawn from surface sources or from wells.

Figure 8:10 is an example of a pond-fed sprinkler system used to water 30 acres of pasture in the Sacramento Valley.   The pond was constructed by damming an arroyo which carries water during the spring period of

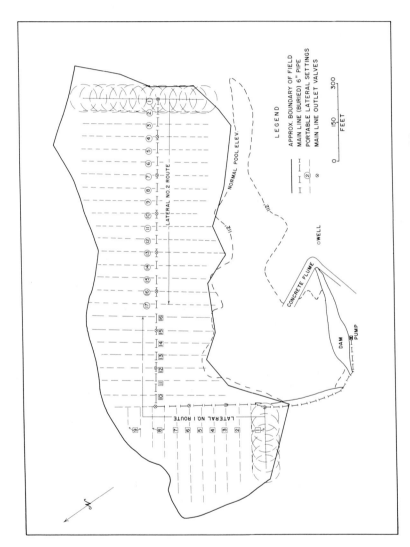

Figure 8:10.   Sprinkler irrigation system—Sacramento Valley, California.

snow melt or after occasional winter rains. Supplementary water is pumped into the pond from a well during the summer. Irrigation water is conveyed to the pasture through a buried system of 6-inch diameter cement pipe, and pressure is supplied by a pump. Three-inch diameter lateral aluminum pipes equipped with fittings for revolving sprinklers are moved manually from day to day along the routes shown on the map. The circular areas watered by the revolving sprinklers overlap, for there is not enough water or pressure in the 6-inch mains to support more than a few laterals at a time. That is why the laterals are moved on a rotational schedule. A sprinkler system is more costly to operate, principally because of the labor involved in hooking and unhooking the laterals and moving them, but it is the best solution to the problem of watering undulating or steep-slope lands.

EROSION UNDER IRRIGATION

Orange County, California, is one of the leading producers of citrus in the United States. It is also one of the fastest-growing residential areas in the country, for it is part of the Los Angeles metropolitan area. Consequently, there is extreme competition for land between the growing suburban populations and the farmers. The citrus industry is caught in the squeeze. Already thousands of acres of level land once in citrus have become subdivisions in which a few trees were left to ornament the new houseyards. On the undulating land of nearby mountain foothills the pressure of human glaciation is not so irresistable. The citrus groves on these sloping lands are being damaged by soil erosion because irrigation water is commonly applied, not by sprinklers, but by various surface-distribution methods. To make matters worse, citrus does not tolerate grass around the trees; otherwise the groves could be protected by a sod cover crop which would help to stabilize the soil. Avocados do grow well with grass as a soil cover crop, and for that reason a number of citrus plantings have been removed to make way for avocados.

Figure 8:11 classifies the land slopes of a 20-acre citrus grove in the piedmont section of Orange County, California. All the slopes are too steep for the application of surface-spread water without danger of erosion. The 15 to 35 per cent slopes are far beyond the optimum limits and consequently show evidence of severe surface erosion and considerable gullying which has been combated, not very successfully, with small cement check dams. The development of irrigation systems and cultural methods which will permit keeping such land in citrus, and at the same time minimize erosion, is now the object of research.

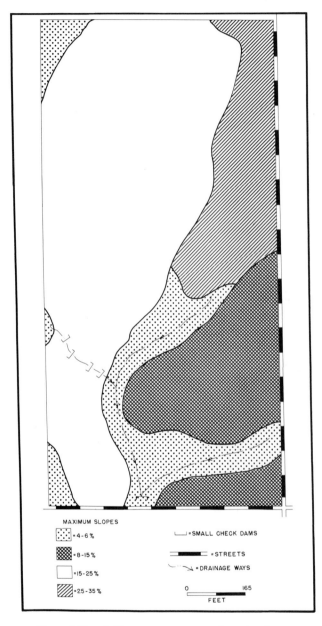

Figure 8:11.   California orange grove—slope classification.

URBAN PRESSURE UPON FARM LAND

It is apparent that only the most unusual types of farming can resist the encroachment of the suburbs upon the limited level lands surrounding metropolitan areas. In fact, only the protection afforded by zoning has helped to preserve the most efficient dairy industry in the United States against the spreading concrete of Los Angeles. The very people for whom the milk is intended threaten to engulf the land now occupied by the dairies. Citrus groves are not so capable of concentrated operation as the dairies, which now import hay as well as other feeds from outside the Los Angeles area. The citrus is therefore more vulnerable.

Los Angeles and Orange counties are extreme examples of the competition between those human pressures for living space and for food producing space. It is a problem observed across the nation, particularly where flat land is scarce or where that flat land is so strategically located that it has greater monetary value for a highway, industrial park, airport, or suburb than for cultivation. As the map of the citrus grove in Orange County illustrates, the day is already here when we are covering some of our best agricultural land with concrete and brick while shunting our food production onto the marginal slopes. In this chapter we have seen how an oasis grows as population and markets grow. We have noted the increasing costs of bringing land on valley flanks into production. In these patterns there is at least the suggestion that as larger populations require more room and the metropolitan areas push the farmer onto poorer land the difficulties and costs of producing food will increase.

In 1941 the Regional Planning Commission of the county of Los Angeles prepared a graph which projected the trends in the urban absorption of agricultural land. At that time the population of Los Angeles County was 2,650,000 and there were 464 square miles (297,000 acres) of agricultural land in the county. In 1954 the population was approaching 5,000,000, and the area of agricultural land had shrunk to 351 square miles, or 225,000 acres. This was only slightly less than the shrinkage projected in the graph (Figure 8:12) which was prepared thirteen years before. By the time the population again doubles in numbers there will remain very little land in the county suitable for farming. In a recent report published by the Los Angeles County Board of Supervisors the following comment was made:

In connection with adequacy of food supply, an interesting paradox occurs in a farm-city transition area such as this. Demand for food is obviously increased by the growing population, yet ability of the area to produce food is decreased as the demand is increased. To indicate what increased population means in food requirements and equivalent land requirements for each 100,000

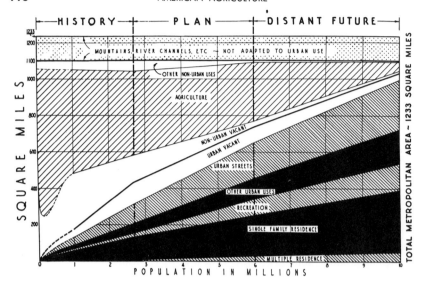

Figure 8:12.   Land-use trends in Los Angeles County. (Source: Reference 2; p. 9.)

new people, the table which follows has been prepared using U.S. Department of Agriculture estimates of national per capita consumption even though these are well below local consumption levels for most of the items listed. Yields assumed are California averages for a recent year.

Crop Acreage and Livestock Required Annually per 100,000 Population Increase.

(Source: Reference 2; p. 10)

Oranges, fresh	241 acres	Potatoes	450 acres	Beef	12,130 head
Avocados	12 acres	Lettuce	166 acres	Milk	7,600 cows
Peaches	98 acres	Tomatoes	283 acres	Eggs	269,000 hens
Grapes	77 acres	Sweet Corn	271 acres	Turkeys	23,000 birds

Between 1925 and 1950 the county of Los Angeles grew at the rate of 100,000 persons annually. This rate has since greatly increased to 165,000 annually. Barring unforeseen developments, it will continue for the immediate future. (Reference 2; p. 6.)

REFERENCES

1. Atrushi, Siddik, *Geographic Elements in Irrigation Agriculture in Boise Valley, Idaho,* a doctoral dissertation in the library of Clark University, Worcester, Mass., 1950.
2. Agricultural Department, Los Angeles County Chamber of Commerce, *Crop Acreage Trends for Los Angles County and Southern California,* Los Angles County Board of Supervisors, 1955.

3. Regional Planning Commission, *Annual Reports*, County of Los Angeles, 1947–1948 and 1953–1954.

4. Stevens, Will, The Big Push, The *San Francisco Examiner* (A reprint of a series of articles which appeared in the *San Francisco Examiner* between May 22 and July 7, 1955).

5. *Southern California, Its Growth and Development*, Cass and Johansing, Los Angeles. (A fine pictorial record of the growth of Southern California. Photography by Spence Air Photos of Los Angeles.)

the
decline
and
renovation
of oases

9

It is possible to put too much water on desert land. Too much, improperly applied without provision for drainage, can drown both plants and soil. Desert lands, like cacti, are not accustomed to much water and may perish by it. By looking at the surface of potentially irrigable land a farmer or even a soil technologist cannot always judge what will happen when water is applied. Sometimes even the examination of soil profiles does not eliminate some guesswork. The principal reason is that no one knows exactly how seepage waters will behave once irrigation has begun. That seepage waters will form swamps somewhere in the immediate irrigated district is a common probability.

The basic reason for uncertainty about future subsurface drainage patterns is the desert itself. Enough rain does not fall to test naturally the potential underground drainage ways of the lands which will be watered. In humid regions a farmer seldom faces such a problem, especially if he examines an area of potential cropland during the rainiest season of the year or in the spring during the melting of snow. He will spot the

natural swamps which develop.   Later he will either avoid those areas or
provide for their artificial drainage.

In the Imperial Valley of California, where a number of early irrigation developments were ruined by seepage swamps, every new farm must
install a drainage system before it is eligible for irrigation water.   The
purpose is not only to protect the new farm coming into cultivation but
the adjoining lands as well.   It would be quite possible for one operator
to commence irrigation without preparation for drainage and suffer no ill
effects.   The penalty for his neglect might be paid instead by someone
else whose land would be swamped by his seepage waters.   We noted in
Chapter 8 how farms in the bottom lands of the Boise River Valley
suffered because seepage accumulated there from new canals and newly
watered fields on the flanking terraces.

TYPES OF DRAINAGE SYSTEMS

The administrators of California's Imperial Valley do not leave such
possibilities to chance.   Figure 9:1 illustrates the water delivery and tile-
drain removal systems of a new Imperial Valley farm.   In essence the two
systems constitute something like the plumbing of a modern house.
Water is led in, used, and the effluent is led away from the property.   In
the plan of Figure 9:1 it should be noted that the main delivery canal
overpasses the principal drainage canal.   The ditches distributing water
about the farm have a slight downgrade to permit gravity feeding.   The
drainage tile are laid at depths of 5 to 6 feet, packed with gravel, and
then covered with soil.   They are set at a slight grade to permit gravity
drainage into the open-ditch outlet canal.   Drainage waters may also be
led into a well and then lifted into an open drainage ditch by means of a
sump pump.   The diameters of drainage tile are in accordance with estimates of the amount of water they carry.

The installation of a grid system of tiles, such as that illustrated, is
costly.   When farmers are not obliged to undertake such construction
they often do nothing.   They prefer to wait until trouble occurs and
then adopt remedial measures.   This may be the soundest approach
economically, for only in an area of unusually favorable winter growing
weather, such as the Imperial Valley, could a farmer be quite confident
of a return commensurate with an investment in a complete grid drainage
system for his entire property.   When remedial measures are taken after
damage is done it usually happens that only portions of a farm need to
be provided with drains.   Other portions do well without them because
seepage waters do not collect there.

In the upper South Platte Valley of Colorado seepage trouble has be-

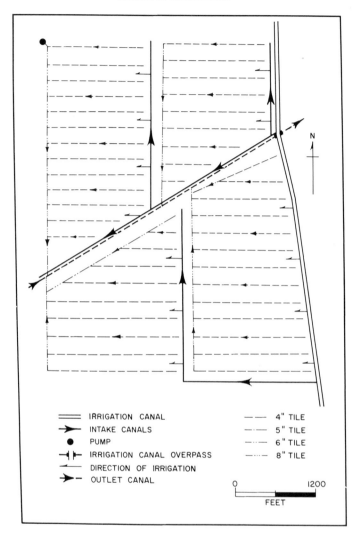

Figure 9:1.   Tile drained-irrigated farm in the Imperial Valley, California.

come commoner as more land is served with the additional water brought into the region via the Colorado-Big Thompson transfer system.   Figure 9:2 shows how one farmer on the South Platte attempted to draw off accumulated seepage waters from 15 acres of land which he had been unable to cultivate because of swamp conditions.

The tile line labeled "old tile line" was installed at a depth of about 5

feet and in correspondence with the drainage pattern of the surface contours of the field.   In other words, had sufficient water been turned on
the land to permit surface runoff it would have run downgrade and off
the field in approximately the same direction as the farmer chose for his
subsurface tile line.   But the seepage was not drained away by this
installation!

The farmer thought when he laid the old tile line that the subsurface
drainage pattern of his field would correspond with the surface drainage pattern.   In terms of the hydrograph discussed in Chapter 6 (Figure
6:2) the farmer believed that the direction of subsurface flow on his wet
field was the same as the direction of surface runoff.   Soil technologists

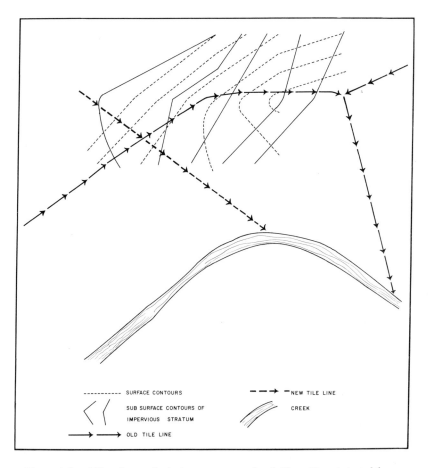

Figure 9:2.   Old and new tile drain systems on a South Platte River irrigated farm.

in irrigated areas know that such correspondence in direction of flow is
so rare that the only rational approach to the drainage problem is a
systematic grid survey of the *subsurface* contours of the impervious clay
stratum upon which the subsurface flow travels. Such a survey can be
accomplished by punching out cores of the soil profile to a depth that
perforates the impervious clay stratum. The cores are taken at points in
the field which correspond with the intersection of grid lines on graph
paper of appropriate scale. The precise position and the exact depth to
the impervious stratum are recorded as each core of the soil profile is
taken from the ground. By connecting points of equal depth on the
graph paper or by interpolation it is possible to draw the contour lines
of the subsurface impervious stratum with considerable accuracy.

When a survey of this type was made with a hydraulic core borer by a
soil scientist he found that the contours of the impervious stratum were
those shown in Figure 9:2. It was at once apparent why the original tile
drain did not function properly. From the point of maximum subsurface
flow the old tile line did not lead the effluent away. The new tile line
intercepted the subsurface flow at its point of concentration and maximum pressure. Instead of carrying off a trickle of effluent, it discharged
at the rate of one half second-foot. The field was once again useable.
Just a few feet of tile properly placed made possible the reclamation of
the original 15 acres which had been swamped. In addition another 100
acres or more can be irrigated with the water recovered.

SURPLUS WATER IN THE JORDAN VALLEY

Irrigation agriculture in the West began in pre-Columbian times. The
Hohokam Indians of Arizona possessed a well-engineered system of
canals in the Salt-Gila Valley which maintained an oasis civilization for
approximately 800 years. As an identifiable people the Hohokam had
disappeared and their irrigation works had fallen into disuse by the time
the Spaniards arrived in the sixteenth century. The Spaniards, themselves, at their mission settlements, developed irrigation along patterns
which they had used in the Old World. The purpose of their agriculture, however, was to assure the subsistence of sparsely populated
Spanish-Indian colonies; so the total area of reclamation was not great,
although there were many settlements.

It was not until 1847 when Anglo-Saxon Mormons settled in Utah that
the modern period of commercial irrigation agriculture began. Shortly
after the Mormon's initial success in raising potatoes by irrigation gold
was discovered in California. The California gold rush and the good

fortune of prospectors in many other parts of the West stimulated strong demands for food in those desert areas in which little could be had without irrigation.   Successful Mormon irrigators were invited to settle in a wide scattering of western mining communities to demonstrate and teach what they had learned in the Jordan Valley of Utah on the rim of Great Salt Lake.   The incentive of commerce, aided by railroad construction after the Civil War, led to the very rapid development of many oasis communities.

In 1947 the centennial of Mormon settlement in the Jordan Valley was celebrated.   Many were the compliments bestowed upon the descendants of Brigham Young and his associates for their achievements in industry, mining, and commerce.   Only in the field of irrigation agriculture were there reservations.   At least one observer ventured the prediction that unless better methods were developed thousands of acres of productive land would become useless in another hundred years.   The cause—not a lack of water but rather the mismanagement of water now used.   As new lands are brought into cultivation on the outer, elevated flanks of the Jordan Valley, the first settled lands in the bottoms are gradually being swamped by seepage from above.

Some years ago the farmers of west Salt Lake County organized a Soil Conservation District in order to qualify for the assistance of federal technicians in dealing with their difficulties.   As is customary in such districts, these farmers elected a committee of supervisors from among their number to discuss policy with the government technicians assigned to help them.   One result was a reconnaissance survey of the district and a division into problem areas.

The map resulting from the study by farmers and technicians divides the district into various regions of land use (Figure 9:3), some of which are subdivided into problem areas.   The types of land utilization represented are rather typical of places in the western states where the average annual rainfall is just sufficient to support dry farming but where irrigation greatly stabilizes agricultural activity and increases yields.   The range lands are used neither for irrigation nor for dry farming because of unfavorable topography and soils.   In the dry-farming sections irrigation has not advanced farther because either, (1) the water reservoir and distribution system has not yet been expanded to include them or (2) because soils and topography do not warrant such expansion.

It will be noted that the outer limits of the irrigated areas are defined by canals.   These irrigated areas are ranked according to whether their problems required urgent attention (priority 1) or gradual correction (priority 2).   The principal objectives outlined for the priority 2 areas

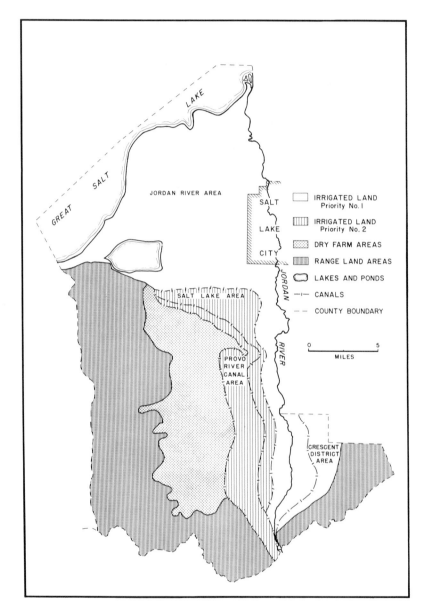

Figure 9:3. Problem areas in west Salt Lake County, Utah. (Source: U.S.D.A.)

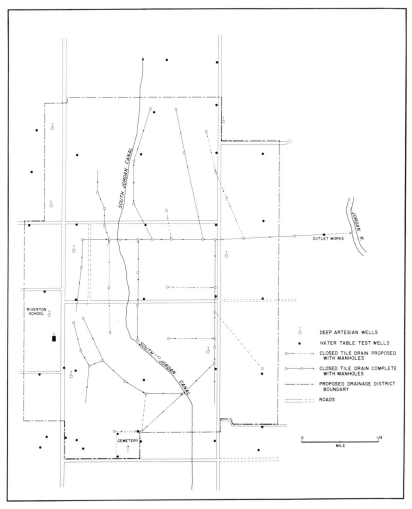

Figure 9:4.   East Riverton Drainage Project—Utah. (Source: U.S.D.A.)

which lie on the elevated slopes of the west flank of the valley are

1. Increased water supply.
2. Elimination of flood-borne silt from irrigation ditches.
3. Flood and flood erosion control.
4. Reduction of ditch erosion.
5. More land leveling to reduce soil erosion and eliminate the waste of water.
6. Control of weed seeds disseminated by the main canal system.

These are all worthy objectives deserving attention. But they do not suggested immediate danger. By good cooperative planning and effort most of them can be achieved in time in an economical way.

The priority 1 lands of the river bottoms are in greater trouble. About 4000 acres are in need of drainage. In some instances seepage has been collecting and evaporating for so long on field surfaces that toxic alkaline salts have accumulated. The Jordan River bed itself has been filled in with so much erosional sediment that it drains sluggishly and needs dredging to serve as a better discharge ditch for farm drainage systems. Seepage from unlined distribution canals is aggravating a waterlogged condition. Slow progress with land leveling is also responsible for over application of water and consequently for excessive percolation. It is to remedy these conditions that the district is now working to preserve the first oasis established by Anglo-Saxon irrigators in the West.

East Riverton is a small town on the banks of the Jordan south of Salt Lake City. There are several small farms in the community, some of which are operated on a part-time basis because their owners also work in town or in nearby industrial centers. In 1950 basements of houses and civic buildings in East Riverton began to show signs of seepage. Cultivated fields had been left idle because of waterlogging long before that. Then a church and a school were condemned because of weakened foundations. It was as if a hydraulic jack were slowly being applied to the community's underpinning. A cemetary, converted into mire, became useless. Tax delinquency forced a few people from properties none would purchase, and suburban building tapered off in potential development areas. East Riverton was not alone. In other places along the Jordan symptoms of a similar condition were developing.

In 1953 the whole community, both farms and village, was traversed by a grid of underground tile drains with an outlet to the Jordan River. Within a single year the seeped basements drained, buildings were renovated and reoccupied; and farm lands were restored by flushing the soil with sweet water to remove excess salts which had accumulated during previous years. It is by such methods of drainage and flushing that seeped and salted fields are being reclaimed in western oases from Nebraska to California.

the
use
of the
range

10

More land is devoted to range for domestic livestock than to any other agricultural activity, and no important commercial use of land returns lower dividends per acre. The grazing area of natural vegetation in the seventeen western states covers about 755 million acres. (Reference 2; p. 27.) From the western Dakotas and the Sand Hills of Nebraska the range areas of the Great Plains extend southward through the panhandles of Oklahoma and Texas to the Rio Grande. Most of the great expanse of the mountain states is range. The principal exceptions are deserts, limited areas under cultivation, and the truly forested uplands. There are also important range districts in the states of the Pacific coast.

The greater part of the western states is range because of low and uncertain rainfall which renders crop cultivation or forestry impossible or hazardous. In many places where the annual rainfall might otherwise support some field culture the terrain is too rough, the growing season is too short, or the soils are too thin or sandy. Although ranching is said to be a conservative form of land use, it has sometimes proved to be too

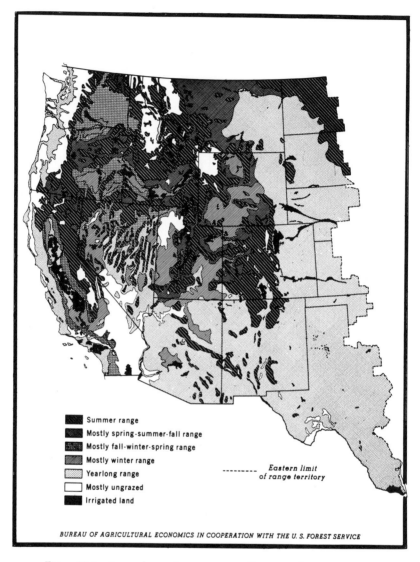

Figure 10:1.   Seasonal use of western range. (Source: Reference 2; p. 38.)

intensive because of overstocking and the consequent destruction of vegetative cover.

There is considerable variation in the character of the western range
and in the ways in which portions of it are used.   These are chiefly the
result of differences in climate or patterns of land ownership.   In the six

plains states private landholders own 93 per cent of the range, whereas the federal government owns only 7 per cent. In the eleven mountain and Pacific states private landholders hold about 40 per cent of the native range, the Federal Government approximately 60 per cent. There are vital reasons for these regional differences in ownership. When national lands were opened to homesteaders it was believed that a family could make a living by crop cultivation in the semiarid plains states. The lands of this part of the country, therefore, were released. Because of the arid climate of most of the mountain states hardship was averted by awarding only those exceptional lands which could be farmed. Most of the remainder was withheld from public entry.

In the plains states, even though erratic rainfall is a problem for field cultivators, it is often possible to conduct a family range-livestock enterprise on two to four thousand acres of land. The returns from such small ranch properties seem to be sufficient for a very modest existence. Frequently, crop cultivation by dry-farming methods can be combined with a range-livestock enterprise on as little as two thousand acres. However, in truly arid New Mexico, Arizona, and southern California ten times as much land may be required for a single range-livestock unit, unless irrigated land is available on which to raise forage crops. Eighty-five per cent of the state of Nevada is public domain, most of it Federal range. In 1955 47,523,865 acres were leased to 1152 permittees. This was an average of about 41,250° acres each and was believed to have been an equitable allotment sufficient to keep the operators in business. (Reference 4; p. 186.) Throughout most of the intermountain region irrigation agriculture is a standard supplement to range operations wherever water is available. Combinations of public range and private irrigated homesteads are more frequent in the north than in the south because water supplies are more commonly available in the north. More than half of the range belonging to the federal government (about three fifths of the total) is in grazing districts.

Although the total water runoff from range land in the intermountain West is small because of the desert climate, nevertheless, flash storms occur. Severe erosion and consequent siltation of costly irrigation reservoirs result from overgrazing this land. Some of it, located in national forests, is potential woodland which, with less grazing or by the exclusion of domestic livestock, might revegetate and offer better protection against erosion. By its ownership the federal government is in a position to control the intensity of grazing on the public range. Wherever grazing is feasible leases are granted to private individuals who may then turn their livestock onto the federal lands.

°This is more than 64 square miles of land.

Figure 10:2.   Federal grazing districts.   (Source: Reference 3; p. 7.)

DIFFERENCES IN REGIONAL USE OF THE RANGE

In the southern plains states range use continues the year around.   In the northern plains it may be seasonal or it may continue on an annual basis, depending upon the locality.   However, the livestock of the plain states are generally confined to one ranch and do not migrate.   If supplementary winter forage is essential in the north, portions of the range are reserved as hay lands and clipped for winter feeding.   In some sections of the northern plains range livestock are carried over winter on forage crops raised on irrigated lands, just as in the mountain and Pacific states. This system is increasing as irrigation itself is developed, either by pump operations or by storing and spreading surface waters. Because higher productivity of the range in the plains states makes ranch units possible on a few thousand acres and because ranching in that area is usually nonmigratory it may be conducted efficiently on private lands. Ground water which may be pumped to supply stock ponds is widely distributed.

There has been and still is competition for land between livestock and the plow in the plains states because of their slightly higher average rainfall. It is thought best, therefore, to reserve discussion of great plains grazing problems for later chapters when the peculiar complex of crop and livestock husbandry is considered in detail.

Crop agriculture seldom competes with grazing in the mountain states, even in those portions which lie in the western Great Plains. This is because low annual precipitation precludes dry farming from all but a few areas. Irrigation farming, on the other hand, is necessarily limited to those few million acres where water is available. Often the irrigated oases are surrounded by vast expanses of terrain which would be of no use to man at all if they were not grazed by his domestic animals or by wild creatures which he might hunt. Throughout most of the intermountain region irrigation agriculture is a standard supplement to range management because the forage production of the native range is so low. It would be impractical to harvest forage clippings for winter feeding on land which generally yields as little as 100 pounds of dry forage per acre annually. By the same token, because of the severe winter climate at high altitudes in the intermountain country it would be foolhardy to leave livestock in the uplands. As we have already noted, the irrigated districts are in the lowlands. A type of migratory range management is therefore essential in the northern intermountain province. Cattle and sheep must be brought to the lowlands in winter.

Frequently the lowlands are not irrigated. In other cases they are. For instance, sheep graze the rims of the Great Salt Lake basin in the winter time. Part of this region is irrigated, most of it is not. As one farmer southeast of Great Salt Lake once remarked:

The land is very poorly watered for stock-grazing purposes. When the area was traversed by sheep, it wasn't unusual to see the sheep make a break and run eight miles to get water. There is a stream in Harker Canyon and one in the canyon over at Bingham. Other than that, there are few springs and not too much chance for development. That is about the story of the low rangeland area.

Other animals in the Salt Lake area are more fortunate because they are brought to irrigated lands for winter feeding.

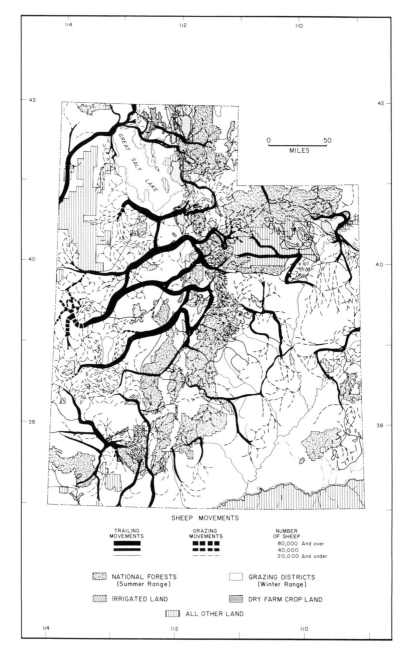

SHEEP MOVEMENTS

TRAILING
MOVEMENTS

GRAZING
MOVEMENTS

NUMBER
OF SHEEP
80,000 And over
40,000
20,000 And under

NATIONAL FORESTS
(Summer Range)

GRAZING DISTRICTS
(Winter Range)

IRRIGATED LAND

DRY FARM CROP LAND

ALL OTHER LAND

Figure 10:3. Major seasonal sheep movements, Utah. (Redrawn from U.S.D.A.)

As noted on the map of sheep migration in Utah, long distances may be traversed between summer and winter ranges. The fact that the federal domain includes both winter and summer range, as well as grazable space over which the animals may travel in their migrations, makes the seasonal shifting practical. Because large spreads of land are necessary to make a ranch unit and because livestock must be transferred from uplands to lowlands and back again with the seasons it is feasible that the federal government retain ownership of the range it holds. It would smack of favoritism for the government to award tens of thousands of acres to a few individual operators. For one thing, there would not be enough land to satisfy everyone who would want a share if there were to be a division. Considering the function of range vegetation as a guard against silt damage to the costly and far more productive irrigation developments, it is essential that this vegetation be subject to public supervision and control.

Since the use of the range is granted to private operators who own the livestock, the government does not compete with private enterprise by being a landlord. Operators with present leases are almost certain of renewals as long as they comply with conservation regulations. In exceptionally dry years the numbers of animals admitted to the public range must be reduced. It is at such times that some ranchers complain. Rather than reduce their herds temporarily they would prefer to allow overgrazing. The nation very likely has forstalled periodic economic depression in sections of the mountain range country by retaining ownership and supervisory control of its grazing lands.

There are about 513 million acres of grazing lands in the eleven Mountain and Pacific states. That is 68 per cent of the total area. (Reference 2; p. 27.) Grazing lands include considerable thinly timbered, parklike woodlands. However, for the most part they are covered with grass, sagebrush, creosote bush, piñon pine, juniper, and desert vegetation in various mixtures and degrees of density. It is impossible to determine accurately just what the feed production of the western range really is, but the estimate in Table 10:1, which was compiled by the Department of Agriculture, gives us a good indication.

As we know, large acreages of irrigated land are devoted to the production of forage crops to supplement the feed supply of range animals. In addition, there are approximately 2 million acres of irrigated pasture in the Mountain and Pacific states. (Reference 2; p. 29.) In these eleven states more animal feed is produced on a few million acres of irrigated land than on a half billion acres of overgrazed native range. According to the Department of the Interior, which administers the federal range, the average production of its millions of acres is 70 pounds

Table 10:1. Sources of Feed for Western Livestock
(Source: Reference 1; p. 91)

	Livestock on Farms January 1	Animal Unit Months Grazed On			Percentage Of Livestock On Farms Grazed On		
		Grazing Districts	National Forests	Total	Grazing Districts	National Forests	Total
	1,000 AUM	1,000 AUM	1,000 AUM	1,000 AUM	Per Cent	Per Cent	Per Cent
Sheep and goats							
1942	54,288	7,170	2,994	10,164	13.2	5.5	18.7
1945	41,971	6,391	2,386	8,777	15.2	5.7	20.9
1949	30,159	5,291	1,792	7,083	17.5	5.9	23.5
Cattle and horses							
1942	168,960	7,856	6,729	14,585	4.6	4.0	8.6
1945	186,024	9,325	6,515	15,840	5.0	3.5	8.5
1949	173,976	9,183	5,636	14,819	5.3	3.2	8.5
All livestock							
1942	223,248	15,026	9,723	24,749	6.7	4.4	11.1
1945	227,995	15,716	8,901	24,617	6.9	3.9	10.8
1949	204,135	14,474	7,428	21,902	7.1	3.6	10.7

Table 10:2. Land Ownership in Western States
(Source: Reference 1; p. 88)

| State and Region | Lands in Federal Ownership | | | | | | State Lands Per Cent | Privately Owned and Local Government Lands Per Cent | Total Area of State Per Cent |
	National Forests Per Cent	Grazing Districts Per Cent	Indian Lands Per Cent	National Parks and Monuments Per Cent	Other Federal Lands Per Cent	All Federal Lands Per Cent			
Arizona	15.8	15.7	26.7	3.2	12.2	73.6	14.8	11.6	100.0
California	19.6	2.9	0.7	4.1	18.1	45.4	4.0	50.6	100.0
Colorado	20.6	11.9	1.1	0.8	3.4	37.8	5.0	57.2	100.0
Idaho	37.9	23.4	1.6	0.1	2.3	65.3	7.7	27.0	100.0
Montana	17.5	7.2	6.9	1.2	4.3	37.1	6.2	56.7	100.0
Nevada	7.2	45.8	1.6	1.2	29.3	85.2	0.2	14.6	100.0
New Mexico	11.5	21.0	8.6	0.2	3.1	44.5	16.4	39.1	100.0
Oregon	23.8	20.1	2.8	0.3	5.9	52.9	2.0	45.1	100.0
Utah	14.9	45.3	4.8	0.5	7.3	72.8	5.1	22.1	100.0
Washington	22.5	–	6.4	2.6	3.8	35.3	4.1	60.6	100.0
Wyoming	13.7	23.6	3.4	3.7	7.6	52.0	5.8	42.2	100.0
11 western states	18.0	18.7	6.0	1.7	9.5	53.9	6.7	39.4	100.0

of dry forage per acre annually. (Reference 3; p. 4.). Just seven thousand acres of good irrigated land producing 5 tons of alfalfa per acre annually will equal the productive capacity of one million acres of federal range.

As indicated in the foregoing chart (Table 10:2), the federal government is the dominant landowner in the western states. Nearly three quarters of those federal lands are open to graziers. Their apportionment is shown in Table 10:3.

Table 10:3. Allotments of Lands in Federal Grazing Districts, 1955

(Source: Reference 4; p. 186)

State	Acres 1955	Number of Operators 1955	Animal-Unit-Months of Use	
			Livestock 1955	Wildlife 1955
Arizona	12,814,086	557	669,416	24,062
California	4,310,076	426	377,586	43,535
Colorado	7,993,759	1,846	906,360	313,331
Idaho	13,062,164	2,792	1,608,125	115,720
Montana	5,970,898	2,606	945,219	69,301
Nevada	47,523,865	1,152	3,147,530	180,977
New Mexico	14,434,263	3,853	2,089,139	40,726
Oregon	13,297,598	1,259	1,139,200	162,324
Utah	25,593,706	3,099	2,471,856	201,622
Wyoming	14,347,183	1,347	2,012,857	121,155
Total	159,347,598	18,937	15,367,288	1,272,753

Despite the vast federal territory open to livestock in the national forests and in the organized grazing districts, the total contribution of these millions of acres to the support of western livestock is relatively small, as we have seen by an appraisal of their forage production in Table 10:1. The forage production capacity of western range lands is calculated in terms of what is called the *Animal Unit Month*. One AUM is one head of cattle, or 1 horse, 1 mule, or 5 sheep or 5 goats grazed for 1 month. Instead of referring to a grazing lease as being so many acres, it is preferable to describe it as being so many AUMs. The value of this term is that it states the grazing capacity of a piece of land. Acreage, on the other hand, would be meaningless to a rancher when one section might have a carrying capacity of 50 AUMs and another section might have a carrying capacity of only 10 AUMs. Obviously, when the quality of grass and other forage is poor it takes far more land to sustain 1000 AUMs than when the range is in better condition.

In terms of the total feed supply for domestic livestock in the eleven Mountain and Pacific states the federal grazing districts and national forests provide less than 11 per cent. Obviously, the private lands are far more productive, since they account for about 89 per cent. There are 224 million acres of private grazing lands compared with 212 million acres of combined federal grazing districts and national forests open to grazing. It would be a mistake to assume that the quality of private range is above that of the federal properties, for both are utilized by the same individuals. From observation and from the accounts of field inspectors, private lands generally have been more severely damaged by overgrazing than public lands, large portions of which are under regulation, particularly in the national forests. The basis for the disparity in AUMs between public and private lands is the fact that irrigated pastures and croplands devoted to raising livestock feed are almost entirely in private hands. Thus, in essence, the basis of the western reputation for livestock production rests on the cultivated and irrigated lands and not the virgin range, whether public or private.

Some technicians have estimated that the carrying capacity of the native range is only two fifths of what it was three quarters of a century ago. The decline is due in large measure to the fact that most grazing has been largely unregulated. Until the Forest Service began to restrict and regulate animal numbers in the national forests and until the Bureau of Land Management began to enforce the Taylor Grazing Act of 1934, the federal range was open to all comers who could stand the competition. Throughout the federal territories, and particularly in the zones of nineteenth-century railroad grants, private lands are interspersed among public lands. Wherever there were waterholes and the possibility of irrigation, homesteads were claimed and granted. Thus by the time supervision on federal lands was instituted it was already custom for ranchers to use and sometimes fight for the use of adjoining federal properties. How complicated the pattern of land ownership may become is illustrated in Figure 10:5.

Today many leases to federal lands are granted legally on the basis of prior use. (Reference 2; p. 40.). The philosophy of "first come, first served" left a scorched earth in its wake, for no cattleman or sheepman proud of the name left forage for someone else's stock if his could get it first. Good grassland management had no chance under such a set-up. The Department of the Interior reports that about 50 per cent of federal rangelands are in a state of severe to critical erosion; 32 per cent are

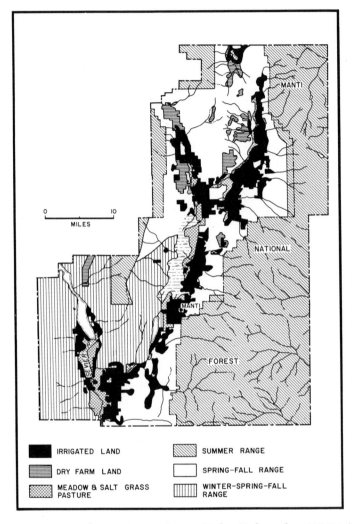

Figure 10:4. Land use in Sanpete County, Utah. (Redrawn from U.S.D.A.)

eroding moderately; and only 18 per cent are in a condition of slight to no erosion. Conscious of its responsibility for developing dams, reservoirs, and irrigation canal systems, the Department of the Interior comments,

Thus the major protion of Federal rangeland is contributing to downstream sedimentation and presents some of the most critical watershed problems of our western river basins. (Reference 3; p. 8.)

As far as the western national forests are concerned there has been a slow but rather remarkable trend to reduce the numbers of domestic livestock permitted to graze in them. At the same time, a significant increase in big-game animals has been encouraged. Today it is just as possible to regulate big-game populations as it is to regulate the numbers of domestic livestock. The pressure for hunting licenses upon the Forest Service is an assurance that there will be no overstocking by wild species. As the human population of the United States increases and takes up more land for living space, wilderness areas open to public hunting are becoming scarcer. The one big opportunity to extend our hunting grounds is to utilize national forests for the purpose.

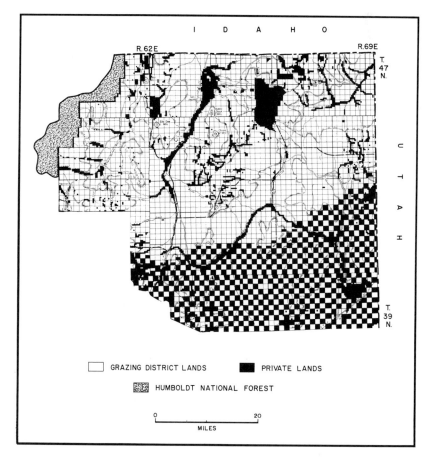

Figure 10:5. Land ownership in northeast Elko county, Nevada. (Source: U.S.D.A.)

Since the same forage will sustain elk, deer, and antelope which now supports sheep, cattle, and horses, any reduction in the number of grazing permits will help to increase the food supply for game animals. It is perhaps only a matter of time before the grazing of domestic livestock in the national forests will be a thing of the past. The nation's meat supply will not suffer, for even now only about 1 per cent of our beef and about 5 per cent of our mutton and lamb are produced on forage obtained in the national forests. Our farms are perfectly capable of expanding production to take care of our needs. Of course, the meat of wild animals obtained by hunters will serve to satisfy a small portion of their requirements.

REFERENCES

1. United States Department of Agriculture, *Domestic Wool Requirements and Sources of Supply*, Production and Marketing Administration and Bureau of Agricultural Economics, Washington, D.C., 1950.
2. United States Department of Agriculture, *Grass—The Yearbook of Agriculture, 1948*, Government Printing Office, Washington, D.C.
3. United States Department of the Interior, *Rebuilding the Federal Range*, Bureau of Land Management, Government Printing Office, Washington, D.C., 1951.
4. United States Bureau of the Census, *Statistical Abstract of the United States—1955*, Government Printing Office, Washington, D.C., 1956.

management
of the
western
range

11

The present low productivity of the western range is the result of mis-management in the past. Improved methods of range use can redeem much of the damage. If these methods are widely adopted the pro-ductivity of range can be more than doubled, but it will take a long time. Because of the very dry climate prevailing in the range country, vegeta-tive growth is slow even when the palatable grasses and browse are in their best condition. Over much of the range the most desired forage plants have been stunted by excessive grazing and in many instances they have been eliminated. Their places have been taken by other species which must now be removed so that the preferred forage types may be restored to their former dominance.

The United States Forest Service has reported that there are 96.5 million acres of sagebrush on the western range. (Reference 5; p. 1.) A large portion of this sagebrush is partly or wholly unproductive, although good forage grasses once grew in many places where sagebrush is now dominant. With man's help and by better range management in

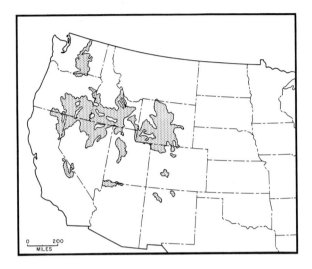

Figure 11:1.   Major sagebrush areas. (Source: Reference 5; p. 1.)

the future, good grasses, such as crested wheatgrass, may replace sagebrush.

The forage on 10 to 15 acres of rough sagebrush land is required to graze 1 cow for 1 month (one AUM per 10 to 15 acres). If converted to grassland 1 to 5 acres might be expected to provide one AUM. Many sagebrush areas have suitable soil, topography, altitude, and rainfall for grass, but western sagebrush lands today present many problems. In some areas the brush is too dense for animals to penetrate. In others the desired grasses which once grew among the sagebrush have been suppressed until they cannot come back naturally. The root system of the sagebrush plant is a spreading one which fans out around the plant just under the surface of the soil. Thus, although it would seem that sagebrush offers no competition to grass, its roots rob most of the moisture which falls on the ground. The mesquite bush of the southern range areas has the same type of root development. These vigorous, drought-resistant shrubs hold their own against livestock and dry weather because they are less palatable than grass and because their root systems are designed to monopolize whatever rain may fall. They must be removed if grass is to come back either by natural propagation or by seeding.

Some years ago the geneticist Oliver Fuller Cook made a study of the invasion of mesquite into former grasslands in the southern range country. He found that in early ranching days fire occasionally swept the range in autumn. Grazing was not so intense then because there were great expanses of grassland and fewer cattle. In the fall of the year dry grass, only partially grazed, served as fuel to feed the fires which were fanned by the wind. The fires suppressed the woody plants, such as the mesquite but did little harm to the grasses, which recovered quickly in the spring. Because the grasses had not been overgrazed their roots were vigorous. As cattle increased and the quality of grass deteriorated, there was not enough grass fuel to keep the occasional range fire running. Then the mesquite came in, both because the fires were checked and also because the grass was so heavily grazed it offered little or no competition. Today one may drive through hundreds of miles of mesquite range in New Mexico and western Texas and see very little grass or few cattle.

Before the prairies were grazed by cattle the luxuriant growths of grass could accumulate for several years until conditions were favorable for accidental fires to spread. With these large supplies of fuel the fires which swept over these prairies were very besoms of destruction not only for man and animals but for all shrubs and trees which might have ventured out among the grass, and even for any trees or forests against which the burning winds might blow. . . . Settlers in south Texas early adopted the practice of burning over the prairies every year; partly to protect their homes against the fires, partly to give their cattle readier access to the fresh growth of grass. The fires were often set near the coast, the strong breeze which blows in from the Gulf spreading the flames over many square miles. . . . In spots where the grass is thin, seedling mesquites and oaks escape the flames and in a year or two begin to shade the ground and gain more protection against the dangerous proximity of the combustible grass. . . . The lessened quantity of grass also makes it impracticable to burn the prairie over in the summer, as was customary in former decades. . . . This shrubby vegetation which is threatening the cattle industry and opening south Texas to the truck and cotton farmers will undoubtedly continue to advance and multiply wherever the land is not cleared and cultivated. The south Texas farmer of the future instead of being a cattle king may even find himself without a place to pasture his milch cows except in tilled fields. (Reference 1; p. 8.)

The Department of Agriculture has undertaken a number of range-improvement experiments which have proved successful. The guiding principles of such renovation programs have been outlined by the Department:

1. *Select Grasses.* Use grass species adapted to the lands to be seeded and make sure you get clean, live seed.

2. *Choose Planting Site.* Avoid rocky ground and shallow infertile soils. Annual rainfall must be not less than 8 to 10 inches, with at least 2 to 3 inches during the spring growing season. The best crops of grass can usually be grown on deep, dark, rich soils, where sagebrush and rabbit brush are thickest.

3. *Remove Competition.* Brush species use too much of the ground moisture available for plant growth. They must, therefore, be killed out if a high-yielding stand of grass is to be established. This is the first step in the reseeding operation.

4. *Plant Correctly.* Put the seed in the ground just before the fall rains, so that the rainfall will keep the soil moist for a month or more of growing weather. Plant seeds at a depth of one quarter to three quarters inch. Plant small seed no deeper than one half inch. It is essential that seed be covered.

5. *Graze Conservatively.* Protect the new plants from premature grazing. They should be allowed to become well established with strong root systems. Graze the new stand of grass conservatively so that it can maintain itself. (Reference 5; p. 6.)

The rural economy of no other state is so dependent upon ranching as is that of Nevada. According to the 1954 Census of agriculture there were in Nevada 373 thousand acres of land in crops and 57 million acres of land in range and pasture, a ratio of less than 1 to 150. To the ranchers of northeast Elko County, Nevada, and to nine federal and state agencies must go the credit for demonstrating on a large scale the manner in which the range can be improved when there is a determination to do so. In 1951 the Elko ranches were chosen by the Nevada Association of Soil Conservation Districts to be the pilot district that might serve as an example to the entire state. This group then initiated a 35-year program of practical range improvement.

The northeast Elko County project includes plans for the improvement of 2 million acres of range, three quarters of which is public domain. The expenditure over the 35-year period is expected to be nearly $5 million. It is predicted that the present carrying capacity of the range will be increased 90 per cent. Improved rotational grazing will be achieved by more fencing and by an increase in the number and in the better placement of stock ponds and wells. The vegetative cover on 409,107 acres of range will be improved by reseeding at a cost of $9.00 an acre. When the project is completed in 1986 it is thought the 2 million acres of range will then be yielding 386,443 AUMs annually in contrast to a production of 206,072 AUMs in 1951.

As we have seen, irrigated cropland is vital to a range economy, since it is expected to provide supplementary forage, particularly in winter. Forage production by irrigation in northeast Elko County will be increased five times at a cost of $1.5 million, and 22,855 acres of partially irrigated land will be leveled, tile-drained, and fully watered by 1986. Production will increase from 28,375 AUMs to 171,412 AUMs. The reader will note in considering these statistics that despite the higher cost per acre for the improvement of irrigated land each additional AUM on irrigated land will cost approximately one third as much as each additional AUM on improved range.   The ratio will be $10.94 : $27.79.   It is no wonder that as far as private capital is concerned there has been greater investment in irrigation than in range improvement.

The planned ratio of irrigated lands to range lands in the Elko County development is 1 : 90, whereas the planned ratio between irrigated land and range lands as calculated in AUMs is 1 : 2.2.   In other words, it is expected that each acre of irrigated land will be as productive as 40 acres of well-managed range.

The land-ownership pattern of the range country necessitates close cooperation between private persons and the federal government.   This is particularly true in the areas of the old railroad grants.   The map showing land ownership in northeast Elko County, Nevada, illustrates well the necessity for cooperation between private stockmen and federal technicians responsible for the maintenance of the public range (Figure 10:5).

The checkerboard pattern in the southern portion of the area is derived from an early grant of land to help finance the construction of a transcontinental railroad which passes through the area.   Alternate square-mile sections were given to the railroad company, and the other sections were retained by the federal government.   The railroad company sold its land to private individuals to obtain capital.   Those who bought became ranchers and, of course, turned their cattle on the public lands as well as on their own.   The blocks and ribbons of private lands in the northern portion of the map are generally located where there is a river or where there are springs.   The ribbon patterns are well developed along the banks of creeks and rivers, and the scattered blocks usually indicate private lands with springs or wells.

The distribution pattern of creek banks and ponds is a vital factor in proper range management.   Cattle are not inclined to graze very far from water.   Consequently, portions of the range farthest away from this necessity are likely to be undergrazed.   By dividing large areas into smaller ones with stock ponds the cattle are encouraged to graze an area more equitably.   Smaller grazing areas may be provided by additional fencing, making it possible to rotate the cattle from one area to another. When cattle stay only a short time in any one place they do a minimum of damage by tramping.   Of course, an ideal distribution of cattle is seldom achieved because ponds and springs can be developed only where there is water.   These locations are not plentiful where the rainfall is 8 to 14 inches annually.

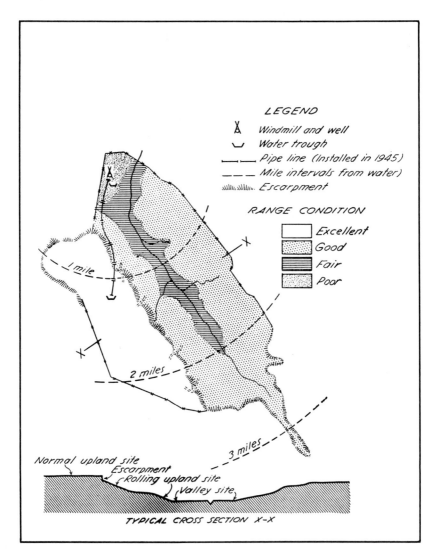

Figure 11:2. *Poor water distribution on a western range.* The improper placement of watering facilities led to the uneven use of forage on a 1690-acre ranch near Marfa, Texas. The cattle grazed too much around the windmill and trough, and the forage there fell off 75 per cent. The area near the stream (indicated by heavy shading) was next most heavily grazed. The animals were not forced to go for water to the upland area, where the forage was excellent. An additional water trough was installed on high land to encourage cattle to graze the upland area. (Source: Reference 2; p. 237.)

OVERGRAZING AND FLOOD DAMAGE

Reference has been made to the fact that surface runoff from over-grazed lands may cause soil erosion.   When both runoff and erosion are excessive, flooding and silt deposition may occur in valleys, and the damage may be costly.   Careful studies of the causes and remedies of excessive runoff and siltation have been made in many places.   Data from such research in Davis County, Utah, are significant.

Directly east of Great Salt Lake there are several communities and some fine irrigated farm land.   Beyond this thickly settled area rise the

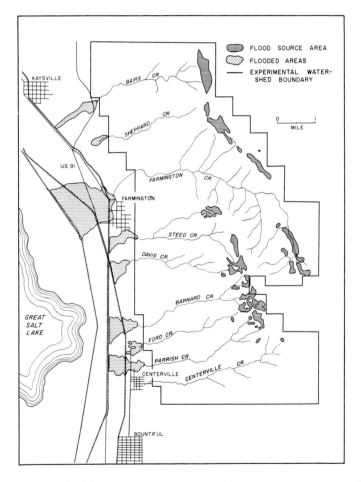

Figure 11:3.   Flood damage in Davis County, Utah. (Source: Reference 4; p. 3 ff.)

foothills and mountains of the Wasatch Range. The district has been settled for over a century, for the pioneers cut trees on the mountain slopes to build their homes in the lowlands. They and the generations after them also allowed their cattle and sheep to graze the slopes. Figure 11:3 shows the location of nine creeks which flow from the mountains to the plains below. As indicated, flood damage, including the deposition of mud and rock debris, has occurred in eight of the nine watersheds. The most serious destruction has been suffered at the mouth of Farmington Creek, whereas at the mouth of Centerville Creek no damage at all has occurred. Between 1923 and 1930 floods took a toll of six lives and caused more than $1 million damage to properties in the shaded areas on the map.

In 1930 the local people organized a flood control committee, and after some investigation of the causes of their troubles Congress was requested to extend the boundary of the Wasatch National Forest to include the watershed area shown in Figure 11:3. The people wanted grazing restrained on that portion of the public domain. Congress was also petitioned to provide money to purchase private lands which were inside the forest boundary, so that they, too, could be placed under federal supervision. The people were impressed by the history of the

Table 11:1. Relation of Vegetative Cover to Soil Erosion
(Source: Reference 4; p. 14)

Before Treatment
Storm date: July 10, 1936
Total rainfall (inches): 1.14
Maximum rainfall rate (in/hr/5 min): 5.04

Plot No.	Plant Cover Condition	Storm Runoff (per cent)	Soil Eroded (cu ft/A)
6.	Depleted annual weeds	40.5	268
7.	Dense aspen, herbs, and litter	0.5	0

After Treatment
Storm date: July 10, 1950
Total rainfall (inches): 0.70
Maximum rainfall rate (in/hr/5 min): 4.20

Plot No.	Plant Cover Condition	Storm Runoff (per cent)	Soil Eroded (cu ft/A)
6.	Recovered by grass and aspen	5.3	0
7.	Denuded by cutting and burning	51.8	374

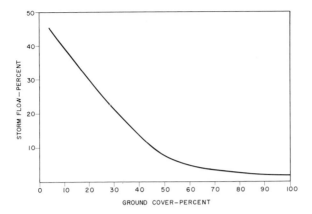

Figure 11:4. Ground cover and summer-storm runoff. (Source: Reference 4; p. 15.)

Centerville Creek watershed which had never experienced a damaging flood. This was due to the fact that many years before, the Centerville community had acquired title to part of the lands in Centerville Canyon and had arranged for conservative grazing in the watershed. In contrast to the unmanaged, excessive use of the forage in the other watersheds the plant cover in Centerville Canyon has always been maintained in a healthy condition. After Congress had complied with the local requests, efforts at revegetation of critical upper-watershed areas were undertaken. Since 1935 there have been no damaging mud-rock floods wherever the revegetation measures were successful.

Experimental plots were installed in the upper portion of Parrish Creek watershed to measure surface runoff and soil erosion. Some of the plots were installed in depleted areas where signs of erosion clearly indicated that they were sources of flood runoff; others were installed on relatively undepleted sites where a lack of erosion indicated that they did not contribute much storm runoff. After records had been obtained for ten years some of the sparsely covered flood-source plots were artifically seeded to grass: on some the plant cover was allowed to increase naturally. The vegetation was also altered on the nonflood-source plots, and in one of these areas all plant cover and litter were removed. Data from two plots during two storms are given in Table 11:1.

The Parrish Creek runoff plots have also supplied information as to how much plant and litter cover is needed to prevent dangerous amounts of summer-storm runoff and to keep soils stable. A study was made of 146 storms. It was found that very little soil erosion occurred when less than 5 per cent of the rainfall ran off the land as surface flow. It was also found that 65 per cent or more of the ground surface should be covered by plants and litter. The curve in Figure 11:4 shows how storm runoff increases above the safe figure of 5 per cent when the amount of plant and litter cover on the ground is less than 65 per cent.

REFERENCES

1. Cook, O. F., *Change of Vegetation on the South Texas Prairies,* U.S. Department of Agriculture, Bureau of Plant Industry, Circular No. 14, Government Printing Office, Washington, D.C., 1908.
2. U.S. Department of Agriculture, *Grass—Yearbook of Agriculture, 1948,* Government Printing Office, Washington, D.C.
3. U.S. Department of Agriculture, *Major Uses of Land, Summary for 1954,* Government Printing Office, Washington, D.C.
4. Marston, R. B., *Guide to Davis County Experimental Watershed,* U.S. Forest Service, Ogden, Utah, 1953.
5. U.S. Forest Service, *Sagebrush to Grass,* Government Printing Office, Washington, D.C., 1945.
6. U.S. Soil Conservation Service, *Coordinated Land Program—The Northeast Elko Soil Conservation District* (second edition), Portland, 1952.

the
Palouse

12

The map that outlines the types of farming in the United States
(Figure 4:2) shows that there is an extensive area of wheat cultivation
on the Columbia Plateau in the northwestern section of the Intermontane
Region. This is an unirrigated area and thus stands out conspicuously
because nowhere else between the Rockies and the Sierra Nevada-
Cascades is dry farming dominant over such an extensive and continuous
territory. The eastern portion of this wheat district is known as the
Palouse. It is one of the most curious as well as one of the most productive agricultural provinces in the West. Peculiar soil and climatic
conditions have made an intensive agriculture possible on land which is
often steeply sloped. Tillage agriculture began in the Palouse about
eighty-five years ago. Since that time there has never been a crop
failure. The average wheat yield is 33 bushels per acre, a phenomenal
record for a region in which the average annual rainfall is approximately
20 inches.

The larger wheat district, of which the Palouse is a part, extends over

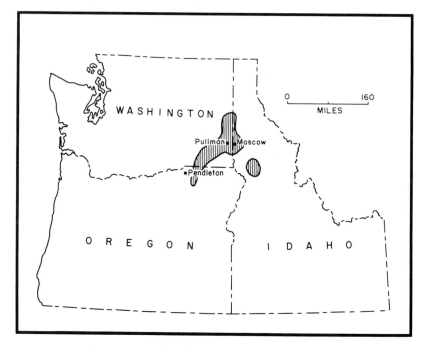

Figure 12:1.   The Palouse. (Source: Reference 3; p. 3.)

most of southeastern Washington with minor projections into adjacent Idaho and north-central Oregon. The Palouse itself may be rather in-exactly defined as the eastern portion of this wheat belt. Its borders are zones of transition rather than precise lines. However, it may be said that the heart of the Palouse lies between the Washington State Agricul-tural College and Experiment Station at Pullman and the Idaho State Agricultural College and Experiment Station at Moscow. The chief crops of the Palouse are winter wheat and peas. For many years Whit-man County, Washington, has been among the top wheat-producing counties of the United States. It is rather consistently the leading county in the production of dried field peas. Umatilla County, Oregon, heads the nation's counties in the production of fresh green peas. As might be anticipated from these foregoing facts, the dominant rotation of the Palouse is an alternation between wheat and peas. This rotation is the basis of the region's prosperity and the cause of soil deterioration and erosion which is becoming a major problem.

PECULIARITIES OF THE PALOUSE

The name Palouse, which denotes grassland, is thought to have been given to this area by early French explorers. In appearance the land surface of the Palouse resembles the Sand Hills of Nebraska, but the dunes are of silt rather than sand. One might carry the analogy farther by indicating that the average annual rainfall of the two districts is similar and their native vegetative cover was grass. That is about the end of any coincidence in the character of the Sand Hills and the Palouse. The soils of the Palouse are utterly different, for they are chiefly loams derived from loess. When not truncated by erosion they are rich in organic matter, highly responsive to fertilization, and retain rain water and snow melt so well that practically all precipitation becomes available to cultivated plants during the growing season.

The climate of the Palouse, particularly the precipitation regimen, is its most distinctive asset. Rains are of remarkably low intensity. More than 92 per cent of all rains in the Palouse amount to less than half an inch in twenty-four hours. This factor, more than any other, has made it possible to carry on intensive rotations, such as wheat-fallow and wheat-peas, for nearly a century without complete destruction of the soil. Soil erosion has been severe, but under a more intensive rainfall regimen the steep-sloped dunes would long ago have been eroded into an unplowable condition.

The Palouse lies windward of the northern Rocky Mountains of central Idaho. Air masses traversing the district proceed generally from the Pacific Ocean. In the course of their landward passage they cross the Coast Range and the Cascades, where they lose most of their moisture. The Olympic Mountains of the Coast Range receive the heaviest annual rainfall in the United States. The Columbia Basin to the immediate leeward of the Cascades is the most arid district in the northern half of this country. There, no agriculture is possible without irrigation. The wheat-fallow area between the irrigated Columbia Basin and the Palouse has an average annual precipitation of 12 to 18 inches, and dry-farming techniques are successful. The western margin of the Palouse has about 18 inches; the eastern margin at the foot of the northern Rockies receives about 25 inches. The increased frequency of drizzly rains closer to the Rocky Mountains is due in part to a corresponding gradual rise in elevation of the Columbia Plateau from about 2000 to 2500 feet above sea level. This increase in elevation, together with the prominent barrier of the nearby Rockies, forces the air masses upward, cooling them and extracting some of the small fraction of water retained after passage over the Coast Range and the Cascades.

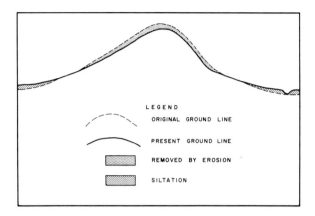

Figure 12:2.   Land condition of a typical Palouse hill.

Gentle, drizzly rains are often a feature of semiarid districts to the windward of mountain masses. What is peculiar about the Palouse is that the rains and snows are just sufficient for annual cropping and they fall chiefly during the winter season. As previously mentioned the soils when not eroded retain practically all precipitation so that it is available during the spring and summer growing season. Because of the moderately high altitude of the Palouse the summer is not excessively warm and evapotranspiration is therefore moderate. The Pacific air masses are generally warmer in winter and cooler in summer than continental air masses at equal latitudes, so that winter wheat is seldom killed by frost in the Palouse. On the other hand, intense winter cold obliges most North Dakota farmers to plant spring wheat rather than winter wheat.

To the eye the most distinctive feature of the Palouse is the intense cultivation practiced on undulating, steep-sided dunes. Slopes vary from 0 to 55 per cent. The flat lands are limited, sinuous, valley plains between surrounding dunes. They are usually poorly drained and, consequently, are generally reserved for permanent meadow. Land use in the Palouse defies all the rules of normal conservative soil management in hilly terrain. The steepest slopes, if not severely eroded, are planted to annual crops, and most of the level lands are kept in grass.

Because the dunes are like round tent-tops, sloping in all directions although at unequal angles, the conventional methods of soil-erosion control, such as contour strip cropping and terracing, are impractical. The steeper slopes cannot be cultivated with wheeled tractors because of the danger of tipping. Low-slung, crawler-type tractors are the standard

Table 12:1. Precipitation in the Palouse
(Source: Reference 2; Table 1)

Station	Years Record	Jan.	Feb.	Mar.	Apr.	May	June	July	Aug.	Sept.	Oct.	Nov.	Dec.	Total
Colfax, Wash.	54	2.37	2.10	2.02	1.35	1.49	1.44	0.33	0.66	1.02	1.50	2.84	2.28	19.42
Moscow, Idaho	48	2.96	2.09	2.19	1.56	1.90	1.43	0.56	0.67	1.20	1.66	2.93	2.76	21.91
Pullman, Wash.	51	2.70	2.13	2.20	1.48	1.50	1.28	0.49	0.63	1.11	1.48	2.86	2.63	20.49
Wawawai, Wash.	13	2.34	1.64	2.53	1.17	1.17	1.32	0.32	0.11	0.75	1.63	2.14	2.97	18.13

source of field power. Implements such as combines may have hydraulic leveling devices with mercury-switch controls to keep them from tipping on steep-sided hills. A large proportion of the farm machinery used in the area has been especially designed for operation on the rolling dunes.

The author of this book is unaware of any other place in the world where such steep slopes are consistently plowed and planted to annual crops without terracing, strip cropping, or contour furrowing. This has been possible for the past eighty five years because of the reasons mentioned:

1. Light, slow, drizzly rains which tend to soak into the soil rather than run off.

2. Absorptive silt loam soils high in organic matter which store water efficiently for future plant growth.

The intensive cultivation of the dunes of the Palouse might continue indefinitely as long as these two conditions prevail.

However, soil erosion is becoming critical in the Palouse. A similar, more aggravated condition has developed in the wheat-fallow district to the west where wind erosion is accelerating. Something is happening to destroy the original spongelike absorptive capacity of the soil, so that rain and snow melt which formerly soaked into the soil now run off in increasing amounts from the tops and upper slopes of the dunes. The obvious change is in the humus content of the soil. When Palouse soils were first broken the surface soil had abundant organic matter. Upon the basis of tests performed on a remnant of undisturbed Palouse prairie, it appears that the original soil absorbed about 3.5 inches of moisture per foot of depth. After years of cultivation much of the soil in the area now has less than half as much organic matter as it did to begin with and it will absorb only about 2.25 inches of moisture per foot of depth. (Reference 1; p. 1.)

The reduction in the organic-matter content of the soil has had important consequences. The U.S. Department of Agriculture states that,

Under virgin sod conditions, total runoff of water was about 5 per cent of the total precipitation. The average runoff from the area now is about 20 per cent. The loss of needed moisture from parts of each field is reflected in lower crop yields. (Reference 2; p. 9.)

With greater runoff, the topsoil itself is being eroded from the steeper slopes and deposited in the valleys where it clogs the already poorly developed natural drainage ways. Sometimes the water runs off with such force that gullies are cut in the lower drainage ways. Loss of topsoil accelerates removal of organic matter, and the speed of soil erosion is further increased.

Moisture is the critical factor in the yields of Palouse crops. Plant nutrients lost through soil erosion can be replaced with commerical fertilizer, but the loss of an inch of water cannot be replaced. In the spring of the year each inch of water that is stored in the soil down to a depth of 6 feet is capable of producing 3.5 to 4 bushels of wheat. So constant is the correlation between water stored in the soil that each spring farmers take thin cores of soil to a 6-foot depth from various places in their fields. Samples from these soil cores are placed in moistureproof containers and sent to a privately financed laboratory for moisture analyses. When informed by the laboratory as to the moisture content of various fields the farmers purchase fertilizers accordingly. They know that the application of more fertilizer than is required to balance water supply would be a waste of money. Since the size of a crop from a piece of hillside land is basically determined by the amount of moisture stored in the soil, any reduction in the soil's capacity to absorb rain and snow melt results in surface runoff and in lower yields.

Constant plowing and the burning of field straw and stubble over a long period of time has seriously reduced the humus content of Palouse soils. Only new methods of farming which eliminate stubble burning and which include green manure crops in the rotation offer the prospect of keeping the Palouse from declining from its present position as the nation's most consistent producer of bumper crops of wheat and peas. The trend of soil deterioration and erosion is illustrated by the land classification map (Figure 12:3).

The Class IV land areas in Figure 12:3 have slopes between 25 and 55 per cent. Nearly all topsoil has been removed, and it is generally impossible to turn furrows up hill when this land is plowed. Every plowing results, therefore, in moving more soil downhill. Over the period of a century plowing alone could remove 6 to 7 inches of topsoil from a band 100 feet wide. This plow erosion is recognized as a serious condition in the Palouse. Steep lands should be seeded to grasses and legumes. The Class II area is one in which sedimentation may occur. Slopes range from 0 to 5 per cent. This land is nearly level and can be cultivated if drainage is satisfactory. The Class VI lands represent gullied drainage ways which are swampy. These areas should not be cultivated but should be planted to permanent sods to prevent further gullying. The Class III lands have slopes of 5 to 30 per cent. Loss of organic matter and topsoil is severe, and the only way to prevent further deterioration lies in the use of rotations, including green manure crops. Progressive farmers who are using such rotations as peas-sweet clover-wheat-peas-wheat have noted improvements. Although they produce cash crops in only four years out of five with such a rotation, total

Table 12:2. Wheat Yields as Affected by Soils, Slope, and Erosion
(Source: U.S. Department of Agriculture)

Area No.	Soil Type	Average Per Cent Slope	Depth of Topsoil Average (inches)	Depth of Topsoil Range (inches)	Depth of Topsoil Original (inches)	Physical Condition of the Plow Layer	Average Depth of Moisture Penetration	Average Bushels Per Acre
Lower south slope 1	Palouse silt loam	11.7	24.0	14–36	30″	Open, mellow and friable. Some silt deposition.	72″	50.0
Middle south slope 2	Palouse silt loam	20.8	10.7	4–15	18″	Slightly puddled and cracked.	60″	35.1
Upper south slope 3	Palouse silty clay loam	22.0	4.7	0–16	14″	Puddled to subsoil. Very hard and cracked. Definite plow pan.	30″	22.7
Hilltop 4	Palouse silty clay loam	0–5.0	0	0	9″	Puddled, hard and cracked. Baked in large blocks. Definite plow pan.	15″	15.3
Upper north slope 5	Palouse silt loam	21.5	13.5	0–36	18″	Mellow and open. Some tendency for plow pan.	22″	29.1
Middle north slope 6	Palouse silt loam	41.7	18.7	6–36	40″	Slightly puddled and cracked on surface. Mellow under surface layer.	50″	18.5
Lower north slope 7	Palouse silt loam	11.0	27.4	15–36	36″	Friable and mellow. Slightly cracked. Some silt deposition.	72″	42.6
Drainage-way 8	Johnson silt loam	0–3.0	7.3	0–14	—	White colored. Surface baked and cracked. Considerable inundation.	—	4.6

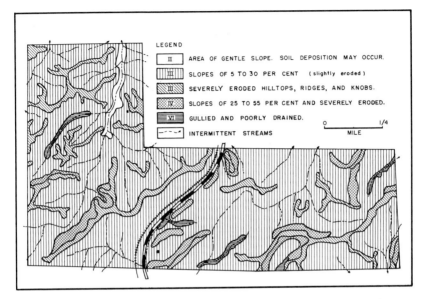

LEGEND

II	AREA OF GENTLE SLOPE. SOIL DEPOSITION MAY OCCUR.
III	SLOPES OF 5 TO 30 PER CENT (slightly eroded)
III	SEVERELY ERODED HILLTOPS, RIDGES, AND KNOBS.
IV	SLOPES OF 25 TO 55 PER CENT AND SEVERELY ERODED.
VI	GULLIED AND POORLY DRAINED.
	INTERMITTENT STREAMS

0   1/4
MILE

Figure 12:3.   Land capability classes on a Palouse farm. (Source: U.S.D.A.)

yields for those four years are higher than for a five-year period without sweet clover as a green manure crop.

Data from the South Fork of Palouse Soil Conservation Project show a distinct correlation between yields of wheat, steepness of slope, loss of topsoil, and depth of soil-moisture storage (Table 12:2).

LAND-USE HISTORY

Settlement of the Palouse by the white man began about 1864. The region was then a grassland world dominated by bunchgrass types which are generally characteristic of the West where the rainfall is low and occurs chiefly during winter months. Dry summers are not conducive to sod-grass types, even to those which are tolerant of drought. The roots of bunchgrasses go deeply into the soil and are capable of sustaining the plants during arid summers by withdrawing moisture stored in the soil profile. Wheat, which is an annual bunchgrass, will send roots six feet into the soil if there is moisture throughout the profile to that depth. Once cultivation began, wheat became the logical plant to dominate the crop history of the Palouse.

The first settlers were not farmers but ranchers. The steep-sloped dune topography did not seem appropriate for plowing, and cattle

PERCENT

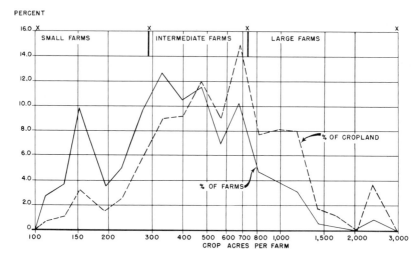

Figure 12:4.   Farm size and cropland in the Palouse. (Source: Reference 3; p. 8.)

grazed the prairies most of the year.   Some wild grasses were cut for hay
to tide the livestock over periods when snow covered the ground.   The
earliest attempts at cultivation were made on small patches of well-
drained land in the valleys between the dunes.   Flax and small grains
prospered.   Gradually less steeply sloping dunes were put into cultiva
tion, and eventually all slopes were plowed.   In the heart of the Palouse,
a few years ago, the author was unable to find any area of virgin grassland except a small remnant of about 3 acres which had been preserved
on the campus of Washington State University at Pullman.   It is said
that in 1938 the last extensive area of 1200 acres of native prairie was
put under plow when the efforts of a few scientists and others interested
in the preservation of native flora failed to raise funds to purchase it.
They had hoped to keep it for research and as a reminder of what all that
land was like when first explored by white men.

The influence of ranch settlement is still noticeable in the large size
of individual farms.   In 1950 the average number of crop-acres per farm
was 446.   When one considers that 33 bushels of wheat or 1000 pounds
of dried peas are average yields per acre these are very prosperous and
highly productive properties.   In the local vernacular they are still referred to as ranches and the operators call themselves ranchers.   Livestock are of minor importance, although many owners keep a few head of
dairy cattle to utilize the forage available in the narrow, winding
meadows which cover the poorly drained lands between the dunes.
From the standpoint of soil conservation, more grasses and legumes

should be grown in rotation with wheat and peas in order to maintain the humus content of the soil. However, because of the low human population of the Pacific Northwest the local market for additional beef and dairy products is not nearly so attractive as is the national market for wheat and peas. The use of sweet clover and alfalfa, insofar as it is increasing, is justified chiefly as a soil-conservation practice and because yields of wheat and peas improve after legume-grass sods are plowed under.

REFERENCES

1. Anonymous, *Facts About Your Soil*, Soil Conservation Service, Portland, Oregon, 1951.
2. Anonymous, *Program of the South Palouse Soil Conservation District*, Uniontown, Washington.
3. Hurd, E. B. and O. L. Brough, Jr., *Farm Size and Land Use in the Wheat-Pea Area of Washington and Idaho, 1935–1950*, The State College of Washington, Pullman, 1951.
4. Rockie, W. A., Snowdrifts and the Palouse Topography, *The Geographical Review*, Vol. 24, No. 3, pp. 380–385.
5. Rockie, W. A., Snowdrift Erosion in the Palouse, *The Geographical Review*, Vol. 41, No. 3; pp. 457–463.

the
Willamette
Valley

13

Agricultural development in the dry West is usually handicapped by
the inadequacy of a resource. We have observed that rough topography,
lack of water, and sometimes poor soils have prevented optimum development, but the principal misfortune of the Willamette Valley is the
lack of a strong market. In the Pacific Northwest the expansion of
Portland, Seattle, and satellite urban centers has been phenomenal.
Grand Coulee, Bonneville, and the Dalles hydroelectric projects have
stimulated industry and encouraged an influx of people from other sections of the United States. It is a testimony to the productive potential
of the Willamette Valley that all this impressive growth has not yet
forced it into anything approaching the agricultural development of
which it is capable. However, the trend in that direction has definitely
begun.

The Willamette is singled out for special discussion because it is the
largest and richest of those mountain valleys which collectively are called
the Pacific Northwest dairy region (Figure 4:2).

Here dairying is the dominant occupation of farmers, but the valley is also a center of a diversified horticulture known for its fresh vegetable and canning crops, cane and orchard fruits, filberts, grass seeds, and oil of mint. However, almost everything that can be grown in the Willamette Valley can also be produced in the humid eastern United States. Freight costs make it difficult for Oregon farmers to compete in eastern markets. Unlike southern Californians, with their subtropical specialties, they cannot count the whole nation as a market. Consequently, maximum land development in the Willamette and in other valleys of the Pacific Northwest will not be achieved until the cities of that region have grown to the point at which they can absorb most of the produce that would result from a more intensive agriculture. This does not mean that the region's farmers are not busy. It means that they are practicing extensive rather than intensive systems of agriculture because the latter type is not yet warranted on a wide scale.

There are approximately 1.7 million acres of tillable river bottom and bench-terrace soils in the Willamette Valley. In addition, there are over a million acres of useable hill lands in the central portion of the valley and along its piedmont borders. These hill lands are suitable for improved meadows and to some extent for tree and cane fruits. It is estimated that 1.3 million acres of these various soils are potentially irrigable. The Bureau of Reclamation reports that about 140,000 acres were irrigated in 1955. (Reference 1; p. 98.) The Oregon Agricultural Experiment Station has conducted irrigation research since 1907, and its studies indicate a promising future for the irrigator.

Four classes of valley land are distinguished in Figure 13:2. Their respective areas are indicated in Table 13:1. The Class 1 soils are made up of recent alluvial deposits along river and stream bottoms and are suitable for a wide variety of crops, including garden vegetables. Fairly abundant and shallow gound water is usually available for well and pump irrigation, much of which is on Class 1 land. The surface of this land is often undulating as the result of occasional winter floods which have caused considerable erosion. Because of uneven land surface the sprinkler-type irrigation systems are most appropriate.

Bordering the immediate river bottoms and 30 to 40 feet above the channel level are the older alluvial soils grouped into Class 2. These are bench lands above present flood crests with surfaces which are usually quite level and satisfactory for gravity-flow irrigation. Ground water is neither so plentiful nor so easily available as on the Class 1 lands. Canal systems, storage dams, and water-distribution organizations will be essential to bring large areas of Class 2 lands under irrigation.

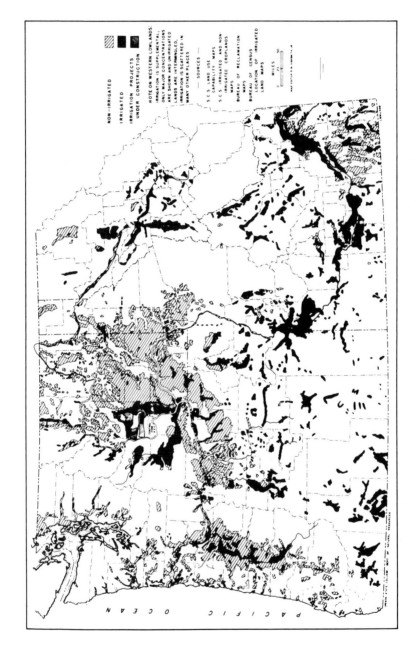

Figure 13:1. Croplands in the Pacific Northwest. (Source: Reference 2.)

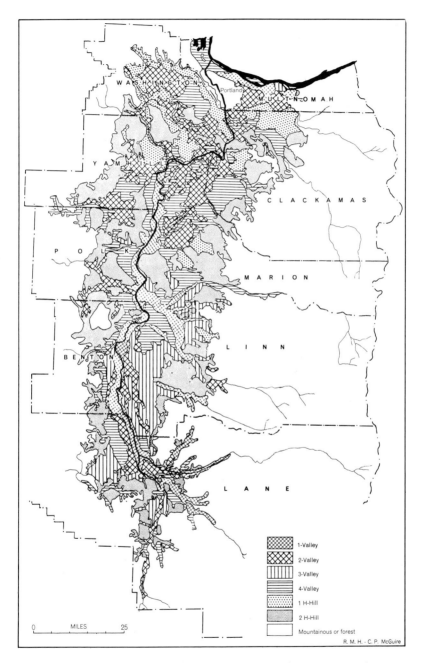

Figure 13:2.   Land adaptability classes. (Source: Reference 1; p. 103.)

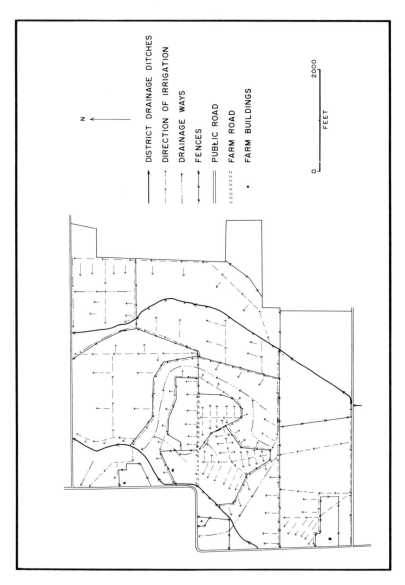

Figure 13:3. Irrigated farm in the Willamette Valley.

The soils of Classes 3 and 4 are compact, poorly drained, and, consequently, require special attention before they can be made productive. The greater area of these lands is on bench terraces, although there are also poorly drained soils in the bottoms. They are capable of very high yields of forage crops when properly drained, limed, and fertilized.

It may seem strange that irrigation is stressed as a prerequisite for intensive land use in the Willamette when it is considered that the average annual rainfall approximates 40 inches and that the soils of the region are neutral-to-acid in chemical reaction rather than alkaline. Alkalinity is typical of the soils of arid areas, and an acid reaction is characteristic of soils in humid zones. The Willamette is as dry in midsummer as the Central Valley of California. However, rainfall is heavy during winter months.

If it were not for the fact that autumn, winter, and spring temperatures are mild despite the latitude, the heavy winter rainfall would not be so effective as it is in providing forage crops for the dairy industry.

**Table 13:1. Acreages of Selected Land-Capability
Classes in the Willamette Valley**
(Source: Reference 1, pp. 5–6)

County	Class I Acres	Class II Acres	Class III Acres	Class IV Acres
Benton	31,733	16,047	37,863	12,080
Clackamas	6,190	66,448	99,763	—
Lane	57,245	53,417	69,642	65,632
Linn	68,380	35,456	73,084	181,624
Marion	34,594	97,459	126,287	12,647
Multnomah	29,127	66,179	23,336	3,099
Polk	17,885	33,926	66,561	4,610
Washington	17,580	100,769	34,617	—
Yamhill	10,539	58,147	56,694	—
Total	273,273	527,848	587,847	279,692

**Adaptability of Land for Irrigation
in the Willamette Valley**

Generalized soil type	Good Irrigability Acres	Fair Irrigability Acres	Total Acres
Old valley fill	434,000	309,000	743,000
Recent alluvial	261,000	253,000	514,000
Residual	—	116,000	116,000
Total	695,000	678,000	1,373,000

It is the precipitation that averages 4.5 to 6 inches per month between November and February that accounts for the flooding of lowland areas and for the puddled condition of many soils. Thus it is that to attain maximum production many farms are in need of both drainage and irrigation, albeit at different seasons of the year. Some of the best-designed, gravity-flow irrigation ditches serve their owners as drainage ditches during the rainy season. Figure 13:3 is a map of the irrigation system of a farm near Harrisburg. The main canals become drainage-water outlets during the winter.

Impressive progress is being made in land drainage. This type of engineering requires cooperation among neighboring farmers, for outlets to creeks and streams must be secured for the excess waters collected in drainage ditches. This generally involves running main-line ditches through several properties, and objectors might thwart the plans of several neighbors by not joining in a community project. This is not a problem unique to the Willamette Valley. It is faced wherever drainage is essential to optimum land use. Figure 13:4 illustrates how eighteen farmers south of Corvallis resolved the problem in an equitable manner. Costs always play an important part in a farmer's decision to undertake any kind of land reclamation. In this instance the Linn-Lane Soil Conservation District made a soil survey of the watershed through which it was proposed to construct a main drainage canal. As a result of this survey the lands of all properties were mapped and classified according to the extent of benefit which would be derived from drainage. Each owner agreed to pay assessments which were determined by acreage, type of land, and percentage of benefit. The project was constructed accordingly.

One reason that many farmers in the Willamette Valley are not much concerned about the pace of future development is that they are already doing well. With the exception of properties on the river bottoms, many of which are now highly developed, the farms are generally larger than a single operator could handle under more intensive systems of cropping. The upland bench-terrace area, which constitutes the broader portion of the valley, lies in rather large units of 200 to 1000 acres. This is in contrast to the smaller farms of 20 to 100 acres along the river bottoms. Yet the potentials of the soils of the elevated valley floor are not so disparate as these figures would suggest.

This is a rather old region as western settlement history is recorded. It was first occupied over 100 years ago and used as range and for the cultivation of wheat. Through the generosity of the 1850 Oregon Donation Land Law any married man who was willing to homestead in the Willamette Valley and forego California's gold rush received a square

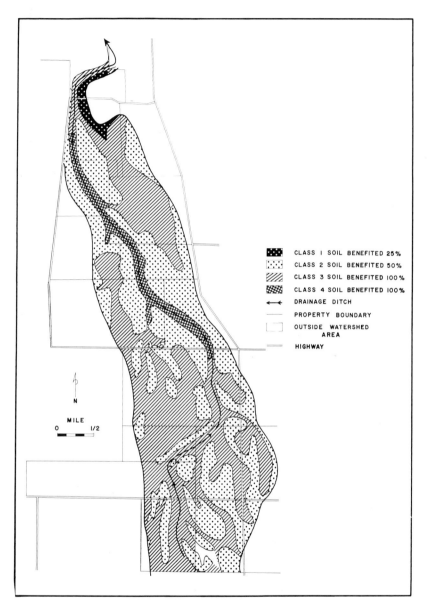

Figure 13:4. Community drainage project in the Willamette Valley, Oregon. (Source: U.S.D.A.)

mile of land. This liberal land policy lasted only five years, but it filled up the Willamette Valley with large-sized farms which to this day are a feature of that country. To be sure, the summers are dry, but sufficient forage crops can be grown between the beginning of autumn and the end of spring to make a cattleman quite satisfied with his lot. Then, too, there are cash crops which can be raised profitably. This is one of the best areas in the country for the production of vetch and grass seeds. The cultivation of Italian ryegrass, alta fescue, and hairy vetch are specialties particularly well adapted to the region's peculiarities of soils and climate. These crops are sown in the fall on the better-drained lands, such as those of the Amity and Willamette soil series. No cultivation is essential during the winter months of heavy precipitation. The dry summers are just what the grower wants when he combines seed. Not all of the land is suitable for commercial grass-seed production, but the returns from these crops have been sufficient to satisfy many owners. Consequently, the balance of their properties is often used as range with little improvement.

Soils of the Dayton series are typical of the compact, poorly drained, bench-terrace soils which are so extensive in the Willamette Valley. With a reasonable drainage system to remove surplus surface water in winter and with irrigation in summer, these soils can sustain excellent pastures of Ladino clover, fescue, and orchard grass. This was demonstrated by a farmer in Linn County who in one year harvested 350 tons of green ensilage from 20 acres and also carried 40 head of Guernseys from June to November on the same ground. He irrigated every two weeks during the dry season and made very heavy applications of ammonium nitrate and superphosphate every four months. This farmer explains that the reason he has not made further drainage and irrigation improvements is that his present enterprise already absorbs all of his time.

As the cities of the Pacific Northwest continue to grow and as the demand for fluid milk increases, more Valley farms will shift gradually toward intensive systems of management. Winters are so mild that pole-barn resting sheds and milk parlors can be used satisfactorily. The cost and maintenance of these efficient structures is moderate. They are the kind of buildings one commonly finds on the Atlantic coast from Chesapeake Bay southward. The mild winters of Virginia and North Carolina are comparable to those of the Willamette Valley and Puget Sound.

The Oregon State College Experiment Station has made studies of the effect of irrigation on bench-land soils. The results are given in Table 13:2.

In view of the previously stated fact that ground water is not easily or

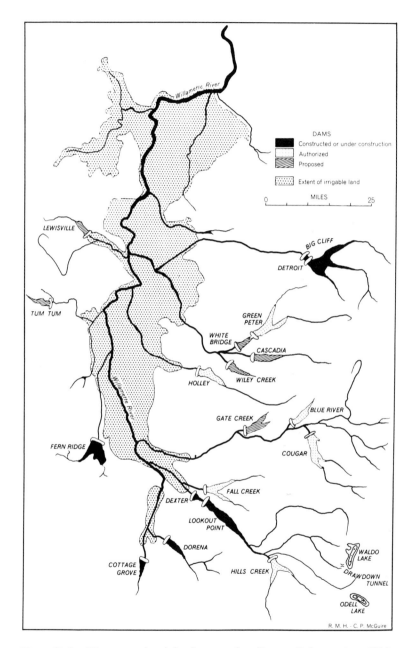

Figure 13:5.   Water control and development plan. (Source: Reference 1; p. 109.)

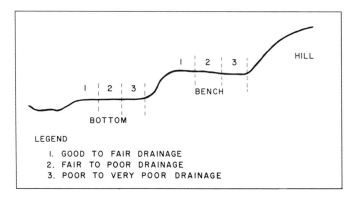

Figure 13:6.   Land condition in the Willamette Valley. (Source: U.S.D.A.)

cheaply secured from beneath the bench lands, community cooperation will be necessary to bring surface waters to most of these farms. The Army Corps of Engineers has made a study of water resources and the possibilities of conserving and distributing them for irrigation. Some dams have been constructed. Of course, the Corps of Engineers also has in mind the beneficial influence upon flood control along the main stream which will result from a series of reservoirs on tributary rivers. Some such project as the Corps of Engineers envisages will doubtless be completed in the future as the cities of the region grow and the demand for farm produce makes additional irrigation feasible.

The rather level surfaces of the bench lands of the Willamette at present contribute to poor drainage conditions. In the future an even surface will be an asset when gravity systems of irrigation and artificial drainage become more popular. Expenses for land leveling and land planing will be reasonable, as already indicated by preliminary use of such heavy equipment.

The great breadth of the bench-terrace surfaces makes the Willamette Valley unique in the Pacific Northwest. These lands are composed of alluvium which has filled in an old structural valley behind a wall-like basalt formation which crosses the valley at Oregon City. This natural dam, known as Willamette Falls, was one of the consequences of vulcanism which created the numerous ridges and hills extruding from the valley floor.

The present river channel is 30 to 40 feet below the level of older fluvial deposits. One might compare the Willamette Valley as it is now with a reservoir which has become completely silted in behind its dam. As the upper levels of the dam itself have crumbled, the stream has cut

Table 13:2.   Average Increase in Crop Yields with Irrigation
(Source: Reference 1; p. 108)

Crops	Number of Years	Average Yield Per Acre Unirrigated	Irrigated	% Increase
On Valley Floor Soils				
Alfalfa hay	23	3.46 tons	5.21 tons	50
Clover hay	28	3.34 tons	5.46 tons	63
Potatoes	30	130.00 bushels	209.00 bushels	61
Dry beans	28	10.43 bushels	18.58 bushels	78
Corn ensilage	30	6.56 tons	9.80 tons	49
Grass	8	3.33 tons	5.13 tons	54
Kale	3	10.67 tons	13.95 tons	31
Stock beets	6	10.98 tons	15.61 tons	42
Flax	11	1.87 tons	3.00 tons	60
Carrots	3	10.56 tons	18.14 tons	72
Ladino clover	4	not grown	500 animal-unit days	
On Bottom Soils				
Potatoes	13	106.00 bushels	227.00 bushels	115
Sugar-beet seed	2	1395.00 pounds	1395.00 pounds	42
Clover seed	10	1.95 bushels	3.31 bushels	61
Spring barley	4	38.00 bushels	49.00 bushels	30
Evergreen blackberries	3	3.212 tons	5.443 tons	70
Red raspberries	3	2.226 tons	3.525 tons	58
Loganberries	2	3.508 tons	7.051 tons	100
Black raspberries	3	0.723 tons	1.521 tons	110
Strawberries	2	4.337 tons	7.929 tons	83
Green beans	2	not grown	11.300 tons	

down to a lower plane to expose the layers of sediments previously deposited. Thus a type of staircase profile has been created. Figure 13:6 illustrates in a generalized fashion the relative positions of well-drained and poorly drained soils on the staircase profile.

REFERENCES

1. Highsmith, Richard M. Jr., Irrigation in the Willamette Valley, *The Geographical Review*, pp. 98–110, January 1956.
2. Highsmith, Richard M. Jr., *et al*, *Atlas of the Pacific Northwest Resources and Development*, Oregon State College, Corvallis (undated).
3. Selby, H. E., and Leland Fryer, *Willamette Valley Land Adaptability*, Oregon State College, Corvallis, 1937.
4. Upchurch, M. L. and E. L. Potter, *Irrigation for the Willamette Valley*, Oregon State College, Bulletin 675.

the
dry
plains

14

The dry plains are the arid to subhumid lands which lie between the Rocky Mountains and the humid eastern United States. The student interested in the dry plains will not overlook the writings of John Wesley Powell and Walter Prescott Webb. Powell submitted his *Report on the Lands of the Arid Region of the United States* in 1878. This report recommended that the western dry lands should be used for ranching and irrigation farming, for Powell believed that dry farming on small homesteads would prove to be impractical. This was four years after barbed wire had been invented and just before uncounted miles of the new "thorn" fence converted the open cattle range into thousands of individual homesteads. Webb's book *The Great Plains* was published in 1931 at the commencement of a drought-stricken decade when the whole nation was beginning to realize that Powell had been right.

As chief of the Geological Survey, Powell had headed a government field party in the arid West. After careful study he recommended that Congress revise the laws governing disposition of the public domain.

The Homestead Law, which granted 160 acres to a family, was appropriate only for settlers in the humid zones of the United States, according to Powell's conclusions. It was thought that widespread suffering and economic disaster would result if nonirrigable grasslands in dry regions were disposed of in units of less than 2560 acres. Powell advocated ranching rather than crop cultivation, an extensive rather than an intensive form of land use.

Powell could only anticipate events. He could not be sure because he was considering the open range before the grass had been plowed for wheat:

The limit of successful agriculture without irrigation has been set at 20 inches . . . at 20 inches agriculture will not be uniformly successful from season to season. Many droughts will occur; many seasons in a long series will be fruitless; and it may be doubted whether, on the whole, agriculture will prove remunerative. On this point it is impossible to speak with certainty. A larger experience than the history of agriculture in the western portion of the United States affords is necessary to a final determination of the question. (Reference 7; p. 3.)

These tentative conclusions were rejected by Congress, and the Homestead Law continued in force. By the time public grasslands of the Great Plains were disposed of, hundreds of thousands of men had been settled on 160-acre plots where the annual rainfall averages 14 to 20 inches.

Nearly sixty years after Powell's prophetic judgment, and while the "Oakies" were being blown from the dust bowl, Webb commented in *The Great Plains,*

The failure to recognize the fact that the Plains destroyed the old formula of living (developed in the humid eastern United States) and demanded a new one led the settlers into disaster, the lawmakers into error, and leads all who will not see into confusion. (Reference 8; p. vi.)

As though his words were an editorial postscript to Powell's forecast, Webb observed,

Practically every consideration in certain semi-arid regions of the Great Plains, particularly in the High Plains, points to the *stock farm* as the most economical land unit that can be adopted, one that is well suited to the natural conditions—in fact one that is made necessary by those conditions . . . and one needs only to make a trip through the West to find that the *stock farmer* (author's italics) is on the whole the citizen best prepared to enjoy life. (Reference 8; p. 395.)

The stock farms that Webb refers to were units of about 4000 acres of land upon which crops were grown by dry-farming methods but an indispensable interest of the operator was "a small herd of cattle . . . which ranged over the pastures." (Reference 8; p. 396.) Farms upon which most land is used for ranching but upon which cropping is economically dominant are considered stock farms in this book.

The question as to whether the plains are better suited to cropping, ranching, or combination stock farms is chiefly one of historical interest because all of these types are prominently established. We note by the map of major types of farming (Figure 4:2) that there are sections of the plains states which are primarily devoted to wheat, cotton, and corn. There are also areas which are characterized by ranches and stock farms. Farmers, ranchers, and stock farmers have all been hurt by drought, and it has become obvious that changes and improvements in grass management, cropping practices, and the size and utilization of properties must occur if man is to make a better adjustment to the uncertainties of the weather.

The most important fact bearing upon land management in the dry plains is not that rainfall is low but that it is *uncertain*. Statistical averages tell little about the reasons for frustrated hopes, bankruptcy, wasted lives, and ruined land. Only systems of farming which can absorb the blows of absolute crop failure from time to time will long survive on the dry plains, and progress toward such systems is now apparent on the landscape. Variation from year to year in rainfall is characteristic of most agricultural regions in the United States. The reason that such variation is of particular significance in the plains states is that they are the transition zone between our deserts and our humid lands. Men on the dry plains are too often tempted to continue the land-management practices of humid regions, even though there is statistical certainty that occasionally desert conditions will prevail.

In the truly arid districts of the West, where precipitation is less than 14 inches annually, the land is not plowed unless it is possible to irrigate. For that reason the desert is not a high-risk region. Man does not gamble here because he knows that it would be futile. Market fluctuations aside, the desert areas of irrigation farming are among the most stable in the nation. The situation is entirely different in many sections of the dry plains where the average annual rainfall is between 14 to 20 inches. There, men have been taking chances ever since Powell warned against crop farming on small units. This will continue until the small units of a few hundred acres on unirrigated land are consolidated into ranches or into stock farms which devote a small proportion of their lands to cash crops and the larger part to permanent grass for pasturage and hay.

The hazard of crop farming is illustrated in the thirty-four-year record of wheat yields at the Agricultural Experiment Station, Colby, Kansas.

**Table 14:1. Yield of Winter Wheat Per Seeded Acre
at the Colby, Kansas, Experiment Station**
(Source: Reference 1; p. 8)

Year	Cropped in Alternate Years Following One Year of Fallow Bushels	Cropped Every Year Without Fallow Bushels
1915	19.5	18.7
1916	26.0	18.5
1917	0.0	0.0
1918	8.3	5.3
1919	13.7	7.5
1920	31.7	15.0
1921	25.2	13.2
1922	18.2	15.3
1923	1.8	5.0
1924	31.8	8.5
1925	27.8	5.5
1926	13.3	1.3
1927	3.0	0.7
1928	37.9	18.3
1929	14.3	5.8
1930	42.8	29.0
1931	23.3	6.0
1932	36.8	6.0
1933	0.0	0.0
1934	5.5	0.0
1935	0.0	0.0
1936	0.0	0.0
1937	2.5	1.7
1938	5.2	4.7
1939	4.2	2.5
1940	0.0	0.0
1941	23.3	10.0
1942	22.0	15.5
1943	28.7	5.5
1944	31.0	12.7
1945	41.0	7.8
1946	15.8	4.3
1947	46.3	24.7
1948	10.0	1.2
Average	18.0	7.9

Colby, the county seat of Thomas County, is known as *The Golden Buckle on the Wheat Belt.*

Drastic annual-yield fluctuations are reported in Table 14:1, but another impressive fact is the increased yield obtained in most years by planting wheat after a year of fallow. The practice of fallowing land for a year before planting wheat was adopted by some individuals very shortly after farming became general in the dry plains in the late eighteen hundreds. But it did not become a prominent custom until the advent of high-speed power implements.

Fallowland wheat is a crop obtained with the rainfall of a two-year period. During the year before cropping the unplanted land is worked clean to keep weeds from withdrawing soil moisture. Several inches of water are thereby stored in the ground and held in reserve for the following season. In the succeeding year, when the land is sown, the crop utilizes the stored moisture with whatever falls during its period of growth. Obviously, a man with a small farm, whose limitation is land rather than time and machinery, is often inclined to gamble on a crop every year rather than let some of his land lie fallow. To be fully occupied the farmer who practices fallowing should have about twice as much land as he plants in any one year. This means that the small crop farm on the dry plains is obsolete for technological and climatic reasons.

The data obtained at the Colby Experiment Station show that fallowing will not eliminate crop failure, although it will definitely reduce the number of failures. Not enough moisture can be stored in the soil after a year of fallowing to assure a crop in the following season if in that subsequent season the rainfall is very low. In 1948 the Department of Agriculture summarized data on wheat yields as related to moisture stored in the soil. Table 14:2 is compiled from 1107 records kept on typical soils under average farm conditions.

Table 14:2.   Yields in the Southern High Plains in Relation to Soil Moisture at Seeding Time

(Source: Reference 9; p. 5)

Depth of Wetted Soil at Sowing Time (inches)	Average Yields Per Acre When Later Conditions Are	
	Unfavorable 1938–39 (bushels)	Favorable 1945–47 (bushels)
0–12	1.4	9.2
13–24	3.1	10.8
25–36	8.5	19.7
37 or more	12.6	26.2

For thirteen years the records of soil moisture and wheat yields were kept on experimental plots at Garden City, Kansas. Alternate years of wheat and fallow were prescribed for some plots, and wheat was planted every year on others. Available water in the soil at seeding time on the fallowed plots averaged 4.67 inches; that on the plots seeded annually averaged 1.08 inches. Yields from the fallowed plots obtained every other·year averaged 15.5 bushels; those from the plots seeded annually averaged 8.2 bushels. Since the cost of the production of wheat amounts to the market value of several bushels, it is obvious that the farmer in the vicinity of Garden City who practiced fallowing made more money per acre during the thirteen-year period than did the farmer who planted every year. (Reference 10.)

Beadle County is in the spring-wheat district of east-central South Dakota. In Table 14:3 the annual precipitation data collected at Huron near the center of Beadle County are compared with wheat yields for the county. The table indicates the close dependence of yields upon precipitation.

The wide fluctuation in yields from year to year is strongly influenced by the fluctuation in precipitation. This is the heart of the problem of land management in the dry plains. A study of the variability of wheat yields was made in 1951 by E. Lloyd Barber of the U. S. Department of Agriculture. (Reference 2.) It showed that in fifty-two of fifty-three counties in North Dakota the yields of wheat deviated at least 30 per cent above or below average over a twenty-three year period. Only Traill County in the Red River Valley on the Minnesota line had a deviation as low as 28 per cent. In twenty-one counties the deviation was as high as 60 per cent. In Billings County the deviation from average was 76 per cent. (Reference 2; pp. 50–51.) In other words, the farmer in Billings County could hardly ever expect to get an "average" yield. The chances are that he would harvest between 2 and 15 bushels in two years out of three; in the other year he might expect either less than 2 or more than 15. These are the kinds of odds that some wheat farmers in the dry plains have been dealing with. Are there ways of reducing the risk? There are several:

1. Ranching rather than crop farming.
2. Irrigation where possible.
3. Crop insurance.
4. Combination of ranching and crop farming (stock farming).
5. Sidewalk farming.
6. Suitcase farming.
7. Conservation measures such as fallowing, trash mulching, lister plowing, terracing, and shelterbelts.

**Table 14:3. Relation of Precipitation to Wheat Yields in
Beadle County, South Dakota**
(Source: Reference 11; pp. 7–8)

Year	Annual Precipitation (inches)	Wheat, Bushels per Acre
1926	16.6	3.0
1927	21.1	14.3
1928	18.1	6.3
1929	17.5	10.1
1930	21.5	11.7
1931	12.7	3.4
1932	13.4	9.0
1933	12.5	0.1
1934	10.7	0.0
1935	19.2	8.2
1936	12.6	0.1
1937	15.6	3.8
1938	20.0	8.3
1939	13.8	5.1
1940	13.4	7.3
1941	17.0	9.6
1942	25.8	12.0
1943	18.2	5.3
1944	26.4	9.9
1945	17.7	19.1
1946	23.3	11.8
1947	19.2	15.4
1948	20.4	13.8
1949	16.2	8.2
1950	17.0	11.4
1951	24.2	15.8
1952	9.7	5.7
1953	20.4	8.3

Ranching and irrigation on the plains are discussed in succeeding chapters.

CROP INSURANCE

Crop insurance reduces the risk of bankruptcy in any one year. It cannot protect the farmer against failure in the long run if he specializes in cash crops where average yields are low and the deviation from average is high. Insurance against crop failure is sold by a federal

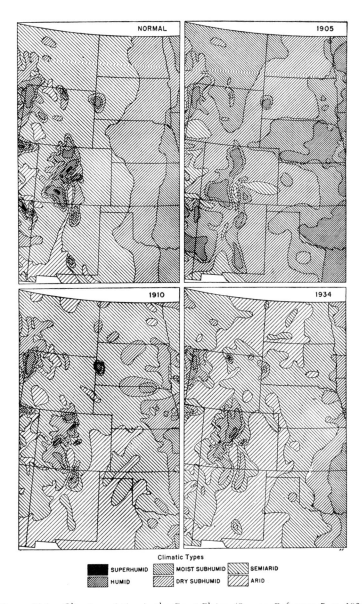

Figure 14:1. Climate variation in the Great Plains. (Source: Reference 5; p. 182.)

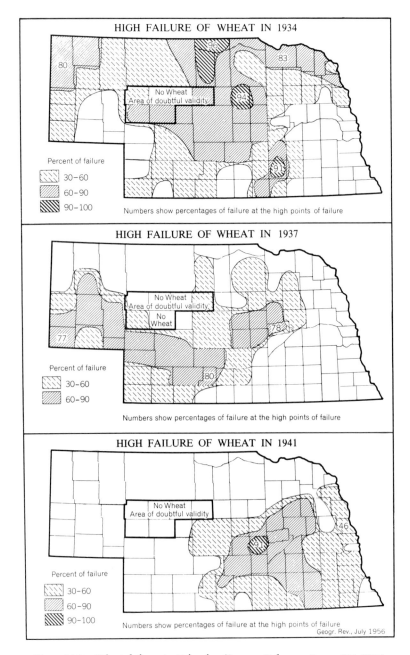

Figure 14:2.   Wheat failures in Nebraska. (Source: Reference 3; pp. 384–386.)

government agency, but premiums charged must cover losses. Therefore, the farmer who takes out insurance year after year ultimately pays during good years for the compensation he receives in years of failure. In case of total failure he receives payment for no more than 60 per cent of a long-time average yield. In high-risk Bowman County in southwestern North Dakota, where the average wheat production is 9.2 bushels per acre, the farmer can get insurance on only 5.1 bushels per acre. For that coverage he must pay 0.8 bushels per acre premium; so that even if he had a total failure his net recovery would be only 4.3 bushels. Ordinarily that is not enough to cover all operating expenses.

In 1950 the Kansas Agricultural Experiment Station issued an income analysis of a prototype family-operated small livestock-wheat farm in the western portion of the state. On the basis of a thirty-four-year record of wheat yields at Colby (Table 14:1), an estimate was made of probable yearly income both with crop insurance and without it. On this theoretical 605-acre farm it was assumed that 75 per cent of income was derived from wheat, 19 per cent from livestock, and 6 per cent from other crops, such as grain sorghums. Commodity prices for all years were calculated at the 1948 level (Table 14:4).

It is apparent that the effect of crop insurance is to ease the impact of calamity and to scale down somewhat the profits of bonanza years. In the long run it cannot add substantially to income.

It is misleading to consider the plains states as a unit. Nearly every year some portions of it are devastated by drought while others are combining bumper harvests. Only occasionally, as in the mid-1930's, is drought general, and only infrequently, as in 1905, does heavy rainfall cover most of the area. It is the scattered pattern of good yields and poor yields, following the scattered pattern of spotty rainfall and drought, which fortunately minimizes those years of region-wide calamity. But, by the same token, because areas of crop failure are widely mixed with zones of adequate harvest nearly every year, national attention is seldom focused upon the private agony of the thousands who lose their gamble with the weather.

The areal patterns of wheat failure in Nebraska during three dry years are given in the maps of Figure 14:2. These maps indicate that the occurrence and intensity of drought are quite variable even within a single state.

THE SIDEWALK FARMER·

The evidence is clear that the farmer who tries to make a living by growing cash crops must expect failure from time to time. This situation

Table 14:4.   Net Income After Tax for an Encumbered Owner-Operator on a Western Kansas Wheat Farm[1]
(Source: Reference 1; Table 9)

Year	Without Insurance Dollars	With Wheat Crop Insurance Dollars
1915	3943	3666
1916	3878	3601
1917	−972	−69
1918	632	307
1919	2806	2531
1920	4377	4100
1921	3736	3461
1922	3742	3465
1923	2414	2103
1924	2831	2554
1925	2280	1955
1926	180	−145
1927	−242	507
1928	4950	4675
1929	1567	1242
1930	7631	7364
1931	2952	2675
1932	3379	3102
1933	185	1214
1934	−834	−187
1935	−1243	−214
1936	−1287	−258
1937	−711	−99
1938	541	216
1939	−215	148
1940	−167	862
1941	3687	3410
1942	3651	3376
1943	2361	2084
1944	4127	3850
1945	3432	3157
1946	1198	873
1947	6541	6274
1948	1019	1222
Average	2128	2148

[1]Crop yields as reported at the Colby, Kansas Experiment Station.

was anticipated by Powell before the plains were settled, and it will continue. The small-unit, cash-crop specialist is slowly dying out. He is abandoning the farm or he is combining the farm with town employment. Gradually small farms are being bought up and annexed to larger units on which a diversity of land-use systems can be employed. On these larger units the risk of total failure is reduced proportionately. The percentage of part-time farmers in the plains states is low but significant. With the automobile and modern mechanized implements, it is possible for a man to be a "sidewalk farmer" who lives in town and holds a town job but drives out to the farm when there is work to be done. By becoming sidewalk farmers, thousands of landowners have been able to hold their properties in the drought-stricken cotton districts of Texas and in the equally dry winter-wheat areas of Texas, Oklahoma, and Kansas.

SUITCASE FARMERS

The machine age has made possible another kind of agriculturist in the wheat districts of the plains states. The so-called "suitcase farmer" owns or rents land in both the winter-wheat and in the spring-wheat regions. He travels back and forth between them with his mechanized equipment mounted on trucks. He does not literally live out of a suitcase, for he may take his family with him and set up housekeeping at both ends of the line. Sometimes he lives in a mobile home. He plants in Texas, Oklahoma, or Kansas in the autumn, and in the early spring he goes to the Dakotas. Then he returns south to combine his winter wheat. In July he rides north to harvest his spring wheat. These men must have good equipment and large areas of land to make a profit from this interstate commuting. The advantages are several. The risk of crop failure is divided among two or more widely separated properties, and the same investment in equipment is made to do double duty, thus reducing overhead. It is a hard itinerant life for several months of the year, but it is a type of commercial farming which good managers are likely to develop on a larger scale. Again, it is no business for a man with small acreages and meager resources. It is a kind of crop farming which Powell could not have imagined in his day.

THE STOCK FARM

The stock farm, or combination ranch and cash-crop enterprise, is not a new institution in the plains states. It is as old as agricultural settlement in the area, but it is becoming far commoner with the passage of

Table 14:5.   Size and Number of Farms in the Northern Great Plains Area During 1935 and 1945
(Source: Reference 6; p. 20)

State	Number of Farms			All Land in Farms (acres)		Average Acres per Farm		
	1935	1945	Percentage Change	1935	1945	1935	1945	Percentage Change[1]
Colorado	63,644	47,618	−25.2	29,978,472	36,217,808	471.0	761	+61.6
Kansas	174,589	141,192	−19.1	48,009,770	48,589,418	275.0	344	+25.1
Montana	50,564	37,747	−25.4	47,511,868	58,787,318	939.6	1557	+65.7
Nebraska	133,616	111,756	−16.4	46,615,762	47,752,941	348.9	427	+22.4
North Dakota	84,606	69,520	−17.8	39,118,136	41,001,158	462.4	590	+27.6
South Dakota	83,303	68,705	−17.5	37,101,871	43,031,964	445.4	626	+40.6
Wyoming	17,487	13,076	−25.2	28,161,911	33,116,554	1610.4	2533	+57.3
Total, Northern Great Plains	607,809	489,614	−19.4	276,497,790	308,497,161	455.0	630	+38.5

[1] Actually this shows more increase in land in farms than happened because considerable land was used as free range in 1935 which was under lease or ownership in 1945, especially in Montana, Wyoming, and Colorado.

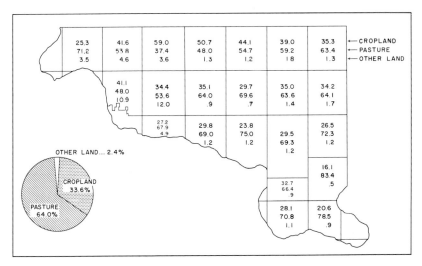

Figure 14:3.   Utilization of land in farms in Hughes County, South Dakota. (Source: Reference 4; p. 5.)

time as smaller units decline in number and consolidation continues. The size of farm is growing in the northern Great Plains, as illustrated in Table 14:5.

Hughes County lies in about the center of South Dakota on the southeastern fringe of the spring-wheat belt. The average size of farm has been increasing in Hughes County since 1890 when the first census was taken. At that time the average farm was 283 acres. By 1920 it was 785. In 1950 it was 1217 acres and the trend continues. Paralleling the increase in farm size has been an increase in cattle from a total of 19,000 in 1924 to 26,000 in 1951. Although it would require a minimum of 2000 to 3000 acres to make a living exclusively with beef, a 1200-acre farm permits the operator to keep enough cattle to hedge himself somewhat against the greater risks of cash cropping. About 20 to 30 acres of well-managed range in central South Dakota may carry a cow and calf for a year. The profit is the calf, which as a yearling may weigh 400 to 500 pounds. The return from wheat on the other hand varies from 0 to 15 bushels annually in Hughes County. The twenty-year average (1928–1947) is 7.7 bushels. (Reference 4; p. 25.) The stockman must have a much larger property than the wheat farmer to make an equal income in a wet year. In a dry year the stockman may survive and the wheat farmer suffer a real loss. The chart (Figure 14:3) shows how farmers in various sections of Hughes County apportion their lands to cropping and grazing.

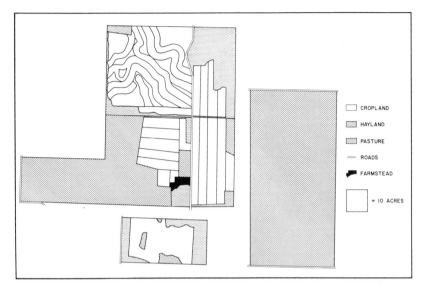

CROPLAND

HAYLAND

PASTURE

ROADS

FARMSTEAD

= IO ACRES

Figure 14:4.   North Dakota stock farm.

A subsidiary cattle enterprise is the wheat farmer's best insurance policy. No matter how bad the year, there will be some grass. If the range is managed with a realization that drought may come at any time, there will always be a reserve of hay on hand to carry the breeding stock through the ordeal. Calves and young beeves can be sold. In such circumstances the farmer salvages something. As those who engage in this kind of operation declare, "We don't expect to make much on the cattle but we don't expect to lose our farms." As for making a good profit occasionally on less than 2000 to 3000 acres—that is possible only with some wheat. In a good year the grower will do well. In a dry year he will make little or nothing. This is a better solution than losing home and livelihood on an out-and-out gamble with wheat alone.

No one familiar with the plains states would seriously suggest that cash-crop farming should be abandoned. The efforts of all serious researchers is to help farmers develop ways to counteract the risk while continuing to grow wheat. The whole agricultural economy of the nation, as we now know it, would be thrown out of joint if we had to raise the bulk of our wheat outside the plains states. Long stretches of level land and efficient modern machinery make the United States plainsman the producer of the cheapest wheat in the world in terms of man-hours per bushel. The trouble, as we are aware from the data already considered, is that, although the nation gets a good wheat crop each year, there are too many individuals who encounter calamity.

The plan of a stock farm in Morton County, North Dakota (Figure 14:4) illustrates the manner in which land may be used wisely as a combination cash-crop and livestock enterprise. The total area of the farm is 960 acres, of which 334 acres are used for cropping, 493 for range, and 84 for permanent hay. The assembly of this property is typical of stock farms. It consists of a central unit and detached pieces. These detached pieces represent annexations some distance removed by road. It is by such annexations that a crop farmer on a small property can become a stock farmer.

CONSERVATION MEASURES

As we have previously noted, *fallowing* helps to reduce crop failure, but twice as much cropland is needed as when fields are seeded annually. Rain often comes to the plains in short but intense storms; even on nearly level lands there is surface runoff of water. *Closed-end terraces* hold water on the land, and much progress has been made with these terraces on the wheat lands of Kansas and the cotton lands of Texas. *Contour basin listing* is also a method of preventing water runoff. Soil erosion reduces the infiltration and water-holding capacities of the land by removing the more friable topsoil. *Shelterbelts* and *strip cropping* serve to check wind erosion which is particularly severe in the Dakotas. *Trash mulching* is a system of tillage which keeps the straw and stubble of the previous harvest partially on the surface of the ground until the next crop is established. A trash mulch is especially valuable in checking wind and water erosion during the years when the cropland is left fallow.

The modern wheat farmer is particularly diligent about keeping the surface of his land in a rough and cloddy condition when it is not planted. This is because stubble-mulched and cloddy ground prevents the wind from blowing individual soil particles into the air. Modern high-speed machinery has made possible better soil management. As one plains farmer remarked to the author,

When we see dust start to fly we get into the fields in a hurry. We couldn't do the job well enough or fast enough with horses. Even if a man could stay out those beasts couldn't take it. The heat and labor of the job that had to be done would have killed them; so we couldn't beat the wind. Now we can run the tractors with lights 24 hours if we have to and cover all our fields before the drifts get going.

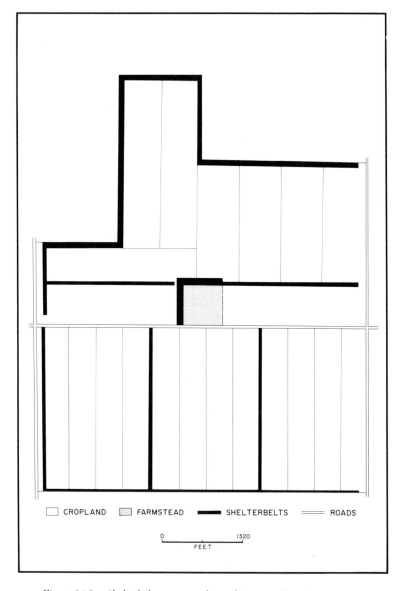

Figure 14:5.   Shelterbelt system in the Red River Valley, North Dakota.

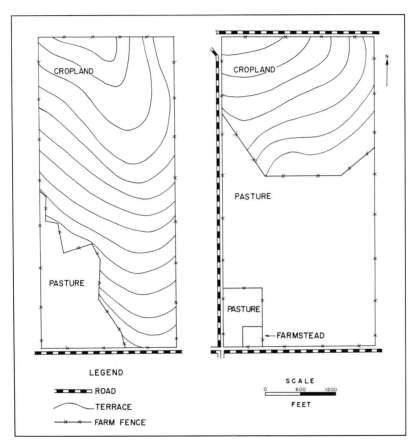

Figure 14:6. Terraced wheat land in Kansas. This farm is composed of several units. It was originally a 320-acre farm and is now a 1080-acre property. Two units are shown.

REFERENCES

1. Barber, E. Lloyd, *Meeting Weather Risks in Kansas Wheat Farming*, Kansas Agricultural Experiment Station, Manhattan, 1950.
2. Barber, E. Lloyd, *Variability of Wheat Yields*, U.S. Department of Agriculture, Washington, D.C., 1951 (mimeographed).
3. Hewes, Leslie and Arthur G. Schmieding, *Risk in the Central Great Plains: Geographical Patterns of Wheat Failure in Nebraska, 1931–1952, The Geographical Review*, New York, July 1956.
4. South Dakota State Department of Agriculture, *Hughes County Agriculture*, Pierre, South Dakota.
5. United States Department of Agriculture, *Climate and Man, 1941 Yearbook of Agriculture*, Government Printing Office, Washington, D.C.
6. University of Nebraska College of Agriculture, *Toward Stability in the Great Plain Plains Economy*, Lincoln, 1950.
7. Powell, J. W., *Report on the Lands of the Arid Region of the United States*, Government Printing Office, Washington, D.C., 1879 (second edition).
8. Webb, Walter Prescott, *The Great Plains*, Ginn and Company, Boston, 1931.
9. Finnell, H. H., *Soil Moisture and Wheat Yields on the High Plains*, U.S. Department of Agriculture, Washington, D.C., 1948.
10. Throckmorton, R. I. and H. E. Meyers, *Summer Fallow in Kansas*, Kansas Agricultural Experiment Station, Manhattan, 1941.
11. Helfinstine, Rex D., *Economic Potentials of Irrigated and Dryland Farming in Central South Dakota*, South Dakota State College, Brookings, 1955.

ranching
on the
dry
plains

15

We have observed that the stock farmer depends upon cash crops for most of his income, and livestock serves him chiefly as a hedge against calamity. The dry-plains rancher, however, is principally dependent upon cattle and sheep, although he often produces some cash crops. Montana is one of the major ranch states. Over half the total annual cash income derived from farming in Montana is received from livestock and livestock products. Normally, the state's total number of cattle is between 1 and 1.5 million head. The number of sheep varies from 3 to 4 million.

Cattle and sheep outfits vary greatly in size. The Montana Agricultural Experiment Station considers 200 head of cattle or 1000 sheep as minimum numbers for efficient operation. (Reference 2; pp. 15–16.) As to the number of acres of land which are required for grazing and feed production, there is again wide variation. In Montana, taking the state as a whole, an average of 32 acres is recommended to maintain one cow or five sheep during the grazing season. This means that each ranch

should have approximately ten sections or 6400 acres of land. An out-
fit of this size should also have 75 to 150 acres of irrigated land devoted
to the production of winter feed. (Reference 2; pp. 15–16.) This is an
ideal that only a minority of ranchers has achieved. Although it is
apparent that ranches in the dry plains require very large acreages,
compared with stock farms, these areas are small compared with the
large spreads necessary in the truly arid districts of the intermountain
states. There, as we have noted, tens of thousands of acres are essential
wherever the average annual rainfall is below 10 inches.

The average cattle ranch in the northern Great Plains has fewer than
200 head of stock and 6400 acres of land. Table 15:1 presents statistics
from a study which included most of southeastern Montana, northeastern
Wyoming, and the western half of South Dakota. The rainfall of the
area averages approximately 14 inches annually, but there is considerable
variation from year to year.

Ranchers did not increase the size of their herds between 1930 and
1952 in the area considered in Table 15:1. However, they did more
than double the amount of land owned. Leased land remained approximately the same. One might have expected that the substantial increase
in the size of the average ranch would have permitted an increase in the
size of the average herd. The researchers who made the study believe
that the additional land represents the cushion which is necessary to
put a ranch on a sustaining basis through anticipated dry periods. This
cushion the ranchers did not have in 1930 when thousands of them were
forced to liquidate their holdings. Between 1930 and 1936 beef production dropped to between one third and one half in South Dakota,
Wyoming, and Montana. (Reference 1; p. 9.)

The gradual growth in the size of ranches, as in the parallel growth
in size of farms, is made possible by the withdrawal of many families
from the business. Purchase of their properties by neighbors has
resulted in fewer, larger, but more stable enterprises. Although it
would be desirable for the average rancher to own even more land, the
risk of buying it would be great unless he had already earned the cash
to do so. If he were to borrow the money and a series of dry years
should occur he could lose everything.

Increase in the size of ranches, together with decrease in their
numbers, is likely to continue at a gradual pace in the future as it has
in the past. The fractionation of the public domain into small parcels
under the original Homestead Act (160 acres in 1862), the Enlarged
Homestead Act (320 acres in 1919), and the Homestead Act for ranchers
(640 acres in 1916) set the stage for economic difficulties and managerial
inefficiencies that have saddled the dry plains for decades. Only by a

Table 15:1. Changes in Size of Ranch and Cattle Populations—Northern Great Plains

(Source: Reference 1; pp. 5 and 7)

Year	Cattle All Ages	Average Acres per Ranch	Acres of Range	
			Leased	Owned
1930	140.8	2606	1303	1084
1931	139.8	2668	1352	1108
1932	132.0	2830	1475	1128
1933	140.7	2624	1411	966
1934	141.4	2561	1362	951
1935	131.5	2661	1442	972
1936	129.0	2890	1598	1043
1937	124.2	2883	1588	1040
1938	131.2	3166	1809	1094
1939	134.2	3408	2002	1137
1940	137.9	3559	2108	1168
1941	138.4	3593	2071	1256
1942	141.0	3391	1881	1242
1943	138.1	3537	1869	1394
1944	137.9	3572	1796	1494
1945	143.2	3667	1772	1611
1946	139.5	3686	1716	1703
1947	143.4	3843	1752	1810
1948	135.9	3804	1719	1802
1949	141.2	3754	1652	1835
1950	136.6	3790	1516	2000
1951	134.1	3813	1213	2317
1952	138.5	3990	1250	2441

slow evolutionary process will the proper readjustments be made. In time, the better managers on larger units will survive and grow bigger. The inefficient, underemployed, and financially weak will be eliminated.

Very few stockmen in the plains area own all of their grazing land. On the other hand, there are many individuals, corporations, and governmental units which own land but are not engaged in either ranching or farming. Sometimes the properties owned by these nonoperators are leased to individual ranchers who use them jointly with their own. In some instances large tracts owned by county and state governments, banks, railroads, insurance companies, and individual investors are leased to groups of small ranchers who use them on a cooperative basis. Cooperative grazing districts organized under state law now administer

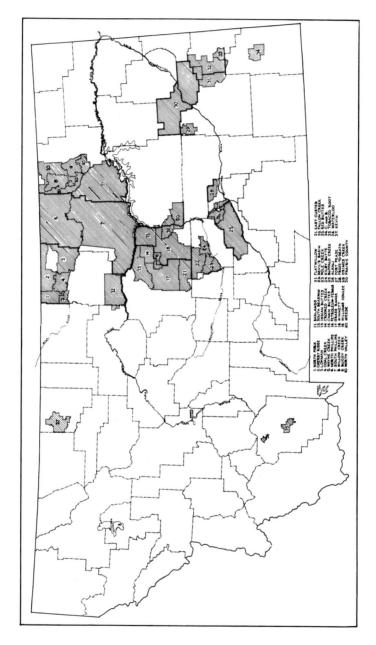

Figure 15:1. Montana cooperative state grazing districts. (Source: Reference 2; p. 44.)

approximately one sixth of the land in the state of Montana. Federal public-domain lands are used by neighboring stockmen, usually under permits issued by the Grazing Service. Grazing lands are available under permit on some national forests on the western fringe of the dry plains. Those familiar with the risks of overcapitalization and with tax foreclosure recommend leasing as a means of acquiring control of land, unless the rancher has the cash to purchase. Even when the rancher has money it might be wiser to invest it in machinery and water facilities on the home property rather than to freeze capital in ordinary range which is low in productivity. Of course, when leasing is impossible, purchase may be the only solution to the shortage of land.

The rancher is not immune to yearly fluctuations in rainfall. His fortunes, like those of the cash-crop agriculturist and stock farmer, go up and down with the weather, but his peaks are not so high and the bottom, when he hits it, is not so hard. Nevertheless, without adequate land resources his chances for economic survival on the dry plains are no better than those of any other type of operator. The grasses of the range are native species or sometimes introduced and improved varieties well suited to withstand drought conditions. They will make some growth and provide some feed in the driest years, whereas wheat will fail. The chief concern of the rancher is to prevent overgrazing and yet keep his livestock well fed. In dry years he must sell surplus animals before they are ready for market unless he has built up reserves of hay to carry them through. An overgrazed range requires some time, often a period of several years with favorable rainfall, before it will come back to good condition again.

The data plotted in Figure 15:2 were compiled over an eight-year period on typical shortgrass native range in east-central Wyoming. The principal species were buffalo grass *Buchloë dactyloides* and blue grama grass *Bouteloua gracilis*. Mixed with the dominants were western wheatgrass *Agropyron smithii*, needle-and-thread grass *Stipa comata*, and six-weeks fescue *Festuca octoflora*. During the years these data were collected the range was utilized but overgrazing was not permitted. Thus the fluctuations in density of vegetation shown in the graph (Figure 15:2) were due chiefly to differences in rainfall. One factor is outstanding: very great differences in vegetative cover result from proportionally smaller fluctuations in rainfall. For instance, in 1937 there was more than twice as much growth as in 1936. Although rainfall is low, the difference of 2 to 4 inches in a year can create pronounced fluctuations in grass growth. From precipitation data already considered in other chapters we are aware that fluctuations of a few inches from year to year may be expected in the dry plains.

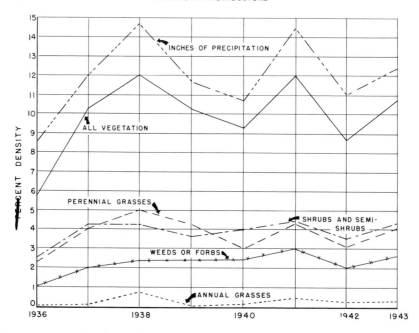

Figure 15:2. The relation of precipitation to yearly changes in density of native vegetation. (Source: Reference 3; p. 8.)

After a study of the effect of drought on both grazed and ungrazed grasslands in the central and southern Great Plains, D. A. Savage concluded that low rainfall definitely has a greater effect than moderate grazing upon vegetative density.

The basal cover declined from an estimated average of 90 percent or more on certain areas before the drought to an average of 25 percent or less on most of the ungrazed areas after the drought.   This estimated reduction of about 65 percent on certain areas was due wholly to the effects of climatic extremes.   The difference between the cover on the grazed and ungrazed areas after the drought usually amounted to about 10 percent, which may be considered the additional injury caused by grazing alone.   (Reference 4; p. 3.)

It seems clear from the foregoing observations that the rancher must expect very great fluctuations in the quality of the range and its carrying capacity from year to year.

The sharp line between the wheat, corn, and cotton areas of the plains states and the grazing areas to the west on the map of major types of farming (Figure 4:2) is deceptive.   There is no sharp line in actuality. Most of the lines on this map are determined by dominance rather than

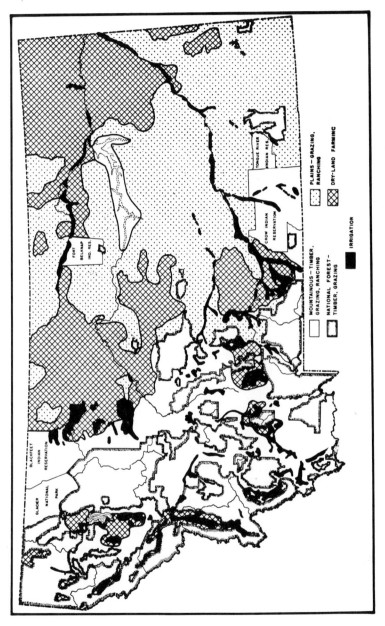

Figure 15:3.   General land use in Montana.   (Source: Reference 4; p. 10.)

exclusiveness on either side. In the plains states there are ranches in the crop-dominant areas and there are crop farms in the range-dominant areas. This is illustrated in the detailed map of Montana's land use regions (Figure 15:3).

A RANCH IN NEBRASKA

What is a ranch like when it is well organized and of adequate size? As an example, let us consider the Flying Y Ranch at Halsey, Nebraska. Halsey is in the Sand Hills, which is one of the best ranching areas and one of the poorest crop-producing districts in the plains states. Flying Y is just over 9000 acres of dune range, with an additional 100 acres of cropland on the banks of the Middle Loup River. The cropland has a high water table and could be irrigated if necessary. An additional 5000 acres of range are leased. The home property shown in Figure 15:4 is divided by good barbed wire fence into thirteen pastures that are 104 to 1472 acres in size. The differences in acreage take into account peculiarities of terrain, water supply, soil, location, use, and quality of grass. Cattle at Flying Y are kept on range the year around, but the grass grows, of course, only in the frost-free season. Winters are sometimes cold, snowy, and windy, but the cattle need only the protection of the dunes and a planted windbreak of coniferous trees in Big East pasture.

All grass, to remain vigorous, must be allowed to nourish its own roots, and this can be done only if the grass is given a period of relief from grazing during the growing season. The division of a range into many pastures permits a rotation of animals so that rest periods for the grass can be provided. Such a division as that shown on the map of Flying Y Ranch is possible only if a well, stock pond, spring, river, or tank provides water in each pasture. In addition to rotational grazing of pastures through the season at Flying Y, there is a biennial schedule of alternate winter and summer grazing for all but two of the largest pastures near the homestead. These two, Big East and Nigger, are exclusively winter pastures and are never grazed when the grass is growing. Consequently, the grass roots are always well nourished and the prospects of deterioration are minimal. According to the biennial schedule, any pasture grazed one summer is rested the following winter and the following summer as well. During its rest, or "off" year, the recuperating pasture is clipped once for hay; then cattle are turned in on it during the winter to eat the hay which is piled in the field. The grasses of the Sand Hills grow shin to knee high when not grazed and may yield as much as 1000 pounds of wild hay per acre. That is because the average rainfall is about 20 inches. In the

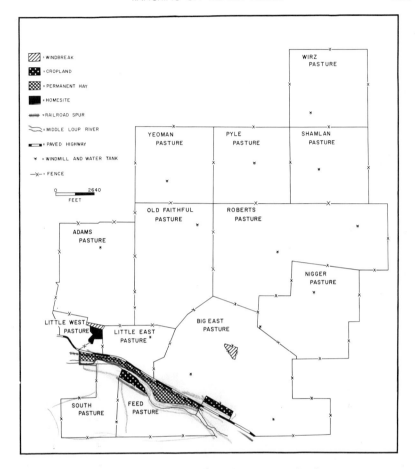

Figure 15:4. A Sand Hills cattle ranch in Nebraska.

drier regions of the western Great Plains the native grasses are very short and to clip them for hay would be impractical.

By such skillful management, the quality of grass at the Flying Y Ranch has been maintained in good condition year after year. There is always enough forage to carry brood cows and suckling calves. If a dry year comes, more yearlings are removed than usual. In a normal year the ranch has 450 brood cows and about 550 calves and yearlings. This rancher's solution to an erratic climate is achieved on the most unsatisfactory soils of the whole region from Canada to Mexico.

The map of Flying Y Ranch tells us something of how it has grown to its present size. Several of the pastures have proper names. A few of these

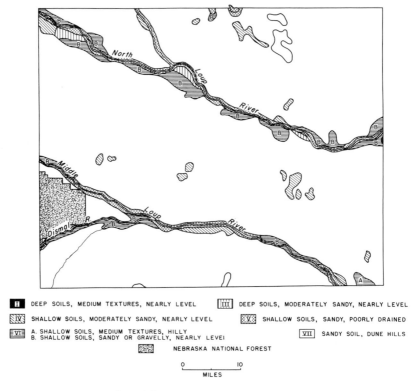

DEEP SOILS, MEDIUM TEXTURES, NEARLY LEVEL   DEEP SOILS, MODERATELY SANDY, NEARLY LEVEL

SHALLOW SOILS, MODERATELY SANDY, NEARLY LEVEL   SHALLOW SOILS, SANDY, POORLY DRAINED

A. SHALLOW SOILS, MEDIUM TEXTURES, HILLY
B. SHALLOW SOILS, SANDY OR GRAVELLY, NEARLY LEVEL   SANDY SOIL, DUNE HILLS

NEBRASKA NATIONAL FOREST

0   10
MILES

Figure 15:5.   Land capability in Blaine County, Nebraska. (Source: U.S.D.A.)

are exactly one mile square (640 acres).   They represent the former homesteads of farmer-settlers who came into the Sand Hills after the passage of
the Kinkaid Act in 1904.   It was Representative Moses Kinkaid of O'Neill,
Nebraska, who was able to persuade Congress that a family could not make
a living by farming in the Sand Hills on a 160-acre homestead.   As a result,
the Kinkaid Act, which permitted allotments of 640 acres, was passed.
Even these proved to be inadequate, except when the grants included some
tillable alluvial soil along a stream course.   Whenever the sand dunes were
plowed wind erosion became severe and annual crops perished for lack of
moisture in the porous soils.   The Kinkaiders or "soddies," as the settlers
were known, built homes of sod and wore their lives out trying to resist the
inevitable.   In the end most of them left.   Their properties, valueless for
anything else, became part of present-day ranches.

Figure 15:5 is based upon a reconnaissance soil survey of Blaine County,
Nebraska, which is entirely within the Sand Hills area, and shows the

capability of the soils. At a glance it is evident that little land is suited to farming and that it is located along the margins of the streams where irrigation is sometimes practiced. As far as land capability is concerned, this is a situation typical of the true ranching country of the plains states as far west as the Rocky Mountains. A ranch without some stream-bank land or land with a high water table where irrigation is possible is at a distinct disadvantage, particularly in the northern Great Plains where winter feeding is a major concern.

HISTORICAL BACKGROUND

With the exception of Texas, the Great Plains were the domain of Indian and buffalo until after the Civil War. Oklahoma remained Indian Territory until 1907. The development of the plains as ranching county, therefore, began in Texas. This was not a new custom so far as pioneer settlement in American is concerned. Ponce de Leon, De Soto, and Coronado had introduced cattle into what are now our southern states early in the sixteenth century. Descendents of these beasts were later encountered running wild from Florida, through Louisiana, to California. The insitution of cattle herding is almost as old as Spanish and English settlement in America. Primeval meadows in the Connecticut Valley became the frontier range of early New England colonies. By 1655 there were cattle drives from the Connecticut to Boston. Santa Fe was founded as a center of cattle raising in 1609.

There were roundups of range cattle on the frontier of piedmont North Carolina in the early eighteenth century, and the branded stock were driven overland by cowboys through the grassy plains of the Great Valley of Virginia to Philadelphia and Baltimore. It was almost an invariable pattern in the course of settlement of this nation that hunters opened the frontiers. Cattle herders and cattle raisers followed them. Finally, as the plowing agriculturists invaded the range outposts and built homesteads, the cattlemen retreated with their stock. There were grasslands in scattered basins and valleys all the way from the Atlantic coast to the Great Plains from the earliest days of exploration and settlement. Buffalo were able to graze as far east as Virginia because of the existence of these islands of grass in the more generally wooded East. The use of grasslands as range was one of the best-understood systems of land management in the early days of this nation, and the eastern grasslands were often established on some of the best soils. Thus it was also an old American custom for the farmer-settler from the humid East to seek out what the rancher had found useful.

The Spanish settlers in the southern Great Plains came from Mexico.

They were thus familiar with the grasslands of arid and semiarid regions; the Anglo-American was not. It is perhaps quite understandable that the Spanish settler in Texas should have made a different appraisal of the dry-plains grasslands which he encountered than did the homesteader who pushed into Nebraska by the backdoor of humid Iowa.

The history of ranching in Texas began on the arid *Mesa Central* of Mexico. Beyond Mexico there had been experience in semiarid Spain, and beyond Spain there was North Africa, the Moors, and their longhorn cattle. Both the custom of dry-land ranching and the animals, born of a near desert world on the Mediterranean's shores, found a congenial and familiar environment in the southern dry plains. As early as 1825, when Texas was a Mexican state, 4000 acres of grassland were awarded to every settler who planned to derive his income exclusively from ranching. Mexican, Spaniard, and Moor had had long experience in semiarid environments. The framers of the Homestead Act in humid Washington had had none. Many Anglo-Americans left the United States for Mexico to take advantage of a wise liberality not extended at home and thus became Texas stockmen. Later, as a Republic, Texas awarded 4605 acres to every citizen-head of a family who had been a resident at the time of its declaration of independence. Even after joining the Union, Texas, controlling its own public lands, continued a comparatively liberal allotment policy, so that in 1850 the average size of all farms and ranches in that state was 951 acres.

After the Civil War the buffalo and the Indians were driven from the plains except in the Oklahoma Territory. The agricultural settler did not follow in significant numbers until after barbed wire was invented and mass produced. Thus between 1866 and 1880 one of the most rapid and dramatic transformations of the American landscape by cattlemen took place.

Within that fifteen-year period 5 million Texas cattle were driven northward, some for slaughter and some to populate the grasslands as far as Wyoming, Montana, and Canada. In those days the ranchers in the states north of Texas were operating without permission, but also without objection, on the lands of the public domain. After 1880 it was only a short time until the farmer-settlers arrived to establish legitimate claims to 160-acre segments of what, until then, had seemed an endless cattle kingdom. The ranchers themselves, in order to survive, homesteaded the lands around water holes and along stream banks. By the consolidation of several claims, they were able to establish ranch headquarters on the better lands, but, as we have previously noted, they were unable for the most part to assemble properties of sufficient size to make real economic units. They are still in the process of trying to reach that goal today.

REFERENCES

1. Gray, James R. and Chester B. Baker, *Cattle Ranching in the Northern Great Plains*, Montana State College, Bozeman, 1953.
2. Kelso, M. M. and H. R. Stucky, *Basic Facts About Montana's Agriculture*, Montana State College, Bozeman, 1952.
3. Lang, Robert, *Density Changes of Native Vegetation in Relation to Precipitation*, University of Wyoming Agricultural Experiment Station, Laramie, 1945.
4. Bolster, H. G. and H. R. Stucky, *Montana's Agriculture*, Montana Agricultural Extension Service, Montana State College, Bozeman, 1945.

irrigation
on the
dry plains

16

Irrigation is not a cure-all for the difficulties of farming and ranching on the dry plains. There are 133 million acres which are dry farmed and 234 million acres which are grazed in the six plains states. There are at present less than 7 million irrigated acres in these same states, and perhaps there are water supplies to irrigate an additional 5 to 10 million acres. Although irrigation has helped to stabilize farming and ranching on the dry plains, and this beneficial assistance can be extended, its limitations are obvious. Theoretically, irrigation would be of the greatest value to the most farmers and ranchers if each could have some irrigated land. Then everyone would be certain that drought could never wipe him out completely. But, being realistic, water is not available everywhere and could not be made available economically.

Because irrigation is possible only where there is water or where water can be delivered at a reasonable cost, let us refer to two maps, one of which we considered in an earlier chapter (Figures 7:2 and 16:1).

Surface water supplies obtainable from rivers are meager in the driest and westernmost portions of the plains. This is because the air masses bearing moisture from the Pacific Ocean have been pretty thoroughly wrung out before they cross the continental divide, and air masses from the Gulf of Mexico generally bring little moisture to the western section of the dry plains. Note how the volumes of the Missouri, the Canadian, Arkansas, Red, and Brazos rivers increase substantially east of the 100th meridian. The best prospect for increasing the extent of irrigated lands by the use of river waters is in the Dakotas, and that, of course, is the basis of the enthusiasm for the Missouri Valley development projects now going forward.

The map of ground-water areas (Figure 16:1) must be interpreted with caution. A minimum flow of 50 gallons per minute will not permit extensive irrigation. However, such flows can greatly aid ranchers who wish to place pump-supplied water tanks at strategic spots on their ranges to make rotational pasturing possible. We have noted in the preceding chapter that the Flying Y Ranch was able to break up its range into many pastures because ground water was available. One well supplying 50 gallons per minute could sustain supplementary irrigation on 10 to 20 acres. This, of course, would be of great assistance to any rancher or crop farmer in the dry plains. Such a weak flow is indicative of a poor supply. If one well were dug for every 20 acres, even assuming that the cost would not be prohibitive, it is possible that the ground-water table would drop for lack of recharge. Let us consider what is occurring in the most highly developed pump-irrigation district of the dry plains where wells supply up to 1000 gallons and more per minute—the redbed area of the Texas High Plains.

One of the most remarkable changes which has taken place anywhere on the dry plains has occurred right in the heart of the worst dust-bowl district of the 1930's. Extending over several hundred square miles of countryside in the vicinity of Plainview, Texas, is one of the lushest, most prosperous farming regions in the West, yet most of it was once among the most depressed and devastated.

Underlying this region, sometimes at depths exceeding 200 feet, is an unusually productive aquifer, called the redbed because of its color which is revealed in well borings. The flow of water is so strong that it taxes the capacity of the best pumps to keep up with it. But there is already some question about the future because even this extraordinary ground-water formation is not recharged as rapidly as it is being drained. Perhaps it is not being recharged at all.

An eight-inch-diameter pipe set down 100 to 350 feet and equipped with a high-speed pump may cost $5,000 to $10,000 per installation. Such a well, throwing about 1000 gallons per minute, will satisfy the

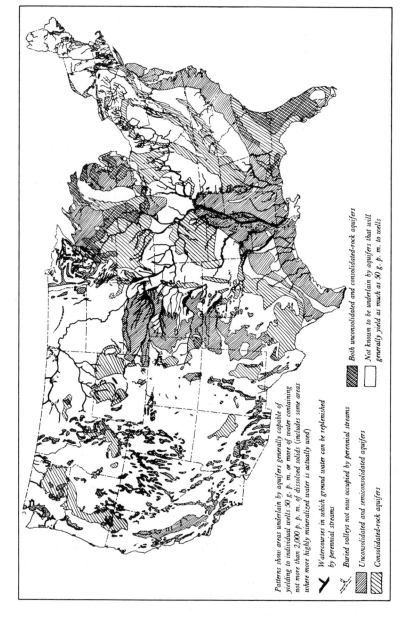

Patterns show areas underlain by aquifers generally capable of
yielding to individual wells 50 g. p. m. or more of water containing
not more than 2,000 p. p. m. of dissolved solids (includes some areas
where more highly mineralized water is actually used)

Y Watercourses in which ground water can be replenished
by perennial streams

⌇ Buried valleys not now occupied by perennial streams

▨ Unconsolidated and semiconsolidated aquifers

▧ Consolidated-rock aquifers

▦ Both unconsolidated and consolidated-rock aquifers

☐ Not known to be underlain by aquifers that will
generally yield as much as 50 g. p. m. to wells

Figure 16:1.   Ground-water areas in the United States.   (Source: U.S.D.A.)

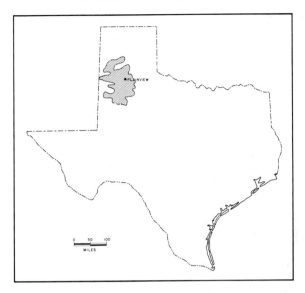

Figure 16:2.   Major area of ground-water development in the Texas High Plains. (Source: Reference 3; p. 3.)

need for supplementary water on 200 to 300 acres of land.   The chief crops in this section of the Texas High Plains are cotton, wheat, grain sorghums, and legume hays.   These crops are not heavy water users, and irrigation is employed only to supplement the natural rainfall, which, although variable, averages 20 inches annually.   This kind of irrigation for ordinary field crops might hardly be feasible if the depth of draw were greater or the climate more arid.   Using low-cost electric power or butane bottle gas, the charge of operating a pump may be as high as $200 a month.   The fact that unirrigable land beyond the redbeds sells for one tenth as much per acre as that equipped with pump and well is an indication of the value of supplementary water in this district.

The difference in land costs with and without irrigation facilities is also a measure of the differences in capital and interest costs which are borne by dry farmers and irrigators.   On the dry plains the situation is very different from that in many irrigation districts of the intermountain West and southern California.   Here irrigation is not the difference between crop farming and no crop farming at all.   It is instead a means of increasing yields in years of drought.   Although this is important, it is like crop insurance—costly.   There is no question that in drought years the irrigation pays.   There is considerable question, however, as to whether increased yields in other years are worth the price.

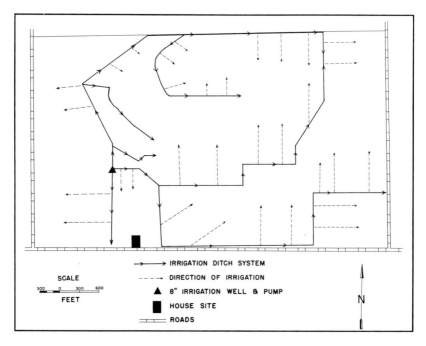

Figure 16:3. Deep-well irrigated cotton farm in the Texas High Plains. The well on this farm will yield 850 gallons per minute. This is sufficient to irrigate about 250 of the farm's 390 acres. The water-distribution system shows complete farm coverage, but some fields are fallowed, grazed, or dry farmed each year and are not irrigated.

The author recalls the remark of one elderly gentleman, an owner of a 400-acre farm near Plainview which is partially irrigated. He would have needed another well if he were to have irrigated all his land. When asked why he did not install it he replied, "It would cost $5,000. A man with $5,000 doesn't need another well, and if he doesn't have $5,000 he shouldn't drill another well." With about half of his farm irrigated, this man felt he had the hedge he needed against drought. He was afraid to overcapitalize and become vulnerable to failure because of low market prices and high overhead. If all ranchers and crop farmers on the dry plains could achieve this happy medium through moderation in pump irrigation, the millennium would be at hand. Unfortunately, they lack the aquifers which would make choice possible.

There is also another risk in becoming dependent upon ground water, as we have observed in other irrigation districts. Unless the aquifer is recharged at a rate equal to withdrawal, the water table inevitably drops. The pace of exhaustion accelerates when neighbors witness a successful operation. They are quick to follow the example, and the periphery of irrigation expands. That is what has been happening in the redbed region. The underground water level is dropping, and there is serious concern about the future. Each drop in water level increases pumping costs. Some irrigators say that in years when rainfall is 20 inches or more the dry-farm operators make a higher net profit per acre than they do. Even though yields on the dry farms are half of what they are on the irrigated land, the overhead is even lower. The fact remains, however, that those who can irrigate are not susceptible to the principal hazard of the dry plains, which is occasional drought. In that sense irrigation is a solution to this special regional problem wherever it is economically and technically possible.

EFFECTS OF IRRIGATION ON AN ADJOINING RANCH ECONOMY

In western South Dakota about 10 per cent of the farms and ranches have some irrigated land. Some obtain their water from streams, small private reservoirs, or wells. Others are irrigated with water made available by large government-sponsored irrigation developments. A few ranchers have feed bases on such projects, even though their main units are some miles away. The remaining 90 per cent of the operators in western South Dakota have no irrigation. Do the larger irrigation projects help adjoining stock farms and ranches which do not control any irrigated land? Can ranchers afford to buy hay from irrigators? These questions are discussed by Willard Schutz of the South Dakota Agricultural Experiment Station in the *Effects of Irrigation on an Adjoining Ranch Economy*. (Reference 6.)

The questions are significant in view of the fact that it is assumed by the planners of the elaborate Missouri River Basin Project that irrigation will greatly aid in overcoming the economic repercussions of drought. What did Professor Schutz conclude after interviews with 166 ranchers in the vicinity of present irrigation projects in South Dakota and Nebraska?

The combination of dryland and irrigated land into single ranch units appears to have much greater promise in affording stabilization than does the sale of irrigated hay. Both ranchers and irrigation farmers expressed a desire for this type of unit. About 85 percent of responding ranch operators expressed the belief that it was desirable to have an irrigated feed base to combine with rangeland, and irrigation farmers, almost without exception, expressed a desire for dryland to combine with their irrigated unit. (Reference 6; p. 19.)

Few ranchers could afford to buy much hay. Professor Schutz reports a number of facts which should be considered in any realistic statement of how expensive public projects may be expected to stabilize the farm and ranch economy in the dry plains.

1. It costs money to irrigate land. Overhead is high, and consequently, the cost of production of any crop is high.
2. The cost of hay raised on irrigated land is too great to make it a profitable substitute for range. Most ranchers bought little hay when it was available on nearby irrigated farms and most declared they did not expect to buy except in emergencies and even then only as little as possible. A ton of legume hay costs as much as two acres of rangeland, which in years with good rainfall will yield a ton of dry grass.
3. Irrrigators generally do not find it so profitable to sell hay as to use whatever hay they raise for their own livestock. The prices which ranchers find too high, the irrigators consider too low. Most irrigators interviewed wished they could lease or buy dry grazing land on which to turn their own livestock. Although this was their preference, only a minority was able to, either because the land was not available for lease or because they could not afford to buy.

On the dry plains the landowner is dealing with a situation distinct from that which prevails in the truly arid West. On the plains the range units of a few thousand acres are really small ranches, but in years of good rainfall the grass grows well and livestock are raised at low cost. Irrigation is most highly regarded as a means to raise supplementary winter feed and to provide hay reserves for drought years. The irrigator, on the other hand, would prefer to raise crops of greater value per acre, such as sugar beets, potatoes, cotton, and dry beans. Hay does not seem to be a profitable crop, unless it is integrated with dry range land stocked by the same operator. These conclusions are born out by other studies. (References 1 and 7.)

Since considerable irrigated land in the northern dry plains is now successfully integrated with both dry-land farming and dry-land ranching, it would seem that this indigenous and popular type of development should be encouraged when the Bureau of Reclamation opens its development projects on the Missouri River. The establishment of specialized irrigated farm units which are not individually integrated, each with a much larger area of dry land, will not mitigate the uncertainties of climate which plague the owners of dry land. Irrigated units which are not integrated with dry land are like isolated oases. They cannot stabilize the fluctuations caused by drought on the dry lands around them. Without integration they are more of an appendage than a functional aid to farmers and ranchers on the dry lands.

Less than 100 acres under irrigation can stabilize production on several thousand acres of dry land if both properties are owned and operated as a unit. It would seem that the development of such units should be encouraged. As we have seen, some ranchers have found it feasible to integrate dry range and irrigated hay land, even when the two units are miles apart. The same principle applies to dry-land stock farms and dry-land, cash-crop farms. A moderate-sized irrigation unit integrated with either of these types of farm would help to stabilize their operations. The most probable trend in the future, as irrigation facilities are extended, will be the joining of such units because the combinations have greater survival value than the separate parts.

THE MISSOURI RIVER BASIN PROJECT

The program, sometimes identified by the names of its originators as the Pick-Sloan Plan, is expected to provide irrigation water for over 7 million acres. Five million acres will be newly irrigated land, and 2 million acres, now inadequately supplied with water, will receive ample quotas. Although these are impressive figures they are dwarfed by the valley's total area of 340 million acres, which includes 107 million acres of cropland. At present 3 million acres are irrigated, and 2 million acres receive an inadequate amount of water. To what extent will the increased irrigation reduce the hazards of cyclic ups and downs in the Missouri basin farm economy?

There are about 582,000 farms, stock farms, and ranches in the Missouri Valley. It is believed that 18,900 of the units, or about 3 per cent, which did not previously have irrigation water will receive it; 15,400 units which previously had some water will obtain more. In addition, 18,600 new farms will be created in new irrigation districts. (Reference 2; pp. 11–12.) Although the 18,600 new farms will in themselves make substantial additions to the productivity of the Missouri Valley, many, particularly in the eastern basin, will contribute little toward easing the uncertainties caused by drought, which is the principal concern of over one half million existing farms and ranches. The farmers and ranchers who will have both dry land and irrigated land will use a large share of the latter to produce hay for winter feed and for emergency use during droughts. The irrigators in specialized irrigation districts in the eastern basin, where most of the new farms are to be established, will concentrate upon crops such as corn, sugar beets, and potatoes. These crops are more valuable than hay to the irrigator who does not also own dry-land range.

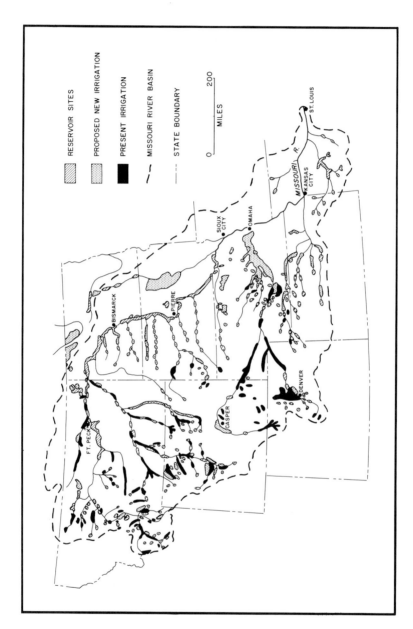

Figure 16:4. Irrigation developments in the Missouri Valley.

Figure 16:4 is a map of the general plan of the Missouri River Basin Project. The locations of present and future irrigated areas are shown in a generalized way. There are two significant features of the distribution pattern indicated on the map.

1. Along the streams tributary to the Missouri, in the western portion of the basin, the irrigated areas are like beads on a string.

2. In the eastern Dakotas and in eastern Nebraska three large concentrated developments are projected.

The necklace pattern of the western basin is basically one of dispersion. Because the irrigated areas are strung out over long distances a greater degree of integration with adjoining dry-land operations has been and will continue to be common and easily achieved. Some present ranches and dry farms will receive water for their lands bordering the new irrigation districts. Other dry-land operators, not far removed from the new irrigation districts, will probably buy small irrigated units and integrate them with their present properties. Real stabilization will result from these types of development.

The three large areas of concentrated irrigation development projected for the eastern Dakotas and eastern Nebraska will be composed chiefly of new, independent units primarily devoted to cash crops. There will doubtless be some integration with dry-land operations, but such integration will not be characteristic—at least not in the beginning. The present plan is to set up most of them as self-sustaining units on which new settlers will be located. They will doubtless prosper as most irrigation districts in the West have prospered when assured of water supplies. But so long as they remain independent units they will not contribute greatly toward stabilizing the economy of the dry-land properties beyond their boundaries. It is quite likely that in the future many of the more successful dry-land operators will buy irrigated units in these compact districts and thus gradually achieve the integration which is not so strongly advocated as it should be in the initial development program. Although much good will come of a full and rational use of the Missouri River waters that formerly went down to the Mississippi, the Pick-Sloan Plan will only ameliorate because it cannot solve the basic problem of cyclic drought with which a half million dry-land operators contend.

REFERENCES

1. Helfinstine, Rex D., *Economic Potentials of Irrigated and Dryland Farms in Central South Dakota*, South Dakota Experiment Station, 1955.

2. Henderson, Sidney, *Changes in Crop Production Anticipated From Proposed Irrigation and Reservoir Development in the Missouri River Basin*, Bureau of Agricultural Economics, Washington, D.C., 1950.

3. Hughes, William F., *Cost of Pumping Water for Irrigation Texas High Plains*, Texas Board of Water Engineers, 1951.

4. Litterer, Oscar F., *The Missouri Basin Development Program*, Federal Reserve Bank of Minneapolis, 1953.

5. Missouri Basin Inter-Agency Committee, *The Missouri River Basin Development Program*, Government Printing Office, Washington, D.C., 1952.

6. Shutz, Willard, *Effects of Irrigation on an Adjoining Ranch Economy*, South Dakota State College, Brookings, 1955.

7. Ward, Ralph M. and M. M. Kelso, *Irrigation Farmers Reach Out Into the Dryland*, Montana Agricultural Experiment Station.

8. Hart, Henry C., *The Dark Missouri* University of Wisconsin Press, Madison, 1957.

part three

the
humid
East

17

Figure 4:1 indicates that there is no absolute boundary between the humid East and the dry West. Thornthwaite's division is a practical one, although it is a statistical line based upon averages. The line dividing pedalfer and pedocal soils appears to have been drawn by nature, but it is only a reflection of average percolation depths. As mentioned previously, drought is possible in the humid areas of the United States, just as ample precipitation may sometimes occur in normally dry regions.

Drought as it is known in the humid East seldom means crop failure. The term is relative. The yields of corn on a farm in central Iowa may be cut from 80 bushels per acre to 50 bushels, but the chances of complete loss because of drought are very small. There is climatic variation in the East, just as there is in the dry West, but the impact upon crops is not so severe. The realization that subnormal rainfall may occur in any humid section of the eastern states has encouraged a growing interest in supplementary irrigation.

There is sufficient precipitation to sustain some kind of crop growth everywhere in the East, from the Atlantic seaboard to Minnesota and Louisiana. The fact that only 212 million acres of a total area of 743 million acres are cultivated indicates that there are other significant restrictions upon farming. One of these is topography.

TOPOGRAPHIC INFLUENCES

In a number of eastern areas poor drainage has retarded intensive land use. On the coastal plains there are numerous undrained lowlands from New Jersey through the Dismal Swamp of Virginia to the Florida Everglades and westward to the bayous of Louisiana and Texas. The Mississippi River's alluvial plain from Cairo, Illinois, to New Orleans is only partially drained. There are still between 10 and 15 million acres of wet lowlands in the glaciated central plains. The beneficial result of drainage is illustrated by the fact that one third of the cultivated areas of the Corn Belt, as well as of Minnesota, Michigan, and Wisconsin, were formerly too wet for agriculture. Wet soil conditions in the East are usually the result of heavy rainfall where natural drainage channels have not developed because of flat topography or where glaciation plugged the channels of previous waterways. Permanently drowned soils are as valueless to the farmer as the unirrigated deserts of the arid West.

It is estimated that there are approximately 112 million acres of land in the United States which have been improved by drainage. (Reference 5; p. 13.) It is also estimated that there are another 72 million acres of wet lands which have not been improved. About 60 per cent of these undrained wet areas are in the eastern states. Because of the costly character of drainage operations they should be preceded by soil surveys and land-capability analyses in order that investments might be safeguarded. Probably the greater part of the undrained wet lands in the United States are not worth reclamation at the present time.

The most important topographic drawback to intensive crop cultivation in the humid East is the large extent of rough land upon which soils are thin, poor, and sometimes nonexistant. In the dry West the mountains and high plateaus are assets to agriculture because they are rain and snow trappers but they serve no such helpful function in the East. As a matter of fact, because the soils on mountains and plateaus are often thin they have little water-holding capacity. Under heavy precipitation the runoff from upland areas is sometimes excessive and floods the thickly settled and intensively developed lands of alluvial plains.

Steep hillsides are not suitable for modern mechanized agriculture, and because of thin soils they commonly do not warrant heavy investment in

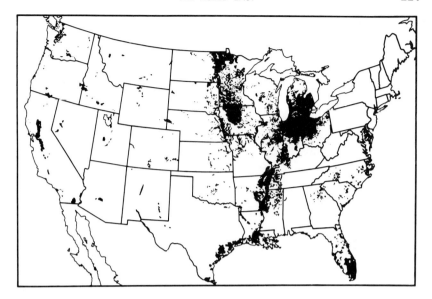

Figure 17:1. Approximate location of land in drainage enterprises. (Source: Reference 5; p. 13.)

pasture improvement. Consequently, many clearings once used for tillage and grazing in the eastern hills are being abandoned to encroaching woodlands. When these woodlands are well managed they make a contribution to the economy by supplying pulp, veneer logs, railroad ties, poles, and some lumber.

The map of generalized soil erosion in the United States shows that the largest areas of intensive destruction are in the humid eastern states. Soil erosion in the East has occurred primarily under corn, cotton, and tobacco crops, which offer very little protection to the soil against the erosive action of heavy rains. The severest damage has been experienced along the fringes of the Appalachian Plateau, in the limestone valleys of the Appalachian Plateau, on the undulating surface of the Appalachian piedmont, and on the dissected coastal plain of Mississippi which lies eastward of the river lowlands. The glacial moraine districts of southern Iowa and Illinois have lost most of their original topsoil.

If it were not for steep slopes, thin soils, and the threat of erosion, there would presumably be much more tillage and improved grazing land in the eastern states where rainfall is not a limiting factor. Figure 17:3 is a strip of counties which commence upon the relatively level Corn Belt plains of Van Wert, County, Ohio, and pass over the severely dissected

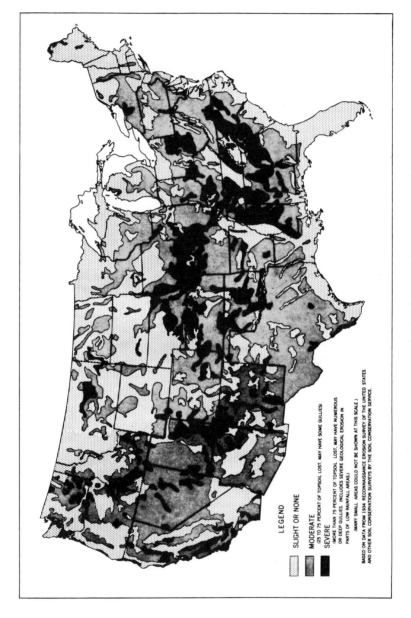

LEGEND

SLIGHT OR NONE

MODERATE
(25 TO 75 PERCENT OF TOPSOIL LOST. MAY HAVE SOME GULLIES)

SEVERE
(MORE THAN 75 PERCENT OF TOPSOIL LOST. MAY HAVE NUMEROUS
OR DEEP GULLIES. INCLUDES SEVERE GEOLOGICAL EROSION IN
PARTS OF LOW RAINFALL AREAS).

(MANY SMALL AREAS COULD NOT BE SHOWN AT THIS SCALE.)

BASED ON DATA FROM 1934 RECONNAISSANCE EROSION SURVEY OF THE UNITED STATES
AND OTHER SOIL CONSERVATION SURVEYS BY THE SOIL CONSERVATION SERVICE.

Figure 17.2.   Generalized soil erosion. (Source: U.S.D.A.)

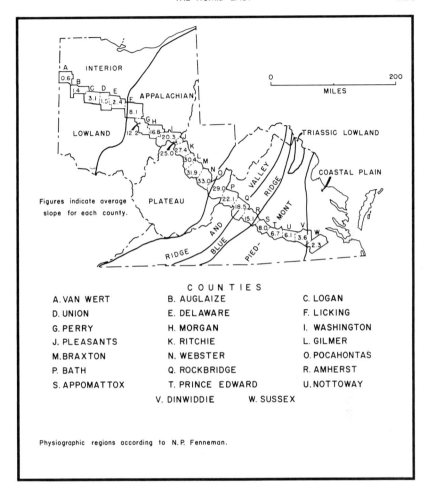

Figure 17:3.   A trans-Appalachian traverse. (Source: Reference 1; pp. 108–110.)

uplands of the Appalachian piedmont.   The traverse ends upon the level-to-gently undulating surface of the Atlantic coastal plain in Sussex County, Virginia.

Figure 17:4 is a sequel to the county traverse illustrated in Figure 17:3.   It correlates average slope with the value of crops and livestock in the respective counties.   The very strong influence of surface relief upon intensity of cultivation and livestock husbandry is evident.

Not only does cultivation and pasturage decline with steeper slope, but the character of farming itself also changes.   In the regions of steeper

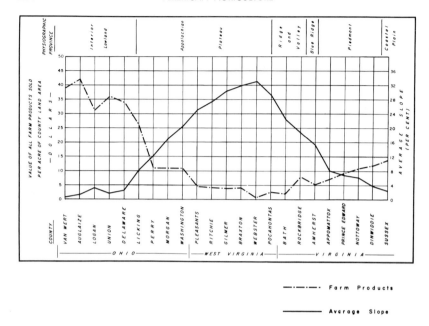

Figure 17:4. Value of all farm products sold per acre of county land area. (Source: Reference 1; p. 114.)

and rougher terrain only a small percentage of the farms are commercial types. Commercial farms are their operator's primary source of livelihood; most of the crops and livestock which reach the market come from them. The farms of the hill country are chiefly part-time, residential, and subsistence farms which yield little except for the operator's families. Their owners usually have other jobs and sources of income. Further studies of the relationship between slope and agricultural activity are contained in the work of Woodford Garrigus. (Reference 1.) They show, for instance, that the proportion of farms with tractors declines as the steepness of slope increases. The values of farm land and farm buildings also decrease as the average slope increases.

LENGTH OF THE GROWING SEASON

The differences in the length of growing seasons, which are shorter in the North and longer in the South, have had a strong, although by no means exclusive, influence upon the regional division of agriculture in the humid eastern states. The northern margin of the Cotton Belt corresponds closely with the line delineating an average frost-free period of 200 days per year. In a sense "Cotton Belt" is a misnomer because cotton is the dominant crop in only a few selected subsections of the belt. However, when soil conditions permit cotton can be grown successfully within this broad region. Cotton itself is a tropical perennial. In the United States it is treated as an annual because frost kills it.

The quality of cotton fiber is poor where rains are common during the autumn harvest season. Consequently, this crop is of minor importance along the Atlantic and Gulf margins of the southeastern states. A variety of specialized agricultural activities characterizes the humid marine-coast districts. Rice dominates in Texas and western Louisiana; sugarcane is important in southeastern Florida; and winter vegetables and subtropical fruits are common in Florida and along the Mississippi-Alabama Gulf coast. When drainage is effective and soils satisfactory there is an intensive production of peanuts, tobacco, and vegetable crops on the coastal-plain fringes of the Cotton Belt from Alabama through Georgia, the Carolinas, and Virginia.

The southern Appalachian Plateau and the Ozark regions are characterized by a variety of crop and livestock enterprises which, collec-

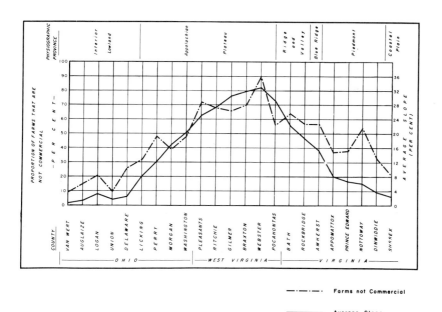

Figure 17:5. Proportion of farms that are not commercial. (Source: Reference 1; p. 130.)

tively, are called *general farming*. A wide variety of crops can be grown in these regions because of the variety of microclimates which are to be found in mountain and plateau areas due to differences in altitude between valleys and uplands. The total amount of cultivation and improved pasturage is small because of the roughness of topography. For instance, in West Virginia only one acre out of ten is under cultivation.

Both climate and topography restrict the possibilities of intensive tillage in the northeastern states from Minnesota to Maine. The Dairy Belt might just as appropriately be called the Hay and Pasture Belt. The growing season is short except along the Atlantic coastal plain and along the south and eastern shores of Lakes Michigan, Erie, and Ontario. Favored spots, such as eastern Long Island and the Delmarva Peninsula, are among the most intensively developed agricultural districts in the northeastern states.

The agriculture of the dairy region, like that of the Cotton Belt, is not uniform. Hay and pasture generally predominate because the grasses and legumes used for meadows are tolerant of cold. They start to grow early in the spring and continue until late in the fall, despite occasional light frosts. The northern dairy farmer contends with the short frost-free season by using plants which can remain green despite some freezing weather and which yield abundantly in a short summer season. Dairying dominates the agricultural activity of the northeastern states for other reasons as well. These are discussed in a subsequent chapter.

The Corn Belt is more properly called the *feed grains and livestock region*. Corn, however, is generally the dominant crop, except along the fringes of the area. Climate has been the most important factor in establishing the northern and western limits of the Corn Belt. Corn is a tropical annual. There are places in the tropics at high altitudes where ten to eleven months are required for corn to mature after the seed is planted. Cool but frost-free weather at these high altitudes slows the rate of growth. In our middlewestern states days and nights must be warm if corn is to mature during the short frost-free period. Warm weather hastens maturity. The northern extension of the Corn Belt is therefore limited by a shorter growing season and cooler summer weather. The cool weather which limits corn production favors the potato, as in Aroostook County, Maine. The potato is a native of the cool Andean highlands.

The western border of the Corn Belt is limited by drought. There it costs more money to produce an acre of corn than an acre of wheat. Consequently, when yields drop drastically for lack of moisture it becomes impractical to plant corn. Under the favorable climatic conditions which prevail in Iowa and Illinois the yields of corn per acre considerably exceed those of wheat. For instance, the ten-year (1942–1951) average corn yield in Illinois was 51.2 bushels per acre. The average yield of wheat for the same ten years was 18.9 bushels. Rough topography rather than climate limits the southern and eastern extensions of the Corn Belt.

RÉSUMÉ

Whereas the pattern of land use in the West is a comparatively simple one and the principal factor limiting intensive agriculture is lack of water, the situation in the humid eastern states is far more complex. Drought is also experience in the East, but its effects are not so devastating. Supplementary irrigation is possible over wide areas, particularly where there are many streams, lakes, and ponds and where the ground-water table is close to the surface. In fact, the removal of surplus ground water by artificial drainage is necessary in sections of the central and coastal plains before intensive land use is possible. Many lowland areas in the glaciated uplands of New England and New York have high ground-water tables as well as ponds and lakes. Supplementary irrigation is becoming more and more common in these districts and much artificial drainage remains to be done to reclaim good valley lands.

Because enough rain falls to make some kind of crop production feasible throughout the eastern states, topography plays a prominent role in determining the intensity of land use. The contrast between plain and hilly upland is vital. There is a major hazard of soil erosion in the production of corn, cotton, tobacco, and potatoes. We have noted that soil erosion was severe on the overgrazed western ranges because of the generally thin and poor vegetative cover. In the eastern states adequate rainfall makes it possible to establish excellent pasture sod except when soils are thin or poor. Good meadows protect soil from erosion; consequently, it is possible in the East to produce as much as 400 to 500 pounds of beef per acre annually on some lands without danger of erosion.

Farmers in the eastern states have a number of alternative ways in which they may use their land. They are not nearly so restricted in their choices as are the farmers of the dry West. The succeeding chapters discuss how past choices have established what we familiarly call our "belts." They also discuss how new techniques are forcing new decisions and changing the land-use systems of established agricultural regions.

REFERENCES

1. Garrigus, Woodford McDowell, *Surface Relief and Agricultural Land Use*, a type-written thesis in the Library of Clark University, Worcester, Mass.
2. Johnson, Sherman E., *Changes in American Farming*, U.S. Department of Agriculture, Government Printing Office, Washington, D.C., 1949.
3. U.S. Department of Agriculture, *Generalized Types of Farming in the United States*, Government Printing Office, Washington, D.C., 1950.
4. Wooten, Hugh H., and James R. Anderson, *Major Uses of Land in the United States*, U.S. Department of Agriculture, Government Printing Office, Washington, D.C., 1957.
5. Wooten, H. H. and Margaret R. Purcell, *Farm Land Development: Present and Future by Clearing, Drainage, and Irrigation*, U.S. Department of Agriculture, Government Printing Office, Washington, D.C., 1949.

the origin and crop systems of the Corn Belt

18

Between the Great Lakes dairy region and the Ohio River-Ozark hill country lies a wide humid plain popularly called the Corn Belt. It extends for almost 1000 miles from eastern Nebraska, across Iowa and northern Missouri, through Illinois and Indiana to the Appalachians' edge in central Ohio. Like a vast wedge, it tapers from nearly 600 miles at its maximum western breadth to 150 miles at its eastern terminus. For general excellence of soil resources, gently undulating-to-smooth topography, and satisfactory climate, the Corn Belt has no rival that approaches it in size anywhere on this globe. The north European plain, Argentina's pampa, and the North China plain are rich agricultural regions, but none is equal to the Corn Belt. In all of Africa there is nothing so productive except the comparatively restricted, irrigated Nile.

There are a number of countries in the world in which the per capita consumption of meat is high. Argentina, Uruguay, Paraguay, New Zealand, Australia, and the United States are particularly fortunate in this respect. In every instance, except that of the United States, this abundance of meat is chiefly attributable to vast extents of natural grazing land, heavy productions of beef and mutton, and relatively small human populations. In the early period of pioneer development in the United States our meat supply was plentiful also because of a great surplus of natural grazing land and a relatively small human population. From previous discussions we are aware that today the native range contributes only a minor portion of our meat supply. We in the United States continue to be heavy eaters of meat because we have an unusual endowment of fertile cropland, only a small portion of which is required to raise food and fiber for direct human consumption. The balance is used to produce livestock feeds. Of all our agricultural assets none is more remarkable than the Corn Belt.

The hope that future generations of Americans will have diets rich in meat rather than vegetarian fare is in large measure dependent upon how well we preserve the soil resources of the Corn Belt and upon how well we learn to increase yields per acre as our population grows.

THE PHYSICAL ORIGIN OF THE CORN BELT

The sequence of events, extending far back into geologic time, which bequeathed to Americans the largest single unit of superb agricultural land in the world is, of course, unique. To better understand and appreciate the soil resources of the Corn Belt let us review their origin in an abbreviated summary. Millions of years ago all of the present region was a sea bottom upon which were deposited deep blankets of erosional sediments as well as heavy accumulations of calcareous marine organisms. During subsequent geologic ages the sea receded and the strata of erosional and marine depositions were uplifted by a flexing of the earth's crust. The former sea-floor sediments, now consolidated into sandstones, shales, and limestones, retained much of their level and horizontal structure. There were also some prominences which extended above the general plain, and these ultimately were worn down by erosion. In time the horizontal surfaces themselves were dissected, but that etching was not drastic, principally because the plains of sedimentary rocks were not much above base level. Then a remarkable rejuvenation occurred.

This concluding episode was the glaciation of New England and the central United States north of the Missouri and Ohio rivers. Enormous ice drifts originating in Canada bore down with tremendous pressure and grinding force. Meeting with little resistance on the gently dissected surface of the present Corn Belt, and losing their transporting powers as they reached the end of their journey, the glaciers laid down enormous

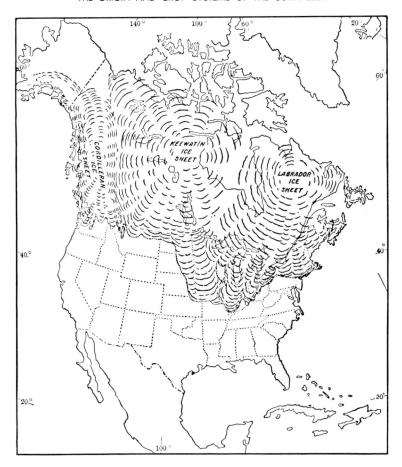

Figure 18:1.   Extent of continental glaciation. (Source: Reference 2, p. 465.)

loads of ground rock powder known as *till*.   The ice drifts had manufactured this till by pulverizing the sedimentary formations over which
they scraped their way.   The till filled in the erosional wrinkles on the
surface of both the level and undulating portions of the plain.   In New
England the preglacial land surface had been severely dissected, and
most of it was constructed of hard igneous and metamorphic rocks which
did not pulverize easily.   Till deposits left by glaciation in New England
generally have more stone and boulders than those of the Corn Belt.   In
addition, they were insufficient to fill in and smooth the surface of the
severely incised landscape which is still hilly.

A particular feature of the western Corn Belt is the deep covering of aeolian silts or loess which blanket many ice-laid till sheets. These loess formations, a few inches to many feet in thickness, are the parent materials of soils in some of the most productive districts. They are believed to have accumulated as the result of repeated dust storms which raged, perhaps for centuries, during the final stages of glacial retreat. As the ice slowly receded, the raw till sheets were uncovered. Additional sediments were flushed into drainage ways by streams of melt-water rushing from the dwindling ice lobes. Wind storms blew away the finer silt particles from the exposed rock powder of till and outwash. Carried aloft by the winds this silt was later deposited over a vast area. Composed of relatively unweathered minerals, both the glacial tills and loess developed into soils that were rich in nutrient elements. It is, of course, most unusual that soils rich in mineral nutrients should occur in humid regions. Glaciation not only rejuvenated the land surface, but it also provided fresh rock minerals for the development of new productive soils.

This remarkable geologic sequence terminated where rainfall is adequate for abundant plant growth. It would seem that here nature has done her best. As if this unique combination of climate and geologic origin were not sufficient to distinguish the Corn Belt, ancient man apparently had a hand in adding to its unusual character. Climate would have permitted forest growth throughout the region. However, many accounts of explorers and early settlers in the Middlewest tell about the Indian custom of deliberate burning which encouraged grazing animals and made hunting easier. The prairie-soil districts of Illinois, Iowa, and Missouri are very likely the gift of pre-Columbian man, for it is probable that forests would have covered those areas if they had not been suppressed by fire.

Among his observations along the Illinois River in 1821–1823, Ogden records:

The prairies on this river are numerous and many of them are large, extending further than the eye can reach; and some of them for 60 or 70 miles. These savannas or prairies resemble large, flat plains—here the traveller is struck with wonder and amazement—here he may in many places travel without once having seen a hillock or a tree . . . nothing but grass of luxuriant growth, waving in the breeze. These places, it was supposed, were once covered with sturdy timber, but owing to their continual burning over by the aboriginals, in order to better take their game, makes them appear what they now do. (Reference 3; Vol. V, p. 55.)

It is the high humus content of the Prairie soils which has enhanced their productivity even beyond the potentialities of their mineral constitution. So rich a store of humus on well-drained soils could have accumulated only under a heavy growth of grass. Thus, in summary, a remarkable geologic sequence followed by the development of unusually productive soils in a humid region has given Americans the most extensive of the world's rich agricultural provinces.

THE CULTURAL ORIGINS OF THE CORN BELT

The cultural origins of the modern Corn Belt are traceable to colonial antecedents east of the Appalachians, particularly to southeastern Pennsylvania. Early in the eighteenth century an industrious group of immigrants from the German and Swiss Rhineland came to settle in the shale and limestone lowlands of what are now the counties of Chester, Lancaster, and York. These people built fine barns, bred high-grade livestock, and were adept at maintaining soil fertility by the use of ground limestone, gypsum, and animal manures. They were successful at clover culture, and practiced crop rotations which generally included corn, wheat, barley, oats, and clover-grass meadows. They were good dairymen as well as cheese and butter makers and kept hogs to dispose of such dairy wastes as skim milk, buttermilk, and whey.

After the American Revolution opened up the trans-Appalachian territories to pioneer settlement, hogs and cattle from backwoods hill-farms were driven on the hoof to Atlantic coast seaports for sale and slaughter. Professional drovers took up the business of collecting and driving the livestock. The major gateway from the back country to the coast in those days was Harrisburg Gap, and the principal destination was Philadelphia. Pickled meats from Philadelphia's abattoirs were disposed of in the growing towns of the Atlantic coast and were shipped to European sugar colonies in the West Indies.

The thrifty German and Swiss farmers on the western approaches to Philadelphia were quick to recognize an opportunity. The cattle and hogs, which arrived from the mountains, lean and worn from the journey, brought a poor price. Clever farmers with rich green pastures and bursting graneries purchased them, fed them well until they improved in flesh and quality, then marketed them at handsome profits. The crop and animal-husbandry practices of these farmers of early Pennsylvania set the style for the modern Corn Belt. To this day descendents of the original Pennsylvania Dutch farmers continue operations in the manner of their forefathers. It is only the limited area of good productive land in this original corn belt which prevented a greater growth. The economic soundness of the enterprise was so obvious, however, that as the American nation grew in population and wealth new corn belts were born to the westward when good productive lands occurred in the vicinities of market centers and shipping points.

In 1839 the nation's chief areas of corn production and livestock fattening were in the limestone basins of Kentucky's Bluegrass and Tennessee's Nashville basin. Even today these are two of our richest agricultural regions, although they are not part of the modern Corn Belt. A location on navigable streams, leading to the Mississippi River and to plantations of the Cotton South, gave the limestone basins of Kentucky and Tennessee a market advantage similar to that enjoyed by southeastern Pennsylvania. Northward, across the Ohio River, Cincinnati began its career as hog butcher of the West. It drew its supplies from Kentucky and from the valleys of the Scioto and Miami rivers, tributaries to the Ohio.

The farmers on these rich soils bred some of their own animals, but they also tried the Pennsylvania system. They purchased lean hogs and cattle from drovers who brought them into the valleys from pioneer farms in the plateau uplands of eastern Ohio, Kentucky, and Tennessee. They turned this stock onto their fine bluegrass pastures and fattened them with corn, oats, hay, and barley.

By 1859 the central and eastern outlines of the modern Corn Belt had taken shape. Several important developments had occurred in the two preceding decades. The population of the United States had grown phenomenally, and the market for meat continued strong. The steel plow was being manufactured in mass quantity so that the grasslands of Illinois, Iowa, and Missouri could be opened to tillage. In 1860 Illinois led the nation in corn production for the first time with 115 million bushels, and Chicago had surpassed Cincinnati as a slaughterhouse. Of major importance was the extension of railroads into the Middlewest. Thirteen railroads serviced Chicago in 1856. Four years before, in 1852, there had not been one. The Illinois Central alone had 700 miles of track which made cheap and rapid transportation available to a rich and fast-growing prairie region.

Again, this greatly expanded Corn Belt functioned as did its prototypes. Some hogs, beef, and dairy cattle were bred and raised on local grain and pastures. It was also a practice to fatten cattle which had propagated on what remained of the unsettled middlewestern prairies. Cattle, herded on native grasslands in northwestern Iowa, were brought to cultivated corn fields and pastures in the eastern section of the state. There they were given a good market finish. Farmers with surplus corn, oats, barley, and hay bought feeder stock from Texas as soon as western drives began after the Civil War. Cattle, driven to railheads in Missouri and Kansas, passed through the feed lots of northern Missouri, Illinois, Indiana, and Ohio before going to their final destinations. In the past hundred years the intensity of grain and hay production in the middle-

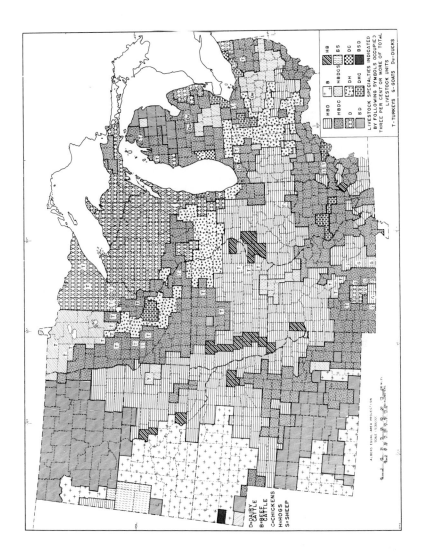

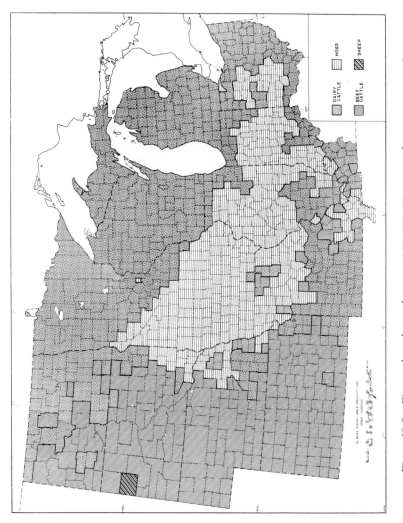

Figure 18·3. First ranking livestock type, 1949–1950. (Source: Reference 7; p. 244.)

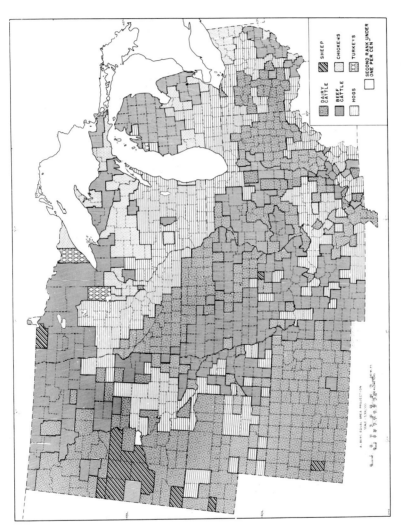

Figure 18:4. Second ranking livestock type, 1949–1950. (Source: Reference 7; p. 245.)

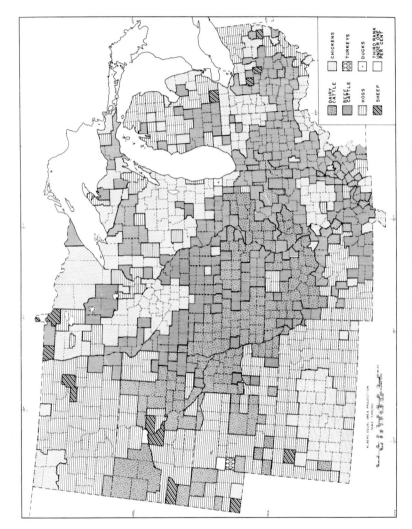

Figure 18:5.   Third ranking livestock type, 1949–1950.   (Source: Reference 7;   p.   248.)

western Corn Belt has increased and the boundaries of the area have been extended. The essential pattern of operation remains much the same, although there are many variations on the theme. Some of those variations and the regional influences which promote them are considered in the following paragraphs.

LIVESTOCK SYSTEMS OF THE CORN BELT

The Corn Belt, as it is outlined in Figure 4:2, is definitely the heart of corn and hog production in the United States. The details of Figure A-1 and A-19 in the Appendix make that clear. However, it has been mentioned that other crops besides corn as well as other livestock besides hogs are characteristic of the intensive husbandry systems of both the contemporary Corn Belt and its historical antecedents.

Figure 18:2 is a presentation of dominant livestock combination systems in the twelve north-central states. This map encompasses not only the Corn Belt but also the Great Lakes dairy land and the Wheat and Livestock Belt of the northwestern dry plains.

The mixed interest in hogs, beef, and dairy cattle is clear at the very heart of the Corn Belt, which extends from central Indiana through Illinois, Iowa, and northern Missouri into eastern Nebraska. Along the north, south, and eastern fringes of this core area chickens are added in significant numbers. The preference for specific livestock types in different sections of the north-central states is demonstrated in Figure 18:3. In this cartogram we see defined the boundaries of the popular but oversimplified hog, beef, and dairy belts. The manner in which these belts are intruded by other types of livestock is illustrated in Figures 18:4 and 18:5. The principal influences which induced middle-western farmers to create these patterns are climate, topography, soils, markets, and the systems of cropping and livestock husbandry which blend well.

CROP SYSTEMS OF THE CORN BELT

Although there are important exceptions to the rule, it is generally the custom in humid temperate regions to rotate crops on the cultivated land. In the Corn Belt, the Dairy Belt, and Appalachian General Farming Belt a rotation of corn, oats, and hay is a common one. There are many variations of such a basic rotation. For instance in north-central Illinois the variant is likely to be corn-corn-corn-oats-hay. In southwestern Wisconsin common variants are corn-oats-hay-hay and corn-oats-hay-hay-hay. Because, under the best conditions in the Middlewest, a good

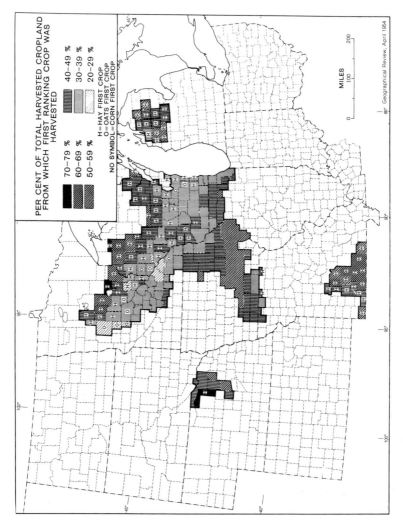

Figure 18·6. COH regions — 1949. (Source: Reference 6; p. 286, Figure 2.)

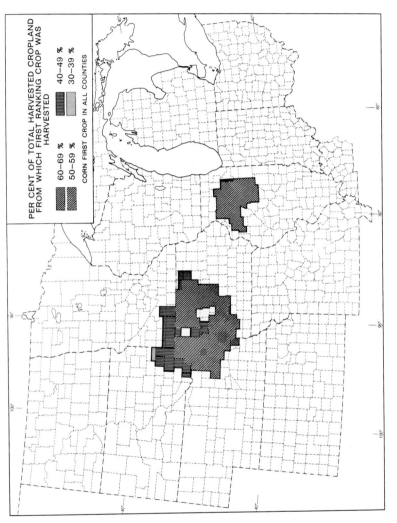

Figure 18:7.   CO regions — 1949. (Source: Reference 6; p. 292, Figure 9.)

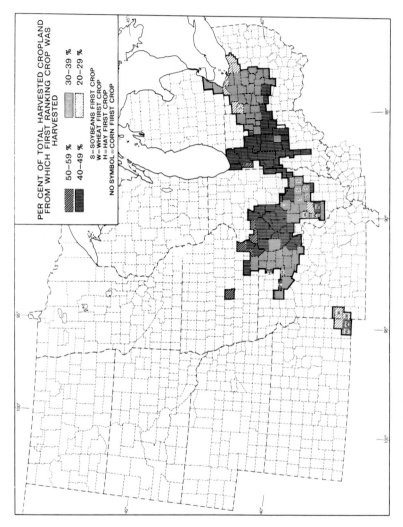

Figure 18.8. COSWH regions — 1949 (Source: Reference 6; p. 296, Figure 17.)

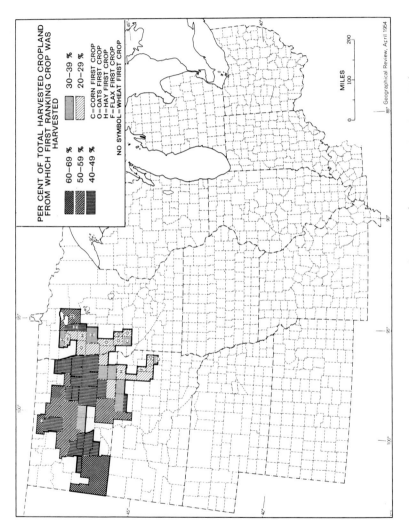

Figure 18:9. WHCOFB regions — 1949. (Source: Reference 6; p. 298, Figure 21.)

corn crop is worth more than a good hay crop it is natural that corn is preferred when conditions permit. However, hay is preferred when the topography becomes hilly, the soils shallow, and the growing season is short.

The preceding fine series of cartograms (Figures 18–6, 18–7, 18–8, and 18–9) by Dean John Weaver of the University of Nebraska illustrate the preferences for certain crops in the middlewestern agricultural regions. As we would expect, comparisons of the maps of crop and livestock dominance show strong correlations between hogs and corn in the central portions of the Corn Belt.

The coincidence of hay and dairy-cattle dominance from central Wisconsin northward is expected. It is the interesting character of the transition area between the districts of strong specialty which will particularly stimulate the student of middlewestern agriculture to active questioning. These cartograms, of course, are based upon the 1949–1950 Census. They represent a situation prevailing at one time only, and the data of succeeding censuses will surely reveal changes in the Middlewest, just as they will elsewhere in the nation. Of outstanding importance is the fact that corn cultivation is symbolic of intensive land use. The soils of the Corn Belt have demonstrated their capacity to support this intensive exploitation. It is logical to predict that the crop and livestock systems in the present Corn Belt, however they may change, will continue to demand heavy yields from the soil. How this soil resource is conserved is thus of paramount importance.

REFERENCES

1. Bidwell, Percy Wells and John I. Falconer, *History of Agriculture in the Northern United States, 1620–1860*, Carnegie Institution of Washington, Washington, D.C., 1925.
2. Bowman, Isaish, *Forest Physiography*, John Wiley and Sons, New York, 1911.
3. Thwaites, R. G., *Early Western Travels*, A. H. Clark Co., Cleveland.
4. U.S. Bureau of Census, *Census of Agriculture, 1954*, Government Printing Office, Washington, D.C.
5. U.S. Department of Agriculture, *Generalized Types of Farming in the United States*, Government Printing Office, Washington, D.C., 1950.
6. Weaver, John, Crop-Combination Regions in the Middle West, *The Geographical Review*, April 1954.
7. Weaver, John., *et al.*, Livestock Units and Combination Regions in the Middlewest, *Economic Geography*, July 1956.

soil
conservation
in the
Corn Belt

19

The climatic advantages of the Corn Belt have been emphasized. But there is one drawback—the frost-free growing season is only 140 days along the region's northern boundary and approximately 180 days along the southern periphery. These periods are long enough for corn, small grains, soybeans, and other annuals which mature quickly. However, if the frost-free periods were longer and if the winters were milder, farmers might be inclined to establish more grass-legume meadows for hay and pasture than is now the custom. It is possible that well-managed perennial meadows, when the growing season is long enough, may yield as many pounds of digestible nutrients per acre as corn—at lower cost and with little, if any, damage to the soil.

Gifted with superb land, the Corn Belt farmer naturally wants to make the most of it. In fact, he is obliged to. Property values have climbed so high that only intensive exploitation makes the investment pay. Corn is by all odds the best yielder and the most attractive money crop, although soybeans, too, may be profitable. Both of these crops are clean-

245

cultivated, and too much clean cultivation leads to deterioration of soil structure and to erosion.

For forty-one years, between 1894 and 1935, the Ohio Agricultural Experiment Station at Wooster, Ohio, studied soil loss and yields on three sets of experimental plots devoted to continuous corn cultivation. The average slope of these plots is 2 to 4 per cent. The results are presented in Table 19:1.

Table 19:1.   Corn Cultivation and Soil Erosion
(Source: Reference 3; p. 102)

Crop Every Year	Fertilizer Treatment	Soil Loss in Inches 1894–1935	Per Cent of Original Organic Matter Remaining in Soil in 1935	Average Annual Yield in Bushels Per Acre 1894–1935	1931–1935
Corn	none	10.3	37	26.3	6.5
Corn	complete (500 lbs. of 10–5–10 per acre)	11.1	35	44.4	28.9
Corn	manure at rate of 5 tons per acre	9.5	53	43.1	30.0

The crucial fact in these data is that although reasonable fertilizer applications improved yields they alone could not sustain them as erosion proceeded. Soil productivity is not simply a matter of available chemicals. It is also dependent upon good structure, aggregation, texture, mellowness, and microorganic life. Without regular incorporation of dead plant tissues, vital microorganic activity diminishes through lack of a food supply. Dead plant tissue is transformed by earthworms, bacteria, fungi, and other living things into humus which mellows the soil and improves its structure. As the humus content in Corn Belt lands declines because of erosion, inadequate replacement, or excessive oxidation, the inherent productivity is also likely to decrease as it did on the Ohio experimental plots.

Figure 17:2 shows the distribution and severity of soil erosion throughout the nation. With the exception of northern Ohio, central Iowa, southwestern Minnesota, and a few smaller areas, the losses of topsoil in the Corn Belt have ranged from 25 to 75 per cent. Extensive portions of southern Iowa and west-central Illinois have suffered even greater damage. About 40 per cent of Illinois is nearly level land of less than 2 per cent slope, most of it artificially drained. On such land topsoil losses exceeding 25 per cent could occur only under the severest mistreatment. Often when there has been little or no erosion, the loss of humus has brought on deterioration of soil structure. Either raw organic matter has not been returned to the land in sufficient amounts, or humus oxidation has been promoted by too-frequent cultivation. Impairment of soil structure can reduce the efficiency of artificial drainage systems previously installed at great expense.

There is considerable difference in the ways various plants prevent or promote soil erosion. They protect the soil if they are perennials and shield the ground from pounding rains. There is nothing better than a good sod of grasses and legumes to hold soil in place. If the Corn Belt were covered with meadows, its soil would not be in danger. But hogs and poultry require more than forage crops. Dairy cattle, beef cattle, and sheep usually do better when fed supplements of grain concentrates. The nation, therefore, needs an abundant corn harvest every year. Corn affords the soil little protection from the impact of falling rain during early weeks of growth, and it provides the ground with no vegetative mantle during winter and spring. It is not the only crop that gives scant protection. Cotton, tobacco, soybeans, and potatoes are other major offenders. Significant soil losses may also occur under oats, wheat, barley, rye, and flax. These crops are prominent in some sections of the Corn Belt.

The amount and severity of erosion depends not only upon the frequencies in the rotation of corn and other nonprotective crops but also upon whether or not the farmer practices contour plowing, terracing, and contour strip-cropping where land relief and slope suggest that they are appropriate. Only the general levelness of the humid Corn Belt plains has saved them from a devastation comparable with that which occurred under cotton on the southern Appalachian Piedmont. For the farmer who finds it uneconomical to plant grass-legume meadows rather than corn, there are new methods of cultivation which help to maintain humus, preserve good soil structure, and prevent erosion.

The University of Illinois College of Agriculture is conducting experiments with annual seedings of corn interplanted with winter rye as a cover and green-manure crop. Indications are that humus and good soil structure are maintained by this technique. The rye is planted between rows of corn every August and gives the soil protection against erosion during the winter months. Of course, exceptionally heavy applications of nitrogen are used not only to satisfy the needs of the corn but also to hasten humification of the rye when it is plowed under before corn-planting time. The following is Professor Roger H. Bray's description of experimental methods which have successfully increased soil organic matter while maintaining good corn yields in successive years.

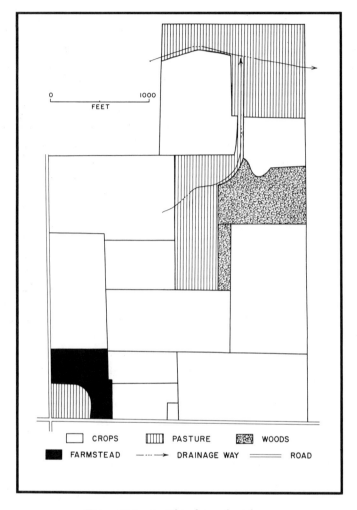

Figure 19:1.   An Ohio dairy-wheat farm.

The waist-high green rye was shredded at corn-planting time, and the corn was planted and fertilized in one operation using an International mulch planter. Most of the chopped rye remained on the surface as a mulch.

Plowing the rye under early in the spring should be equally effective so far as (corn) yields are concerned.

In addition to an average of 89 bushels of corn (per acre), the following objectives were achieved: (a) soil humus was increased; (b) soil erosion was prevented; (c) the physical quality of the soil was improved; (d) a mulch was left on the soil during the summer; and (e) a new high in biological activity was achieved. All of these are objectives which the legume rotations have only incompletely achieved. . . .

Our experience convinces us that in some such nitro-grass program lies the key to high production at a low cost per bushel—and with complete soil conservation. . . .

As yet, we have no definite recommendations for any general use of a nitro-grass rotation. But the basic principle is simple—enough synthetic nitrogen should be used to take care of both the grass and the corn. (Reference 1; p. 12.)

SOME LAND-USE SYSTEMS IN THE CORN BELT

As we have noted in Chapter 18, there are many land-management systems in the Corn Belt. Some farmers, particularly in central Iowa and east-central Illinois, concentrate upon cash crops such as corn, oats, and soybeans. Many keep no livestock. Elsewhere in the Corn Belt most farmers feed their crops to livestock. We will consider three farms, each having a different land-livestock system. These farms are exceptional only in one detail: each follows a crop system designed to prevent soil deterioration. The crops and livestock are representative of the Corn Belt.

An Ohio Cash-Grain and Dairy Farm. This farm is located in north-central Ohio at the eastern limit of the Corn Belt. It was cleared from a timbered wilderness by the grandfather of its present operator approximately a hundred years ago. Less than 3 of its 205 acres have a surface slope exceeding 2 per cent. In other words, it is almost level land. Its principal problem in the past has been inadequate drainage. It is now almost completely underlain with tile drains. Some of these tiles are homemade of local clay, formed and baked on the farm in the days before manufactured tiles were available. There has been almost no soil erosion on this property, and the soil is doubtless more productive today than at any other time in its history.

Because this is a dairy farm as well as a producer of wheat there is a need for hay and pasture. A very conservative system of land management is thus possible. Although every one of the 205 acres is suitable for intensive cultivation, the average year finds the land being used as follows:

Corn	30	acres
Wheat	29	acres
Oats	29	acres
Hay	58	acres
Pasture	36	acres
Woodlot	12	acres
Buildings and roads	11	acres
Total	205	acres

The basic rotation on this farm is corn-oats-hay-hay, and as long as the property continues to be managed in such a provident manner it will continue to yield well without injury to the soil. Dairying is not the most popular type of farming in the Corn Belt for several reasons. To the north and northeast lie the major dairy areas of the United States. There, milk for conversion into butter, cheese, and other processed items is in surplus supply. The value of milk used for processing is therefore low in relation to its cost of production. While prices paid for fluid milk for direct human consumption are usually higher than prices paid for "processors' milk," there is only a limited market for "bottle" milk in the Corn Belt itself. Dairying calls for considerable investment in barns, and labor requirements are also higher per animal unit than for beef cattle, hogs, or sheep.°

The soils of the Corn Belt are generally superior to those of the specialized dairy regions. Because of this most farmers in the Corn Belt find it more profitable to devote the major share of their labor to field crops and a lesser share to animal care. In the dairy regions a better income is derived by doing less work in the fields but more in the barns. Although it is not possible for dairymen in the northern areas of specialized dairying to have the best soils, it is possible for them to have the best cattle. Thus we find the typical farmer of the Corn Belt and of the dairy regions devoting most of his effort to developing his best resources.

An Illinois Corn-Hog and Cash-Grain Farm. North-central Illinois is the cash-grain center of the Corn Belt. Most of the soils are true prairie loams, originally high in humus, and very responsive to cultivation. The farms are not far from Chicago, the principal depot for grain shipments both to industrial processors and to the poultrymen and dairymen of the Northeast and the middle Atlantic seaboard who buy concentrates. Many farmers in north-central Illinois keep no livestock at all. A common rotation on their properties is corn-corn-oats. Some jokesters have said that their favorite rotation is corn-oats-Miami. Sometimes a planting of soybeans is substituted for one of corn. Hay is a poor cash crop, and without livestock the farmer has nothing to feed it to. The constant emphasis upon annual plants without winter cover or green-manure crops has resulted in a serious decline in both the soil structure and humus content of formerly superb prairie loams. This system would be greatly improved by the addition of a winter-rye intercropping program, such as that outlined by Professor Bray and quoted in this chapter.

Other farmers in north-central Illinois do keep livestock. In 1951 the University of Illinois reported on the field and feeding practices of 271

°An animal unit is 1 cow, 1 horse, 5 sheep, 1 bred sow, or 100 chickens.

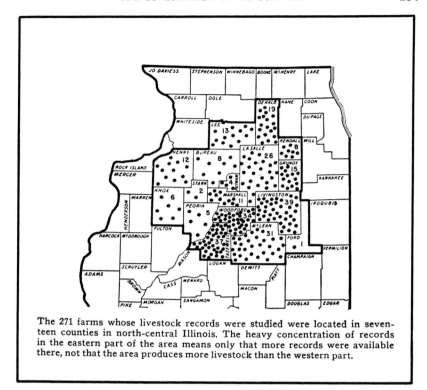

The 271 farms whose livestock records were studied were located in seventeen counties in north-central Illinois. The heavy concentration of records in the eastern part of the area means only that more records were available there, not that the area produces more livestock than the western part.

Figure 19:2.   Location of livestock farms. (Source: Reference 2; p. 258.)

operators who had kept accurate records of their enterprises for ten years.   The location of these farms is shown in Figure 19:2.

One quarter of these farms sold 70 per cent or more of all their crops. Another quarter sold 40 to 69 per cent of all they raised.   The remaining half of the farms sold 39 per cent or less.   What was not sold was fed to livestock.   The total disposition of all crops on all 271 farms is shown in Figure 19:3.

Figure 19:4 is the tile drainage system of a well-managed combination cash-grain and corn-hog farm in east north-central Illinois.   All the land on this 160-acre farm is capable of intensive use.   Five sixths of it has a slope of less than 1.5 per cent, which is practically flat.   The principal land-management problem is drainage.   Nevertheless, a considerable portion of this almost level land has lost more than 6 inches of topsoil in the hundred years it has been farmed.   Obviously, the crop systems used in the past were hard on the soil.   A loss of more than 6 inches of

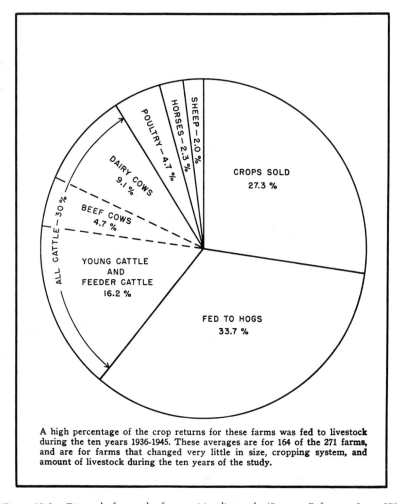

Figure 19:3.   Disposal of crops by farms raising livestock. (Source: Reference 2; p. 259.)

topsoil on well-drained loams with nearly flat surfaces would normally occur only when the soil structure has broken down for lack of humus.

To arrest erosion and prevent further deterioration of soil structure this farm is now one quarter meadow. It supports a very small dairy herd in addition to its principal cash-grain and corn-hog program. The basic rotation is corn-corn-oats-meadow. This is a distinct improvement upon the common practice in north-central Illinois. It is very likely that this rotation, if continued, will not cause further injury to the land, particularly if winter rye is used as a cover and green-manure crop with the corn. In the average year the 160 acres of this farm are used as follows:

Corn	76 acres
Oats	38 acres
Meadow	38 acres
Homestead and roads	8 acres
Total	160 acres

In some years most of the corn and oats are sold. Selling the grain for cash is particularly attractive when hog prices are down and grain prices are satisfactory. Then there are years in which all the grain is fed on the farm, when grain prices seem low in proportion to the value of hogs. The hog-grain enterprise is quite flexible, since the number of pigs on feed can be increased or decreased quickly. By marketing all but a few sows and a boar, the operation can be put on a stand-by basis. To build it up again requires a gestation period of only 114 days. Shelters for

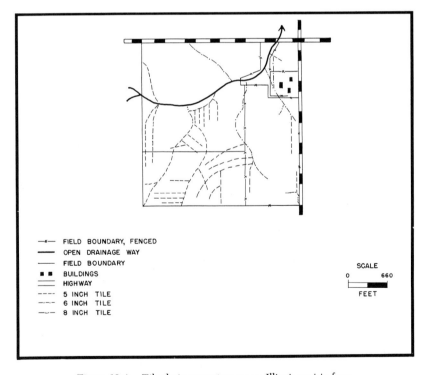

Figure 19:4.   Tile drainage system on an Illinois prairie farm.

hogs require very little capital outlay; and leaving them unused occasionally does not impose a significant overhead expense. [*]

An Iowa Corn-Hog-Cattle Farm. East-central Iowa breeds and fattens a great many hogs and beef cattle. It also puts a fine market finish on feeder cattle bought from western ranches. A few farmers in this part of the Corn Belt also keep dairy cows, raise poultry, and occasionally fatten lambs. This is indeed a paradise for the connoisseur of choice meats and other livestock products. Even the least pretentious short-order, side-street diners serve excellent T-bone and porterhouse steaks, pork chops, and roast pork, often for the price of hamburger in New England. Of course, lobster is a bit expensive in Iowa, so the good people of Gloucester and Portland may have that to console them.

Figure 19:5 is a 240-acre farm which has been in the same family since virgin prairie sod was plowed seventy-five years ago. No cash crops are sold from this property. Everything grown is fed to livestock, and each year more than 300 hogs and approximately 40 head of homebred Herefords are marketed. In addition, this farm supports a dairy herd of over 20 milking cows and the young stock. This is a highly efficient unit with a crop program well designed for high production and soil conservation. Some soil erosion did occur in years past when corn was sold for cash and beef cattle were not a part of the livestock enterprise. A smaller proportion of the farm was in meadow during those years.

The land is typical of east-central Iowa prairie soils. Surface relief is flat to undulating, but a few slopes are as steep as 8 to 12 per cent, which is considerably more than for the Ohio and Illinois farms previously discussed. Soil-erosion control is therefore a major consideration. Contour cultivation is practiced on all the sloping land. The field on the extreme right also has a terrace system with a sodded outlet to carry the runoff water. The southwest section of the property is level land which is drained by a combination of subsurface tile and a surface drainage ditch into which the tile lines discharge. The surface ditch is shown on the map. The basic rotations are corn-oats-meadow-meadow on the sloping land and corn-corn-oats-meadow on the level fields.

It is the divided interest in hogs and cattle on this farm which permits a large proportion of the land to be in hay and pasture every year. This is not merely for soil conservation. It results from a consideration also of markets, animal diets, and labor management. The farm is a large

[*] About 6 bushels of corn plus about 30 pounds of protein supplement are required to put 100 pounds of gain on a young hog. The corn-hog ratio is the number of bushels of corn which 100 pounds of live hog will buy. Naturally this ratio changes with the market prices of corn and hogs. When the ratio is low (around 8) the farmer is more likely to sell corn than to feed it. When the ratio is high (around 14 or above) he is likely to feed as much as he possibly can. (Reference 4; p. 14.)

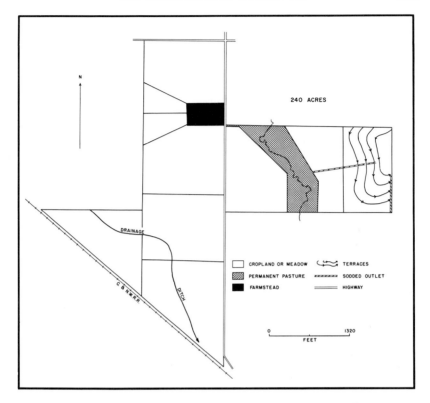

240 ACRES

N

DRAINAGE

C & N W RR

DITCH

CROPLAND OR MEADOW TERRACES

PERMANENT PASTURE SODDED OUTLET

FARMSTEAD HIGHWAY

0   1320

FEET

Figure 19:5. A diversified livestock farm in Iowa.

one. If the operator were to devote all of it to field crops for cash sale, he would have to concentrate upon corn, soybeans, and small grains because the market demand for hay is not good. If most of the farm were in grain crops, the field-labor load would be so heavy that little or no time would be left for the care of livestock unless additional labor were hired. That might not pay. To keep two fifths of the land in meadows reduces the field-labor load and permits time to care for livestock. The cattle are kept to eat the hay and graze the pastures. The result is good soil conservation and a high income. The animal manures and the sod in the rotation maintain soil humus at an optimum level. In some years yields per acre on this farm have been 50 per cent above the state average. Soil erosion is effectively checked, and there is no likelihood that productivity will decline as long as the present crop and livestock system is adhered to.

REFERENCES

1. Bray, Roger H., The New Nitro-Grass Rotation for Corn, *What's New In Crops & Soils*, Madison, Wisconsin, April–May 1954.
2. Mosher, M. L., *Livestock Earnings on North-Central Illinois Farms*, University of Illinois Agricultural Experiment Station, Urbana, 1951.
3. U.S. Department of Agriculture, *Yearbook of Agriculture, 1938*, Government Printing Office, Washington, D.C.
4. Zeller, J. H., *Swine Production*, U.S. Department of Agriculture, Government Printing Office, Washington, D.C., 1952.

the
economic
geography
of
dairy
farming

20

Economically there are two basic classes of commercial dairy farms: (1) those which sell milk to dairies for direct human consumption as fresh whole milk or cream; (2) those which sell milk to manufacturers of butter, cheese, condensed milk, and other processed items. We shall call these Class 1 and Class 2, respectively. Of course, there are many variations of these basic types. For instance, there are farms which have their own milk routes. Some make butter and cheese. Others sell milk to a regional pool out of which some is taken for bottling and some for processed dairy products. The economic significance of how milk is used is made clear by Table 20:1.

The farmer who can sell all or most of his production in the Class 1 market receives a handsome premium. The cost of production of Class 1 milk is usually slightly higher than the cost of production of Class 2 milk because special sanitary regulations must be complied with. A large number of dairymen, however, market through regional milk pools and receive what is known as a blended price. They are paid Class 1 prices

Table 20:1. Prices Paid for Milk
According to Use in the United States
(Source: Reference 5; p. 2045)

Year	Prices Paid Producers by Dealers for Standard-Grade Milk for City Distribution as Milk or Cream Hundredweight	Prices Paid Producers by Condenseries Hundredweight	Ratio of Milk Distributors' Price to Condensery Price
1930	$2.69	$1.67	161
1931	2.20	1.18	186
1932	1.72	0.89	193
1933	1.60	0.98	163
1934	1.89	1.14	166
1935	2.05	1.35	152
1936	2.13	1.56	137
1937	2.32	1.57	148
1938	2.26	1.25	181
1939	2.17	1.24	175
1940	2.21	1.38	160
1941	2.40	1.81	133
1942	2.79	2.08	134
1943	3.16	2.61	121
1944	3.24	2.66	122
1945	3.26	2.63	124
1946	3.92	3.36	117
1947	4.71	3.46	136
1948	5.17	3.90	133
1949	4.76	2.81	169
20-year average	2.832	1.976	151

for milk and cream which are bottled and Class 2 prices for that which goes into processed items. Obviously the Class 2 milk must comply with the Class 1 sanitary codes under such arrangements.

Milk-marketing arrangements and prices paid to producers frequently vary from state to state as well as from district to district within states. The basic factors effecting prices are supply-demand ratios and distances to market. For instance, far more fluid milk is produced within 150 miles of Chicago than the people in that milkshed can consume. The surplus, therefore, must be shipped great distances to deficit areas or it must be processed. Wherever there is a substantial surplus of Class 1 milk the prices for both Class 1 and Class 2 milk are depressed because of the unfavorable supply-demand ratio. Also, any surplus automatically becomes Class 2, and there is a national overproduction of this type of milk. We make more butter, cheese, evaporated milk, etc., than people will buy at prices commensurate with those they will pay for fluid milk for direct consumption. Wherever regional surpluses are insignificant prices paid for Class 1 milk are relatively high. The processed items are shipped into these areas at less cost than they could be produced locally. At Chicago in 1949 the price paid to farmers for Class 1 milk was $3.77 per hundred pounds. At Miami, Florida, where there is little or no surplus, the price paid was $7.09. Chicago is close to the geographical center of the combined Great Lakes dairy region and the central Corn Belt. Within these two areas are 40 per cent of all the dairy cows in the United States.

**Table 20:2.   Milk Cows on Farms and Ranches,
January 1, 1954 (in thousands)**
(Source: Reference 3; p. 48)

North Atlantic states	3,480
Lake states	5,128
Central Corn Belt	4,863
Northern plains	1,807
Appalachian	2,898
Southeastern states	1,206
Delta	1,475
Southern plains	1,610
Mountain	835
Pacific	1,433
Total	24,735

CLASS 1 MILK

Milk is approximately 86 per cent water and highly perishable. Costs of transportation of fluid milk are therefore high per unit of value. This fact limits the ability of surplus milk in one area to depress the price of Class 1 milk at some distant point. Consequently, the Class 1 fluid-milk industry is one of the most widely dispersed industries in the United States, both as to location of production and the location of dairies which distribute it. Every community has its milkshed. All urbanized areas are surrounded by dairy regions extending outward to a point from which it no longer remains profitable or permissible to ship milk in, and in many cases the limits of a milkshed are determined by regulation.

This protects the farmers within the restricted area from outside competition and makes possible the supervision of dairy sanitation by local authorities. Sometimes an unusual situation exists such as that at Los Angeles, where land values close to the city are so high that dairymen cannot afford pastures for milking cows. Farther away from Los Angeles the land is either so mountainous or so arid that dairying is not feasible. Consequently, dairy cows are kept on feed lots within the metropolitan district. The land is especially zoned for dairying to protect it from excessive taxation and the encroachment of residential development. These "milk factories" are the most highly specialized type of dairy farm. All concentrate feeds and hay are purchased. As many as 250 cows are kept on 10-acre plots.

CLASS 2 MILK

The processed dairy products made from Class 2 milk have little or no water content. They are less perishable than fluid milk, and their value per pound is very much greater. Consequently, transportation charges per unit of value are substantially lower. This is illustrated by the costs of shipments of various dairy items from Wisconsin to New York City in June 1950.

**Table 20:3. Freight Rates on Selected Dairy Products
from Wisconsin to New York City**
(Source: Reference 5; p. 2000)

	Unit	New York Wholesale Price June 1950	Freight from Wisconsin to New York	Freight as Percentage of Price
Fluid milk	100 pounds	$4.76–$5.00	$1.81	36–38
Cream	10–gallon can	32.75	2.45	7.5
Evaporated milk	case	5.25	0.38	7.2
Cheese	pound	0.351	0.014	4.0
Butter	pound	0.599	0.015	2.5
Milk powder	pound	0.116	0.0088	7.6

National overproduction of Class 2 milk, as well as regional differences in supply-demand ratios of Class 1 milk, influence the profits of dairy farms from place to place. Figure 20:1 shows the variation in average prices paid to the farmers of different states for all milk deliveries in 1955. If one compares this map with Figure A-18 in the Appendix, which shows the distribution of milk cows in the United States, then the

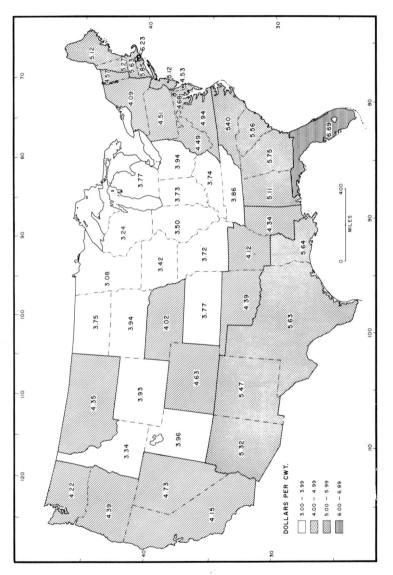

Figure 20:1.   Average wholesale price received by farmers for milk. (Source: Reference 4.)

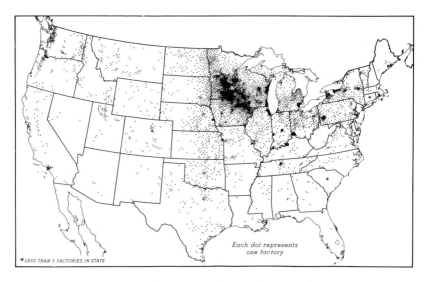

Figure 20:2.   Factories making creamery butter. (Source: Reference 5; p. 2019.)

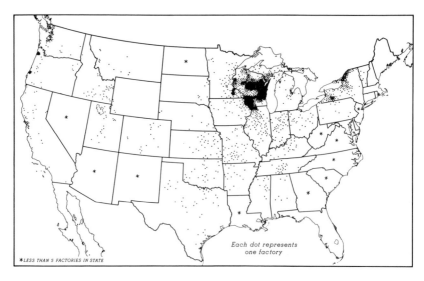

Figure 20:3.   Factories making American cheese. (Source: Reference 5; p. 2020.)

close relationship between low prices and surplus production is easily recognizable. The location of factories making creamery butter and American cheese give an indication of the areas in which most of the Class 2 milk is produced.

THE NATIONAL MILK SUPPLY AND ITS USES

The majority of the nation's farmers have at least one milk cow. In 1944 there were 2,022,000 farmers who kept one or more of these animals just to provide dairy products for their own families. There were also 2,473,000 other farmers who kept sufficient cows to place milk or other dairy products on the market. Of these commercial dairymen only 559,000 were what might be called specialized: they derived more than half of their income from the sale of milk or other dairy products.

In 1949 approximately 23 million cows were milked, and 122 billion pounds of milk were produced. The sale value of all dairy products and of livestock sold from dairy herds represented 19 per cent of the total value of all marketed farm products. The total value of physical assets associated with milk production on farms (including real estate, equipment, and livestock) totaled 21 per cent of the value of all physical assets for farm production in the nation. (Reference 5; p. 1964.) The manner in which the 122 billion pounds of milk were disposed of is indicated in Figure 20:4.

As noted in the above chart, 35.8 million pounds were marketed as Class 1 (whole) milk. This represented about 36 per cent of all the market milk produced. In other words, almost two thirds of the nation's marketed production fell into the Class 2 category. It is this heavy preponderance, entering a depressed market, that has caused economic distress in the specialized dairy areas of the Great Lakes states. In the Corn Belt and other agricultural regions, where dairying is not the major type of farming, the low prices paid for Class 2 milk are not matters of serious regional concern. However, the low value of Class 2 milk is a matter of concern to all individual farmers wherever they may be, particularly if that type of livestock husbandry is essential to a sound soil-management and conservation program.

We have already noted that the best crop rotations and soil-management practices in the Corn Belt are performed by those farmers who do some dairying, even though it is a secondary enterprise on their properties. Of the major types of farming, dairying is one that is most conducive to good soil-conservation practices. This is because of the large quantities of good perennial meadows which are needed for hay and pasture. The dairy cow is not a rugged animal; pastures must be of

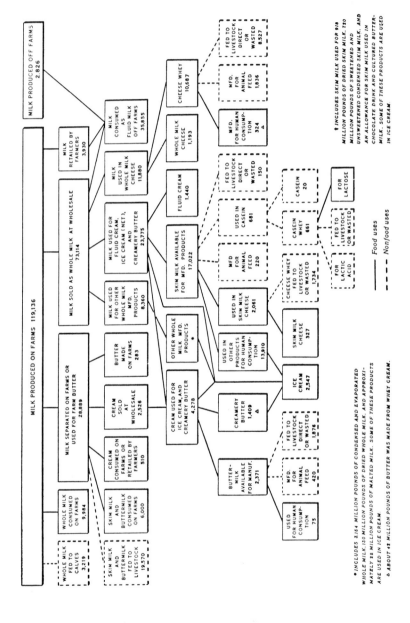

Figure 20·4. Sources and uses of milk. (Source: Reference 5; 1968.)

good quality so that she will not have to expend much energy grazing. Hay must be of high nutritional value, or expensive concentrates will be needed in larger amounts to compensate for deficiencies in the roughage. To maintain meadows of high quality requires the best field management. The dividend is good soil conservation.

Specialized Dairy Region of the Northeastern States. This region includes New England, New York, and Pennsylvania, as well as portions of New Jersey, Maryland, Delaware, West Virginia, Virginia, and Ohio. There are fewer dairy cows in this region than in either the middlewestern lake states dairy area or the Corn Belt. However, it is the most densely populated part of our nation. The significance of fewer cows and more people is obvious. A larger share of the milk produced is marketed as Class 1, and dairying is more profitable. There are several distinctions between the conditions and methods of dairy farming in New England and in the middlewestern Great Lakes area. In New England very little grain is raised on the farms. Instead, most of these concentrates are purchased, chiefly from the Corn Belt. There are several reasons for this. The topography of most of New England is rough. Tillable fields with good, deep loams are interspersed with areas of wooded terrain, steep slopes, thin or gravelly soils, and also with places where boulders are thickly strewn.

As a consequence, the average New England dairy farm has less cropped land than the average dairy farm in Wisconsin and Minnesota. Also, the individual fields are smaller. With a low proportion of tilled land per farm unit, it is more profitable for the New England dairyman to use this land for meadows than to devote it to grain. Cattle consume much smaller amounts of grain than they do of hay or pasturage. The cost of shipping grain into New England from the Corn Belt is not great. In fact, Corn Belt grain can be bought in New England for just about what it would cost the average eastern hill farmer to raise it himself— if he had the land. The Corn Belt grain farmer, as we have seen, is a specialist. He can produce about four times as much corn per man-hour as the typical New Englander because he has better soil, larger fields, more mechanized equipment, and warmer summers. The average cost of production of corn in the Corn Belt is about one third of that in New England.

The New England dairyman has an advantage over the Minnesota-Wisconsin dairyman when it comes to forage crops and pastures. The average annual rainfall in New England is heavier. Summers are cooler, spring and autumn are warmer, and the frost-free growing season is longer. With proper management of grasslands, a longer grazing season and higher yields of hay are possible in New England. Pasture and hay

Table 20:4. Average Value of Production per Man-Hour of Labor, 1935–1939
(Source: Reference 1, p. 38)

Item	New England Dollars	Middle Atlantic Dollars	East North Central Dollars	West North Central Dollars	South Atlantic Dollars	East South Central Dollars	West South Central Dollars	Moun-tain Dollars	Pacific Dollars	United States Dollars
Feed grains	0.46	0.60	0.95	0.83	0.30	0.31	0.36	0.65	1.11	0.60
Hay	1.42	1.35	0.93	0.67	0.91	0.80	0.55	0.70	1.05	0.83
Food grains	—	0.85	1.02	1.15	0.61	0.55	1.33	1.13	2.03	1.11
Trucks crops and gardens	0.58	0.66	0.48	0.32	0.69	0.41	0.36	0.66	0.96	0.55
Vegetables, except truck	1.80	1.21	0.91	0.91	0.79	0.67	0.63	1.08	1.55	0.99
Fruits and nuts	0.69	0.61	0.54	0.36	0.70	0.49	0.36	0.58	0.58	0.57
Sugar crops	0.63	0.77	0.50	0.54	0.28	0.22	0.35	0.60	0.85	0.44
Cotton	—	—	—	0.30	0.26	0.27	0.29	0.45	0.58	0.28
Tobacco	1.10	0.51	0.42	0.48	0.37	0.48	0.26	—	—	0.41
Oil crops	—	1.06	1.51	1.31	0.30	0.22	0.26	0.96	2.05	0.52
All crops	0.93	0.78	0.86	0.79	0.39	0.34	0.36	0.74	0.81	0.55
Milk cows[1]	0.75	0.75	0.51	0.36	0.55	0.39	0.40	0.48	0.72	0.50
Meat animals[1]	1.31	1.82	2.54	2.31	1.43	1.50	1.29	1.27	1.33	1.88
Poultry[1]	2.10	1.60	1.14	0.92	1.22	0.89	0.90	1.12	1.38	1.13
All meat animals and animal products[1]	1.00	0.98	0.94	0.91	0.87	0.70	0.73	0.85	0.97	0.89
All meat animals and animal products[2]	0.49	0.47	0.39	0.35	0.35	0.29	0.28	0.32	0.43	0.36
Gross farm production	0.60	0.55	0.54	0.50	0.34	0.29	0.31	0.53	0.62	0.43

[1] Gross livestock production per hour of labor; includes product added plus the value of feed and pasture consumed.
[2] Product added per hour of labor.

are the cheapest feed for cattle.   Therefore, the expense of purchased concentrates is partially offset by cheaper home-grown roughages.

The specialized New England dairyman usually keeps more cows than his counterpart in Wisconsin or Minnesota, but he does less field work. The average Wisconsin dairyman would not be impressed by the roadside appearance of the usual New England dairy farm.   He would see more woods than fields, and most barns would look old and dilapidated by comparison with his own.   He would, however, admire the pastures and hayfields; most of all he would envy the prices paid for milk, which are over 50 per cent higher than those he receives at home.

It may be seen by reference to Table 20:4 that the New England farmer makes more money per man-hour by producing hay than any other farmer in the nation, but he is one of the least successful in producing feed grains.   He is, on the whole, one of the best paid dairymen. His asset is an attractive supply-demand ratio.   The largest proportion of the milk produced in New England sells as Class 1, yet not all of New England's dairymen are well-off, by any means.   Important intraregional changes are taking place.   The owners of small farms and small herds are finding it difficult to modernize field and barn operations.   Many of them are going out of business.   The age of mechanization is eliminating dairymen just as it is eliminating other types of husbandmen who do not expand their output with labor-saving devices.   Between 1939 and 1954 the number of dairy farms in New England declined 32 per cent.   The more efficient, large-scale operators are increasing the size of their own properties, for there is much wooded and stony hill land in New England with good loam soils well suited to grassland agriculture.   It would not pay to reclaim this land in order to produce Class 2 milk. However, the market for Class 1 milk is gradually increasing as the population itself multiplies.   Rhode Island is the most densely populated state in the Union.   Massachusetts is third in population density and Connecticut is fourth.

Quite a few fine dairy farms in southern New England are going out of business as cities, villages, and rural housing developments take over the land.   The spread of human glaciation is particularly active in those exceptional districts of rather level-to-gently undulating surface relief. In the lower Connecticut Valley, for instance, the competition between suburbanization and the farm is gradually liquidating the latter between Hartford, Connecticut, and Springfield, Massachusetts.

A favorable supply-demand ratio helps the dairymen of New Jersey as well as those of northern Virginia, northern Delaware, central Maryland, and southeastern Pennsylvania.   This is because of the large urban markets—Washington, Baltimore, Philadelphia, and the industrial cities of northern New Jersey. The state of New York is something of an anomaly. It has the largest urban population, but it is also a leading dairy state. The net result is that it produces considerable Class 2 milk. Under the state marketing regulations producers are paid a blended price for their milk. That is, their total production goes into a pool. This pool is an accounting system rather than an actual physical entity. The farmers are paid Class 1 prices for the percentage of their deliveries which corresponds with the percentage of the state's total production marketed as Class 1; Class 2 prices are paid for the balance.

One result of this is that some farmers within easy access of the state's largest urban markets ship to manufacturers of processed dairy items in some nearby village. Other dairymen half-way across the state may ship into New York City to distributors of fluid milk and cream. Certain transportation differentials are paid, but each farmer receives the same blended or pool price for his product, regardless of destination. In effect, the milk-pool arrangement removes the locational advantage commonly enjoyed by those farmers who are closest to large urban fluid-milk markets. On the other hand, it helps those who are so far removed that they would normally have to market most of their production as Class 2. The New York dairyman, as noted in Figure 20:1, is not quite so well off as the New England producers because he has a higher percentage of Class 2 milk. He is in a stronger position than the farmers of Wisconsin and Minnesota because he produces a smaller percentage of Class 2 milk than they do. In the fifteen years between 1939 and 1954 the number of dairy farms in the state of New York declined 22 per cent.

The Specialized Dairy Region of the Western Great Lakes States. This region includes most of Wisconsin, Minnesota, and Michigan as well as small neighboring districts in northern Iowa, Illinois, and Indiana. It is the dairy center of the United States. With the Corn Belt, it is the source of most of the nation's Class 2 milk (Figure A-18). There are several reasons that farmers in this area have specialized in dairying, despite poor price incentives. P. E. McNall and W. J. Roth of the Wisconsin Agricultural Experiment Station stated some years ago:

> Farms of Wisconsin are mostly small in size. These small farms can give their operators larger incomes when the crop products are marketed through the dairy herd than would be possible if marketed directly. Dairy farming requires much labor. More hours of labor are required to take care of a dairy herd than for an equal number of other classes of livestock. This also increases the volume of business upon a given size farm and offers opportunity for larger farm incomes than would otherwise be possible.
> In a sense it may be said that other forces have induced a dairy type because they have prevented the growth of the other farm types. A Corn Belt type of

farming is impossible for most of Wisconsin not only because of rather poor soils and short growing seasons but also because of the cool summer temperatures. Wheat farming is not feasible due to relatively small acreages per farm and to small farm incomes when any appreciable portion of the farm is planted to the crop. Beef cattle and sheep as dominant farm enterprises, while physically possible, cannot offer effective competition to dairying in much of Wisconsin because of the small size of farm and the limited income possible from these types of farming as compared with the income possible from dairying.

Apparently most Wisconsin farmers will continue to milk cows because it fits in with ample pasture, forage crops, small grains, limited corn production and the opportunity to enlarge (income from) the rather small farm unit through this intensive type of farming. (Reference 2; p. 4.)

This statement could be applied to most of the middlewestern Great Lakes dairy region. Nevertheless, it should be qualified by mentioning that soils, topography, and even climate are all more favorable to intensive agriculture in southeastern Wisconsin, northeastern Illinois, and southern Michigan. The sections of the Great Lakes dairy region where climate, soils, and topography restrict most types of intensive crop cultivation are in northern Michigan, northern Wisconsin, central northeastern Minnesota, and also along the Mississippi River in southwestern Wisconsin and southeastern Minnesota. Even in these areas it is possible to find on most farms some acreage of both good soil and level-to-slightly-undulating topography.

Dairymen of the Great Lakes states who do not maintain large specialized farms have found a way to compensate somewhat for the small returns obtained by dairying. Many raise extra cash crops. These cash crops require a large amount of labor per acre and heavy fertilization, but the income per acre is correspondingly high. The dairy herd provides manure which is useful in the fertilization program. Labor is available because farms and dairy herds are ordinarily small. Almost every farm has a few acres of choice land which can be set aside for the favored cash crop. On dairy farms in different parts of these states one may find tobacco, peppermint, canning peas, cabbage for sauerkraut factories, cucumbers for pickling, sugar beets, potatoes, canning corn, market vegetables, orchard and cane fruits, Concord grapes, dry onions, canning beans, and canning tomatoes. A few acres of these cash crops are vital to the economic solvency of small dairy farms producing Class 2 milk. Many of them also have subsidiary livestock enterprises—a small flock of laying hens and usually a few hogs fed on dairy by-products, pasture, and some grain.

The average lake-states dairyman has a smaller proportion of cropland on his farm than any Corn Belt farmer outside Minnesota, but he has a higher proportion of cropland than the New England dairyman. To

Table 20:5.   Cropland Comparisons
(in millions of acres)
(Source: Reference 6; pp. 9 and 37)

Region	State	Crop-land	Non-forested Pasture	State Area	State Area in Farms	Cropland as Percentage of Total Land in Farms
Great Lakes Dairy	Wisconsin	10.7	4.6	35.0	23.2	46.1
	Minnesota	20.9	4.1	51.2	32.8	63.7
	Michigan	9.0	3.0	36.4	17.2	52.3
New England	Connecticut	0.36	0.28	3.13	1.2	30.0
	Rhode Island	0.055	0.038	0.677	0.191	34.5
	Massachusetts	0.47	0.25	5.03	1.66	28.9
Corn Belt	Iowa	22.9	6.8	35.8	34.2	66.9
	Illinois	21.3	4.8	35.7	30.9	68.9
	Indiana	11.7	3.5	23.1	19.6	60.0

make ends meet he must process his field crops through animals.   Because soils, topography, and climate oblige him to put much of his land in meadows dairy cattle are his best bet.   He must, however, raise nearly all of the concentrates the cattle require, for he is not in a financial position to buy as much supplementary feed as is the New Englander.

REFERENCES

1. Hecht, Ruben W. and Glen T. Barton, *Gains in Productivity of Farm Labor*, U.S. Department of Agriculture, Government Printing Office, Washington, D.C., 1950.
2. McNall, P. E. and W. J. Roth, *Forces Affecting Wisconsin Agriculture With Resulting Types of Farming*, Agricultural Experiment Station of the University of Wisconsin, Madison, 1935.
3. Miller, Earl E., *Regional Trends in Livestock Numbers*, Statistical Bulletin No. 146, U.S. Department of Agriculture, Government Printing Office, Washington, D.C., 1954.
4. U.S. Department of Agriculture, *Agricultural Prices*, Agricultural Marketing Service, Government Printing Office, Washington, D.C., 1956.
5. U.S. Department of Agriculture, *Changes in the Dairy Industry United States, 1920–50*, Bureau of Agricultural Economics, Government Printing Office, Washington, D.C., 1950.
6. Wooten, H. H., *Major Uses of Land in the United States (Supplement)*, U.S. Department of Agriculture, Government Printing Office, Washington, D.C., 1953.

soil
conservation
and
dairy
farming

21

The use of land for dairy farming can result in good soil conservation, but dairy farming in itself does not assure proper management of the land. For evidence that soil erosion occurs where dairying is the major type of farming one may refer to the map of soil erosion in the United States (Figure 17:2). The dairy areas of southern Wisconsin, southern Michigan, and central Minnesota have lost between 25 and 75 per cent of their topsoil. With the exception of New England, moderate to severe erosion has also occurred in the northeastern dairy region.

The most efficient and economical system of feeding the dairy cow is likely to result in proper care of the soil. As we have noted previously, soil erosion seldom occurs on a field which is covered with a good sod of perennial grasses and legumes. Dairy cattle can derive most of their needed total digestible nutrients (T.D.N.) from these roughages when they are of high quality. That pasture and hay are also the cheapest feeds a cow can eat is shown by the data of Table 21:1, published by the Michigan Agricultural Experiment Station.

Table 21:1.   Cost of Feeds Fed and Cost per Pound of T.D.N., 1945–1949
(Source: Reference 6; p. 31)

Kind of Feed	Pounds Fed per Cow		Per Cent of Total T.D.N.	Cost of Feed	Cost per Pound T.D.N.
	Total	T.D.N.			
Concentrates	3,033	2,275	32	$ 81.32	$0.036
Hay	4,183	2,091	30	40.16	0.019
Silage	5,034	754	11	17.96	0.024
Other roughage	278	42	1	1.00	0.024
Subtotal	12,528	5,162	74	$140.94	—
Pasture	152 days	1,870	26	20.73	0.011
Total	—	7,032	100	$162.17	0.023

It is just as possible to make good silage from grasses and legumes as to prepare it from corn. The advantage of grass-legume silage from the standpoint of soil conservation, particularly in hilly country, is known to every farmer, although corn is still commonly used. One reason for the continued use of corn is that it will grow on acid soils, and many legumes will not. In the humid regions of the country both ground limestone and superphosphate must be applied to the soil if legumes such as alfalfa and ladino clover are to be established successfully. There are still many dairy farmers who try to get by without lime and who depend chiefly upon barnyard manure for fertilizer. The manure of the dairy cow is low in phosphate because much of that fraction of her diet goes into milk and calves. When she herself is sold in her old age, additional phosphate goes with her in her bones. Without legumes and grasses of good quality for hay, silage, and pasturage, the dairy cow must be fed more corn and small grains in order to supply the T.D.N.'s which are deficient in roughages of poor quality.

It is possible that all pastures and at least one half to two thirds of the cropland on the average northern dairy farm could be kept in perennial grasses and legumes to supply cattle with proper feed. With little risk of serious soil erosion, the remainder of the cropland could be sown to corn and small grains. A few acres might be reserved for cash crops if they are essential to the farm economy. Such a balance between perennial and annual crops would permit the adoption of a convenient strip-crop program. When slopes do not undulate too severely the strips should conform to the contours of the land.

Many dairymen in the North like to turn their cattle to graze on hayfields after the second cutting and on new stands of hay after small-grain nurse crops have been harvested. By dividing hilly cultivated land

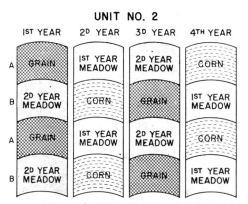

Figure 21:1. A two-unit and four-year rotation schedule for strip-cropped fields. (Source: Reference 4; p. 24.)

A 4-year rotation of corn, grain, meadow, meadow, by strips in a 2-field arrangement. Each year alternate strips are in corn and meadow in one field and grain and meadow in the other.

into two major units and by using a four year rotation, such as corn-small grain-meadow-meadow, it is possible to utilize half of the crop-land as pasture any time following the harvest of the small grain. Such an arrangement eliminates the need to fence individual strips, since one permanent fence around the whole unit suffices. The manner in which cropland can be conveniently rotated and strip-cropped by division into two major units is illustrated in the chart (Figure 21:1) prepared by the U.S. Department of Agriculture.

The two-unit and four-field rotation schedule illustrated in Figure 21:1 is one of many possible solutions to the field division and rotation puzzle which each farmer must solve according to the character of his own farm.

There are several advantages to a contour strip-crop field pattern. All tillage operations are done at close-to-level position rather than up and down hill. The plow furrows, being on the contour, serve as small dams to hold water on the land. In up-and-down-hill farming these same furrows serve as small channels to speed water runoff. Since soil is removed from cultivated fields in proportion to the speed and volume of runoff, a system of contour cropping which has a sod strip between every strip of corn or small grain is ideal. This balance of sod and annual crops is possible in dairy farming because it fits in with the feeding program. When a meadow strip lies between two strips planted to annual crops it serves to trap soil which may be carried off the open field above. Gullies are also checked by the sod, and the quantity of runoff waters is somewhat reduced because there is a smaller proportion of runoff from sodded fields than from corn and grain fields.

The majority of northern dairymen own small farms of 80 to 200 acres. As we noted in the table at the end of the preceding chapter (Table 20:5), cropland on the average dairy farm is generally half or less of the total area. With a small farm and a low percentage of fine cropland, the operator can best increase his income by feeding the produce of his limited fields to the dairy cow. The Wisconsin Agricultural Experiment Station has determined that, "The dairy cow requires in the neighborhood of 150 man-hours of labor per year. Her labor requirement is higher than for any other farm animal. The cost of labor is second to the cost of feed in the annual cost of keeping a dairy cow." (Reference 5; p. 5.) Because of this high labor input per cow the value of milk is high compared with the value of the feed which the cow eats.

We have noted that in New England the value of milk is such that it does not pay the average dairyman to raise any grain. It is cheaper for him to buy these concentrates and to use his time to take care of more cows. Most dairymen close to Los Angeles buy all feed for milking cows. Almost all their time is spent with their animals. Many of them hire helpers who do nothing else but milk cows twice a day for four hours at a stretch with the latest mechanical devices. These professional milkers take their positions in the milking parlors much as factory workers take their positions at lathes and punches. They do not live on the farms and their wages are higher than the net income of most Wisconsin dairymen who operate their own units.

Because the greatest profit in dairying is made by caring for the animals rather than by raising the feed for them, the most efficient farmers are those who raise the best feeds at the lowest cost in terms of man-hours. Perennial grasses and legumes for pasture, hay, and silage are preferred by these operators. As indicated by the data in

Table 21:2. Annual Soil and Water Losses from Row Crops, Small-Grain and Meadow Crops Grown in Rotations, and the Average for the Rotation of Crops. (Soil and Water Conservation Experiment Stations of Soil Conservation Service[1])

(Source: Reference 4; p. 18)

Location, Slope, and Period	Cotton		Corn		Small Grain		Meadow Crops		Average of Rotation	
	Soil Loss per Acre Tons	Water Loss as Compared with Precipitation Per Cent	Soil Loss per Acre Tons	Water Loss as Compared with Precipitation Per Cent	Soil Loss per Acre Tons	Water Loss as Compared with Precipitation Per Cent	Soil Loss per Acre Tons	Water Loss as Compared with Precipitation Per Cent	Soil Loss per Acre Tons	Water Loss as Compared with Precipitation Per Cent
Zanesville, Ohio, 12 per cent slope, 1934–1940			42.7	24.8	9.8	25.8	0.35[2]	17.2[2]	13.3	21.2
Bethany, Mo., 8 per cent slope, 1931–1940			18.8	19.7	7.3	18.5	1.1	10.4	9.1	16.2
LaCrosse, Wis., 16 per cent slope, 1933–1938			53.1	20.6	30.0	18.8	0.9	11.2	28.0	16.9
Guthrie, Okla., 7 per cent slope, 1930–1938	10.6	11.3	30.2	10.3	1.4	12.4	0.5	6.8	4.2	10.2
Statesville, N.C., 10 per cent slope, 1932–1938	23.2	9.9			5.6	13.1	1.6	3.9	15.1	9.3

[1]Investigations conducted in cooperation with the respective state experiment stations.

Rotations:
Zanesville—Corn, wheat, meadow, meadow.
Bethany—Corn, wheat, timothy and clover.
LaCross—Corn, wheat, clover.
[2]Average for first- and second-year meadow.

Guthrie—Cotton, wheat, sweetclover.
Statesville—Cotton, corn, wheat, lespedeza.

Table 21:1 from the Michigan Agricultural Experiment Station, two thirds of the T.D.N.'s required by a dairy cow can be supplied with legumes and grasses at a price which is one half the cost of T.D.N.'s provided by grain concentrates.

A WISCONSIN DAIRY FARM WITH
CROPLAND IN CONTOUR STRIPS

This farm is located in the unglaciated bluff and coulee section of LaCrosse County, Wisconsin, not far from the village of Coon Valley. It consists of 52 acres of cropland, 36 acres of permanent pasture, 46 acres of woods, and a 4-acre houselot. This farm carries an average of 14 head of milk cows and about 7 head of young stock for replacement. In addition, it keeps an average of 2 sows and their litters and a flock of less than 100 hens.

A soil survey made in 1933 indicated that most of the cultivated land had lost one fourth to all of the original topsoil, and there were many gullies which could not be crossed with machinery. Since that time soil erosion on this farm has been reduced to a minimum by better management. Some of the pastures have been improved by liming, by using commercial fertilizers, and by disking and reseeding to legumes and better grasses. All crop fields are contour stripped. A very conservative rotation of corn followed by small grains and three years of legume-grass meadows assures maintenance of humus and very little erosion. The cropland is divided into units so that every year there is an average of 10 acres each of corn and small grains and 30 acres of hay and rotation pasture.

The contour strips on this farm are rotated so that there is always a strip of perennial hay between strips of corn or small grains. Also, at least one entire unit of cropland is in hay at all times for use as emergency pasture if necessary. Most of the contour strips are of even width; this is particularly desirable in the year corn is planted. The terraces are an added precaution against the redevelopment of gulleys which once did great damage to this property. Although the contour-strip design, together with the rotation scheme, may seem complicated, the principle is actually simple. Most dairy farmers in hilly country who have tried this system of land management contend that their soil is now more productive than before the new pattern was adopted. They carry more livestock and they find the field work easier. Needless to say, their profits have increased because hay and pasture of good quality are the cheapest and best feeds for dairy cattle.

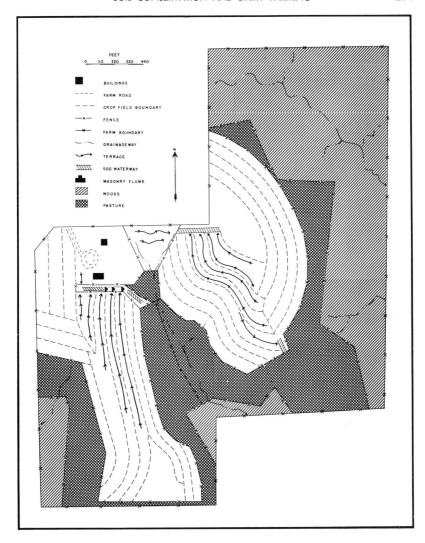

Figure 21:2.   Contour-cultivated farm in Wisconsin driftless area.

A DAIRY AND WHEAT FARM IN THE
FINGER LAKES AREA OF NEW YORK

In hilly country there are areas of gentle slopes and flat land. The problems of land management change with the changes in topography and soils. The Finger Lakes district in northwestern New York is a

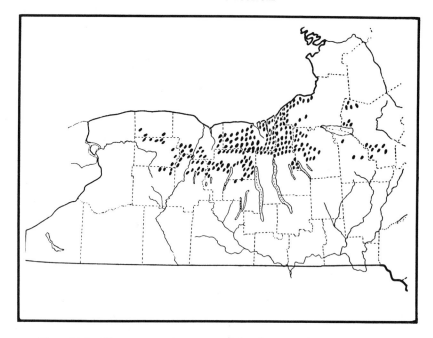

Figure 21:3.   The more prominent areas of drumlins in northwestern New York.

glaciated area in which the surface of the land varies from flat to steep. Drumlins, or hills of glacial till, are a conspicuous feature of the landscape, particularly to the north of the Finger Lakes.

These drumlins may rise 150 to 200 feet above the level of the intervales between them, and their sides may be cultivated when they are not too steep.   Subsoils are often compact and do not admit water readily. In such cases even sloping land must be provided with tile drains.   These same side hills may require strip cropping to prevent soil erosion.   The problem of water removal is even greater in the intervales where the land is nearly level.   Twenty-two per cent of the farm land in Cayuga County has soil that is poorly drained, but much of this land can be made highly productive by drainage and proper management.   Dairying is the major farm enterprise in the Finger Lakes area, although orchards and vineyards are common, particularly on the lake shores.   Most dairy farms raise some cash crops.

Figure 21:4 is a 100-acre dairy farm which also produces dairy stock and wheat for cash sale.   Although this is a smaller farm and has less cropland and pasture than the Wisconsin example already considered, its soil is more productive.   It has been in the same family since it was settled in 1837 and shows the effects of good care.   Soil erosion has been slight.   It carries 21 milking cows and could support 10 more.   However, the operator raises dairy heifers for sale in New England and New Jersey instead of keeping the maximum number of mature cows.   Many farmers in New England and New Jersey do not raise their own herd replacements.   They prefer to buy them from New York, Canada, Wisconsin, and Minnesota where cattle prices are comparatively low.

The hill land on this New York farm is of gentle slope.   It is strip cropped, but the strips do not exactly adhere to the contour, and strips of hay do not alternate with strips of annual crops.   To reduce the hazard of erosion a diversion ditch is constructed across the upper portion of the cultivated land to carry away surface runoff waters so that the fields below will not be damaged.   The land above the diversion ditch is tile-drained to remove excess moisture within the soil.   Other drainage facilities are indicated on the map.   The lowland pastures were swampy until they were drained by means of sodded ditches.   Now planted to brome grass, ladino clover, fescue, and Reed canary grass, they are the most productive land on the farm.

Although there are only 43 acres of cropland and 43 acres of permanent pasture, so much feed is produced for the cattle that 10 acres of cropland are sown to wheat for cash sale.   The basic rotation on the cultivated fields is corn-wheat-oats-hay.   Fields and pastures are well limed and heavily fertilized with commercial fertilizers and barnyard manure.

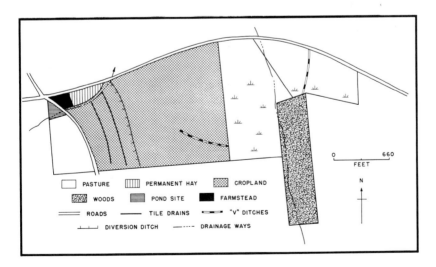

Figure 21:4.   A New York dairy farm in the Finger Lakes district.

Very heavy yields per acre, obtained by expert management, make this farm remarkable, for its soils and topographic character are not the best. There are many properties with similar physical resources in northwestern New York which produce only half as well.

A SPECIALIZED DAIRY FARM IN CENTRAL MASSACHUSETTS

Soil erosion is slight in the six New England states for two reasons: (1) only about 13 per cent of the total rural land is used for crops and pasture; and (2) perennial hays cover 86 per cent of the total harvested cropland. (Reference 3; p. 32.) Dairying, of course, is the major type of farm enterprise, although a number of specialty items, such as potatoes, tobacco, market vegetables, canning crops, and fruits, are produced. Commercial poultry and hog production in New England should scarcely be considered as types of farming in the conventional sense. This is because the methods used resemble factory procedures. The techniques of the textile mills have been brought to the barnyard. The principal commercial poultrymen do not cultivate any land at all, and they buy all feeds, chiefly from the Corn Belt. Broilers are raised by the thousands in feeding sheds. Egg-laying hens, deprived of a country life, are kept in nest-and-roost apartments which they never leave until they are culled and slaughtered. This type of poultry husbandry could be conducted on Main Street as efficiently as on County Road 1A. Only cheaper building sites and lower taxes make this a rural rather than an urban activity. For the most part, swine are adjuncts to municipal sanitation departments, being raised by the holders of garbage-collection contracts. This method of swine husbandry bears little resemblance to those practiced in the Corn Belt. It is a by-product industry stimulated by the clusters of large cities and satellite towns which contribute the feed and buy back the pork. The efficient use of scrap materials is considered a primary feature of modern industry. A comparable recycling technique is here applied to animal husbandry.

Among the wooded hills of New England one will find modern dairy farms, sometimes singly, sometimes in clusters. Their fine meadows of fescue, orchard grass, and ladino clover are in sharp contrast to the surrounding woodlands of sprout-growth hardwoods intermingled with some white pine, spruce, and hemlock. Not all dairy farms in New England are so well developed as these models of modern grassland management, but the trend of commercial farms is strongly in that direction. On the other hand, those farms with small herds and poor meadows are rapidly going out of business.

The reasons are many for the increase in large commercial dairy farms

Figure 21:5.   A central Massachusetts dairy farm.

and the decline of small-herd enterprises.   Increased labor efficiency on
the former is perhaps the major reason.   It is now possible for one man
to care for 35 to 40 milking cows in addition to doing the chores for the
dry cows and the young replacement stock.   This is done with mechanical milking parlors and automatic hay-feeding racks in stanchionless
barns.   Drive-in, concrete-lined ground silos permit rapid removal of
silage with tractor-operated front-end loaders.   The excellent quality of
pastures for seven or eight months of the year in southern New England
is the result in part of adequate and well-distributed rainfall.   Good
management is man's contribution.

Figure 21:5 is the land-use map of a 160-acre dairy farm in Worcester

County, Massachusetts. No hogs, chickens, or sheep are raised. This is strictly a specialized dairy operation. All concentrate feeds are purchased because the farmer's time is more profitably spent with his cattle than if it were used to raise grain. The land is better suited to the production of good pasture and hay than to the cultivation of corn and oats. No roughages are purchased, yet 65 animal units are carried on 64 acres of dual-purpose, hay-pasture meadows and 51 acres of permanent pasture. The 65 animal units are made up of 50 milk cows and 30 head of young replacement stock. More than half of the meadow lands were cleared from scrub woodlots by the use of bulldozers and power-driven tree rakes. Stones were removed with heavy equipment, and the soils limed and heavily fertilized. Only the short growing season limits their usefulness as pastures. However, they produce excellent hay and silage for winter use.

LAND CLEARING

White men have farmed in New England for three hundred years. In 1860 the area cultivated reached its peak. Since that time over half of the improved land has reverted to woods and scrub growth. There are several reasons for this drastic decline. Until 1880 most farms were of a subsistence nature, although such self-sustaining units did sell surpluses. The national development of commercial agriculture made these farms obsolete. Also, industrial development began early in New England, and good job opportunities persuaded many hill farmers to abandon the plow. Poor and stony soils have often been cited as the cause of the agricultural decline in New England, but examination of much of the land does not confirm this opinion. Thousands of acres which had been cleared of stones were later abandoned. The soils cleared by the pioneer farmers were not generally poor. They were acid and low in fertility but they would have responded to good care. According to historical records they did not receive good care at the hands of most subsistence farmers. In *American Husbandry*, a classic account of early American agriculture, we find such comments as the following about farming in New England.

Worse ploughing is no where to be seen, yet the farmers get tolerable crops; this is owing, particularly in the new settlements, to the looseness and fertility of old woodlands, which, with very bad tillage, will yield excellent crops: a circumstance the rest of the province is apt to be guided by, for seeing the effects, they are apt to suppose the same treatment will do on land long since broken up, which is far enough from being the case. Thus, in most parts of the province, is found shallow and unlevel furrows, which rather scratch than turn

Figure 21:6.   Acreage of improved land on southern New England farms in the census years 1850–1940. (Source: Reference 2; p. 12.)

the land; and of this bad tillage the farmers are very sparing, rarely giving two ploughings if they think the crop will do with one; the consequence of which is their products being seldom near so great as they would be under a different management.   (Reference 1; pp. 59–60.)

To this day many New England farms produce little or nothing for the commercial market.   They are homes in the country and the part-time interests of owners who hold other jobs.   As with all farmers in the United States, the contemporary New Englander who wishes to make a full-time commercial business of dairying must enlarge the scale of his operations.   He must utilize the technological improvements which make possible an increased production per man-hour.   Progressive dairymen are now reclearing previously abandoned fields and bringing them back into production.   Thousands of acres of second-growth woods have been replaced with fine meadows.   In the days of oxen and horses some fields strewn with glacial boulders were never entirely cleared of these impediments.   Now they are removed economically by bulldozers, so that tractor-drawn, high-speed implements may be utilized.

The cost of clearing land and filling in stump holes and pits, which are left after boulders are extracted, usually amounts to $75 to $150 per acre. To make such an investment pay the soil must be made as productive as possible with lime, commercial fertilizer, and the seeds of the most desirable legumes and grasses. The Maine Agricultural Experiment Station reports that 2.5 acres of well-managed grassland will provide the roughage requirements for a dairy cow and her young for an entire year.° The pasture season may be extended from May to November. Meadows of ladino clover and timothy can be used for both hay and pasturage. Considering the relatively heavy and well-distributed rainfall in New England, there is no better natural grassland country in the northeastern states. Only the shorter growing season makes it inferior to the southeastern states.

REFERENCES

1. Anonymous, *American Husbandry*, Harry J. Carman (Ed.), Columbia University Press, New York, 1939 (the original published by J. Bew, London, 1775).
2. Fowler, Herbert C., *The Competitive Position of Dairying in Southern New England*, U.S. Department of Agriculture and the Massachusetts Agricultural Experiment Station, Government Printing Office, Washington, D.C., 1942.
3. Swanson, C. L. W., et al., *The Changing Fertility of New England Soils*, Joint Publication of the Agricultural Experiment Stations of Connecticut, Maine, Massachusetts, New Hampshire, Rhode Island, and Vermont, 1952 (mimeographed).
4. Tower, Harold E. and Harry H. Gardner, *Strip Cropping for Conservation and Production*, U.S. Department of Agriculture, Washington, D.C., 1953.
5. Witzel, S. A., et al., *Dairy Cattle Housing*, Agricultural Experiment Station, University of Wisconsin, Madison, 1950.
6. Wright, K. T. and T. L. Hodge, *Dairying for Profit in Southern Michigan*, Michigan State College Agricultural Experiment Station, East Lansing, 1951.
7. Fink, D. S., *Grassland Experiments*, the Maine Agricultural Experiment Station, Orono, 1943.

°"The dairy farmer of the future will make only limited, if any, use of native pasture, because other grassland crops produce more milk per acre and are more easily managed than native white clover and bluegrass. Not more than one-half acre per cow of excellent native pasture can be efficiently used on the dairy farm. This amount of improved native pasture will feed both milk cows and young stock during May and June, and feed the young stock for the remainder of the season. Annual applications of plant foods giving 60 pounds of nitrogen (N), phosphoric acid (P_2O_5), and potash (K_2O) will maintain excellent native pasture in high production.

"The first crop from two acres per cow of ladino clover grown in association with timothy, will meet the winter roughage requirement of a dairy cow and her young stock, and the subsequent growth will furnish abundant excellent milch cow pasture from the first part of July until November. Annual applications of eight tons of manure, fortified with superphospate, per acre will maintain ladino-timothy in excellent production over long periods.

"Ladino-timothy aftermath pasture, following the removal of the first crop for hay or silage, surpasses any other pasture crop, for milch cows, studied to date." (Source: Reference 7; p. 226.)

general
farming
in the
eastern
uplands

22

The areas characterized by general farming in Figure 4:2 are too diverse in their physical features to be treated as a unit. Therefore, the discussion in this chapter applies only to the hills and valleys of the Ozark-Appalachian province. This is the dominant region of general farming in the United States. Scattered areas of general farming on the coastal plain are considered with other agricultural districts in subsequent discussions.

General farming is a term used to indicate that no single type of crop or livestock husbandry is outstanding within a region. Such a definition is relative, for we have noted in previous discussions of other agricultural regions that there is diversity within all of them. There are also specialized farms in the general farming region, but the very variety of specialties from dairying to tobacco culture and from poultry husbandry to orcharding necessitates composite designation. The Ozark-Appalachian general farming region is an exceptionally good one for microgeographic studies of land use. However diverse the uses of land may be, the basic influences upon those uses are

1. Topography and soils.
2. Distances from markets.
3. Sizes of farms.
4. Alternative opportunities for employment.

TOPOGRAPHY AND SOILS

Topography is the major arbiter of farm activity in the Ozark-Appalachian country. Intensive cultivation without soil erosion is impossible if the uplands are severely dissected, the slopes steep, and the soils both poor and shallow. Areas of gentle slope with deep soils are usually small and scattered, but there are a few exceptional valleys and basins of notable size. In general, it may be said that for each few acres of tillable soil on the average upland farm there are many acres suited only to woods and pasture. Often the soils on the steeper slopes are sandy as well as shallow, and even tree growth may be poor. Some pastures are established on slopes which should not have been cleared because the soils are inferior. Consequently, the sods are thin and erosion occurs even under moderate usage.

In pioneer days, when most of these lands were settled, subsistence farming rather than commercial production was the prime objective of the cultivator. In those times of hand-hoe and horse agriculture, when 10 or 15 acres of cultivated crops were all a family needed to sustain itself, the hilly eastern uplands were an ideal environment for homesteading. A few patches of tillable land could generally be found on the knolls and in the coves. The more extensive wooded areas on steep land harbored small game and could be used as pasture for a few head of livestock. From the beginning of white settlement conditions have been very different in valley and basin bottoms and on gentler piedmont slopes. There, soils are usually superior and with good care may be kept productive. The major distinction between farms and between farmers is whether they are located in the hilly uplands or in the basins and valleys.

All states have some rough nonagricultural land as well as some which is desirable for cultivation. However, there are great differences in the respective endowments of different states. For instance, important sections of Kentucky are suitable for intensive agriculture because of favorable topography and soils. The reverse is true of West Virginia, which is mostly hilly upland. Let us consider the statistics.

Table 22:1 shows a drastic difference between the land base of the average farm in the heart of the Corn Belt and the average farm in the

**Table 22:1.   Statistical Aspects of Farming in Two Appalachian States
and a Comparison With One in the Corn Belt—1945**
(Source: Reference 1; pp. 52–53, 60–61, 64–65)

	Regions		
	General Farming		Corn Belt
	West Virginia	Kentucky	Iowa
Percentage of total state area which is in farms	56.4	76.9	93.2
Percentage of total state area which is in cropland	12.3	40.2	69.5
Average amount of cropland per farm in state	20.0	43.2	119.0
Percentage of farms which are less than 70 acres in size	58.0	56.7	15.5
Percentage of farms producing less than $1000 worth of crops and livestock	76.8	52.6	12.3
Percentage of farms producing chiefly for home use	66.0	34.5	4.6
Percentage of farm operators who work at jobs away from the farm more than 100 days a year	39.7	18.6	5.6

heart of the Appalachian general farming region.   But the table reflects
more than that.   There are differences as well as similarities between
Kentucky and West Virginia.   A larger proportion of Kentucky is in
farms, and there is a greater amount of cropland per farm than in West
Virginia.   Kentucky has a smaller proportion of subsistence farms and a
smaller proportion of part-time farmers.   The major statistical similarity
between the two states is the large percentage of small farms in each.

The finest agricultural district in Kentucky is its famous limestone
basin known as the Bluegrass.   In Figure 4:2 it is designated as a
tobacco area.   Within it are also some of the finest dairy, beef, and race-
horse farms in the nation.   The Bluegrass, we will remember, was the
first western corn-hog center before the emergence of the present Corn
Belt.   The Bluegrass, as well as the smaller Nashville basin in Tennessee, was an outlier of concentrated pioneer settlement as early as 1790.

The finest farming districts in the Appalachian country were from the
beginning of man's occupancy right where they are today—in the limestone valleys and basins.   This was just as true of Indian times as it is
now.   The Indians did not cultivate much land, but they did systematically burn the dry natural vegetation of certain Appalachian

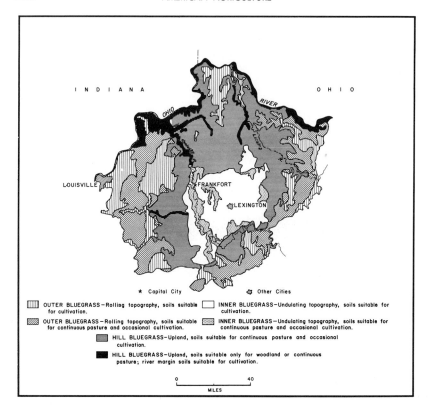

Figure 22:1.   Land types of the Bluegrass. (Source: Reference 4.)

regions to suppress woody growth and to encourage grass for the deer
and buffalo.   In a sense they were animal husbandmen even though their
livestock were not domesticated.   Samuel Kercheval, historian of the
Great Valley of Virginia, recorded over a 100 years ago what he had
learned from conversations with some of the first settlers in that limestone
district.

   At the first settling the Valley was one vast prairie, and like the rich prairies
of the west, afforded the finest possible pasturage for wild animals.   The country abounded in the larger kinds of game. . . .   These prairies had an artificial
cause.   At the close of each hunting season the Indians fired the open ground,
and thus kept it from reverting to woodland.   This was done to attract the
buffalo, an animal that shuns the forest.   The progressive deforesting of the
lowlands of the Valley made the settlement by the whites very easy and rapid.
(Reference 3; p. 52.)

It is important to note that Kercheval refers to the lowlands of the Valley. These lowlands are chiefly limestone, sometimes shale. If one traces the progress of early white settlement in the Appalachians and the Ozarks, one discovers that the limestone depressions were the areas favored by the pioneers. Although the soils are sometimes shallow, they are productive under good management. They are exceptionally good for pasturage, as present landowners will testify—a confirmation of an earlier judgment by the aborigine. When one looks into the historical accounts of the first explorations in the major limestone districts of the eastern states one is impressed by the descriptions of meadows and park lands in those areas. Usually one finds some reference to the fact that the Indians deliberately maintained grassy areas by using fire to suppress tree growth. This was true not only in the Great Valley, but also in the Bluegrass, the Nashville basin, and on the calcareous till and loess plains of the present Corn Belt.

The surface relief of the limestone lowlands is usually undulating to rolling. There are occasional areas of rough terrain, little suited to intensive use, where dissection by solution and geologic erosion has been severe. There are also areas of cherty limestone which may have very uneven surfaces. In general, however, the limestone lands are such that a high percentage is usable for tillage and good pasture. Today commercial farming is dominant in these better Appalachian-Ozark districts as it was from the time of the first white settlement.

The upland flanks and knobbed hills of the Appalachian-Ozark valleys are chiefly sandstone and shale, occasionally cherty limestones. The terrain of the sandstone areas is often rough with steep slopes, and the soils are poor and generally unsuited to tillage or pasture. They are best maintained in woodland in order to reduce the amount of runoff into the valleys below. Erosion and flood damage can be severe where the sandstone uplands are deforested or where the woodlands are heavily grazed. Grazing in woodlands packs tight the otherwise spongelike soils of the forest floor. In a tramped condition these soils are not absorptive. One of the primary efforts of the Tennessee Valley Authority in its cooperation with upland farmers has been to encourage exclusion of domestic livestock from wooded areas. To compensate for thus reducing the pasture acreage of the average farm, nitrogen and phosphate fertilizers have been manufactured and distributed at low cost to improve the productivity of bluegrass meadows.

Slopes of the shale uplands are gently undulating to steep. Soils are sometimes deep and suitable for pastures of high quality, but where the terrain is steep and forests have been removed much erosion has occurred. The majority of Appalachian pioneer families settled in the sandstone, shale, and cherty limestone sections of the uplands because they could not afford the better lands of the limestone valleys which were already occupied by the time they arrived. These uplands are the home of the modern mountaineer, or hillbilly, who is rapidly giving up a subsistence existence and turning to factory employment.

ALTERNATIVE OPPORTUNITIES FOR EMPLOYMENT

Agriculturally, the hill country of the eastern United States is even now influenced by its colonial past. At the time of North America's first white settlement most Europeans made their living by farming. The industrial age was yet unborn, and the era of transoceanic commerce had only begun. For those early immigrants who were without money but who wished to live independent lives, the prospect of holding a family homestead in fee simple was an ultimate objective. For most of them there could be no plantations at tidewater nor even commercial farms in the better valleys and basins beyond. For them, and they were the majority, there were the Appalachian uplands from New England to Georgia. They could go there and settle if they were able to make peace with the Indians or take the soil by force. They could not expect the enterprise or profits of businessmen, but they could expect an independent living on their subsistence farms—a situation impossible for people of their class in Europe.

From Maine to Alabama and westward to Kentucky and the Ozarks the hill country was eventually settled by pioneers skilled in the arts of self-subsistence in field, in forest, and by the hearth. Even in our own time one finds remnants of pioneer living on what are chiefly self-sustaining homesteads in the mountain and plateau uplands from New England southward. The cradle still harvests wheat in remote recesses of the hill country. Horse agriculture and the occasional ox are reminders that our pioneer past is not entirely obliterated. In terms of agricultural techniques and changing patterns of land use the upland peoples of Vermont, Arkansas, and Georgia have more in common than do the uplanders and valley dwellers within each of those states. Crops vary somewhat from north to south, but to this day the tiller of the coastal plain, the rich alluvial valleys, and the limestone basins is a more highly specialized producer of items for commercial markets than is the mountaineer who often is less dedicated to commercial farming than he is to other means of supplementing his living.

Industrial opportunity came early to New England. In 1792 the single Massachusetts county of Berkshire had a total of 233 small industries, most of them powered by water wheels. Like magnets they enticed the subsistence farmers out of the hills and into valley mill towns where they could earn cash and spend it.   In the southern and central mountain states the subsistence farmer waited longer before alternative opportunities of employment came close to home.   Topography had isolated him more surely than space had ever isolated the plainsman.   First came the industrialization of the Carolina piedmont and the improvement of living standards which resulted from factory pay.   Today the coves and ridges of the Cumberlands and Ouachitas no longer represent isolation or opportunity restricted to subsistence agriculture.   Concrete and black-top reach nearly everywhere.

The modern highway, power highline, and industry's invasion of the plateaus and mountains of the southern and central states are concluding an era that began two centuries ago in New England's hills.   The familiar competition between factory and farm for the subsistence home-steaders' labor is being repeated.   In fact, industry has gone to the mountains, not only because new roads and electric power made it feasible, but also because the hill country is one of the last reservoirs of able, underemployed man power in the United States.   Figure A-29 (Appendix) shows the distribution of noncommercial farms in the nation. The largest concentrations are in the highlands paralleling the upper Tennessee and Ohio valleys.   Western West Virginia, southeastern Ohio, eastern Kentucky and Tennessee, southwest Virginia, the western Carolinas, and northern Georgia have the largest proportion of sub-sistence and part-time farms.   The use of these farms is now rapidly changing because their owners, in increasing numbers, are becoming regular workmen at nearby factories.   A man can live in the country and drive his car twenty miles to a town job in less time than it once took him to hitch a team and drive a wagon to the back "forty."   He receives a pay check every week, buys his supplies at the store, and spends week ends hunting, fishing, and, sometimes farming a little.

SIZES OF FARMS

We have noted many times that with increased mechanization of farm operations a man cannot be fully employed on his land unless his acreage increases in proportion to the ability of machines to do the work.   To buy machines and to buy tillable land takes capital.   Few are the farmers in the Appalachian-Ozark uplands who have resources to undertake expansion, but among those who do there is now a growing interest in exploiting the best methods of grassland farming.   By buying-up the holdings of former subsistence farmers who are going out of business, the modern commercial farmer of the uplands is able to consolidate sufficient acreage to compete successfully with commercial farms in the limestone basins and valleys. If slopes are not too steep the shale soils can frequently be brought to a high state of production when limed, fertilized, and planted to perennial grasses and legumes. This is one of the important trends in land use in the general farming region of the Appalachians and the Ozarks. In census reports, however, it is obscured by an opposite trend which is leading to an increased number of part-time and residential farms. The latter development is a reflection of growing opportunity for factory employment. The small farm as a sole source of livelihood is going out of favor. As a consequence, many of these economically obsolete rural properties are undergoing physical fragmentation into multiples of even smaller units. Thus further reduced in size, they are no longer sufficient to support a family, but they make pleasant homes in the country with spacious grounds sufficient for gardening and for keeping livestock for household purposes.

Roanoke, Virginia, is among the many expanding industrial centers in the Appalachians. Only seventy years ago the size of the average farm in Roanoke County was 206 acres, and most operators then made their living at home on the land. Today, through subdivision of properties among heirs, through sales, and through land abandonment, the average farm has shrunk to 52 acres. Now over half of the operators supplement their incomes by working away from home, chiefly in the city of Roanoke. In the decade 1940–1950 in the Cumberland Plateau of Tennessee part-time farmers increased the average number of days spent at off-farm employment from 83 to 150. The emphasis on work in factories, mines, and sawmills became as great here as it had been a century earlier in the hill country of New England. The difference was that on the Cumberland Plateau in 1950 the farmer could keep his rural home and drive to his new job in town. In the days of the dirt road, horse and buggy, and the twelve-hour shift the farmer either had to settle in a mill village or remain in the hills with his subsistence agriculture. Thirty-one per cent of all the farms in 1950 were noncommercial part-time, residential, and subsistence farms. The largest number are in the hilly uplands of the eastern states—from New England south to Alabama and west to Missouri and Arkansas.

Figures 22:2 and 22:3 show the relationship of small land holdings and larger commercial farms to topography and soil parent materials in north-central Kentucky. The limestone basin or "Inner Bluegrass" is dominated by commercial farms (bluegrass farming), whereas the surrounding shale belt, which has a comparatively rough topography, is predominantly a zone of small landholdings, many of them noncommercial.

The principal cash crop in both of these areas is tobacco. One reason

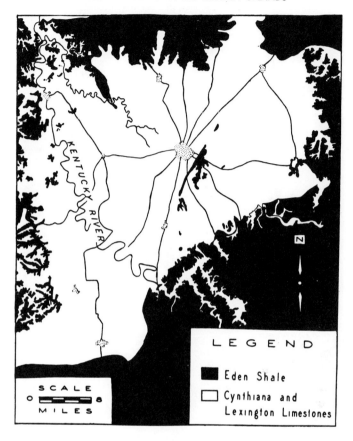

Figure 22:2. Geological limits of the Inner Bluegrass. (Source: Reference 5; p. 288.)

that tobacco has long been a favored crop in Kentucky is that it is profitable to raise on any size of farm. This is particularly true today because most tobacco farmers favor government acreage control and the government price guarantees which go along with it. The common reckoning that each acre of federal tobacco allotment adds $1,000 to the value of a farm is sufficient indication of farmers' respect for the crop. Farms in the uplands which are worth no more than $3,000 in physical property may sell for $5,000 if they have a 2-acre tobacco allotment. This is because tobacco is a *labor* crop rather than a *land* crop. The extra value is not in the soil but in the permission to use one's labor to produce tobacco.

A 100-acre farm need have only 2 or 3 acres of soil suitable for tobacco

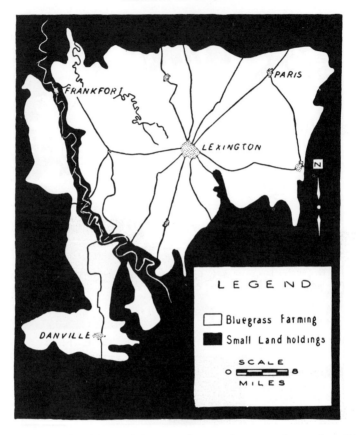

Figure 22.3.   Cultural limits of the Inner Bluegrass. (Source: Reference 5; p. 296.)

to make an economic unit for a thrifty family with willing hands.   Although most farmers, even dairymen, require 30 or 40 acres of good
cropland or meadow to make a bare living, the Appalachian tobacco
farmer can get by if he can raise the food and livestock essential for
subsistence—plus a few acres of tobacco for money income.   Tobacco is
valuable because of the almost incredible number of man-hours required
to raise and process the thousand or two thousand pounds of leaves that
are produced per acre.   The higher the yield the higher the number of
man-hours consumed.   Tobacco farmers talk of making $500 to $1,000
an acre per year by raising the crop, but actually this is the compensation they receive for the hundreds of hours required to complete the
work.   During the four years 1945–1948 an average of 495 man-hours
were spent on each acre of tobacco.   In Table 22:2 we may note that

Table 22:2.   **Man Hours per Acre, Yield, and Man Hours per Unit**
of Production for Designated Crops, United States,
Indicated Periods, 1910–1948[1]
(Source: Reference 2; pp. 70–71)

Crop	1910–1914	1935–1939	1940–1944	1945–1948
Corn				
Man hours per acre	35.2	28.0	26.2	23.7
Yield—bushels	26.0	25.0	32.0	35.2
Man hours per 100 bushels	135.0	112.0	82.0	67.0
Oats				
Man hours per acre	15.7	10.1	9.2	8.1
Yield—bushels	29.4	29.2	31.8	35.0
Man hours per 100 bushels	53.0	35.0	29.0	23.0
Hay				
Man hours per acre	11.9	11.2	11.7	11.6
Yield—tons	1.15	1.24	1.35	1.37
Man hours per ton	10.3	9.0	8.7	8.5
Wheat				
Man hours per acre	15.2	8.8	7.4	6.1
Yield—bushels	14.4	13.2	17.1	17.7
Man hours per 100 bushels	106.0	67.0	43.0	34.0
Rice				
Man hours per acre	55.0	31.8	29.2	26.1
Yield—bushels	35.8	49.7	45.5	46.4
Man hours per 100 bushels	154.0	64.0	64.0	56.0
Potatoes				
Man hours per acre	76.0	69.6	71.4	80.1
Yield—bushels	99.7	117.2	136.7	182.3
Man hours per 100 bushels	76.0	59.0	52.0	44.0
Sweet potatoes				
Man hours per acre	132.0	116.0	115.0	118.0
Yield—bushels	94.4	84.9	87.4	96.3
Man hours per 100 bushels	140.0	137.0	132.0	123.0
Dry beans				
Man hours per acre	47.2	27.5	23.7	20.8
Yield—pounds	778.0	855.0	898.0	988.0
Man hours per cwt.	6.1	3.2	2.6	2.1
Sugar beets				
Man hours per acre	128.0	97.0	95.0	90.0
Yield—tons	10.6	11.6	12.7	13.2
Man hours per ton	12.1	8.4	7.5	6.8
Cotton				
Man hours per acre	116.0	99.0	103.0	102.0
Yield—pounds	200.6	226.2	259.9	268.6
Man hours per bale	277.0	210.0	190.0	182.0
Tobacco				
Man hours per acre	356.0	415.0	448.0	495.0
Yield—pounds	816.0	886.0	1026.0	1164.0
Man hours per 100 pounds	44.0	47.0	44.0	43.0
Soybeans				
Man hours per acre	—	11.8	10.7	9.8
Yield—bushels	—	18.5	18.3	19.0
Man hours per 100 bushels	—	64.0	58.0	52.0

[1]Man hours per acre harvested and include preharvest work on abandoned acreage.

although cotton, potatoes, sweet potatoes, and sugar beets are also labor crops none of them approaches tobacco as a consumer of time.

TRANSPORTATION AND DISTANCE TO MARKETS

There is no great difference between the topographic and soil resources of the hilly uplands in New England, Kentucky, and Alabama. The principal advantage which the New Englander enjoys, if he has the capital to develop a modern dairy farm, is a splendid market for fluid milk. His market is at his back door in the form of the dense urban populations along the sea coast and in the Connecticut and Merrimack valleys. Gradually, as the South industrializes and the urban centers grow, the market for fluid milk will increase there also. Already there are specialized dairy areas within the general farming region. They are the milksheds of the larger cities. In the fifteen years between 1939 and 1954 the number of dairy farms in Tennessee increased 100 per cent. In South Carolina they increased 111 per cent, and in Virginia, 151 per cent. Of course, this industry is still small despite its growth because the market is relatively small compared with the metropolitan markets of the Northeast.

Along the southern border of the general farming region lies the Cotton Belt. There is always a market for cotton, although at times it is a poor one. If the growing season were longer in the general farming region, doubtless cotton would be a common cash crop. A family with a mule cannot take care of more than 10 to 20 acres of cotton because so much labor is required per acre. As with tobacco, this is an advantage to the farmer of the hilly uplands who has time but only a limited amount of cropland. Cotton is relatively valuable per unit of weight so that it easily bears transportation charges. One of the handicaps faced by the upland farmer of the east-central states is that there is no one specialty in very heavy demand that he might concentrate upon. As a consequence, he tries many things, depending upon his particular market opportunities. His products must have a fairly high value per unit of weight to pay transportation charges to consuming centers.

The mountaineer has always preferred a product requiring labor to produce and process so that he might compensate for fewer acres of tillable land. Livestock and livestock products were always favorites because they are concentrated forms of feed and labor which will pay for transportation out of the uplands into the urban centers. Poultry husbandry has become increasingly popular. Feed can be shipped in more cheaply than it can be grown, little land is needed, and labor can be converted to good profit. The end products, whether eggs or meat, can easily be transported. Of all counties in the United States, Washington and Benton in the Ozarks of Arkansas ranked second and third in chickens sold, according to the 1954 Census of Agriculture.. The Appalachian counties of Hall and Cherokee, Georgia, ranked sixth and seventh, respectively. Rockingham County, Virginia, leads all others in turkeys raised.

Apples have long been a favorite crop in the eastern uplands. All sidehill country has the advantage of fine air drainage by which cold night air of the highest elevations sinks to valley floors displacing warmer air which rises to piedmont slopes. This air drainage reduces the danger of early frosts which are a particular hazard to orchards. According to the 1954 Census of Agriculture, Frederick County, Virginia, ranked sixth among all counties in the United States as an apple marketer. Adams County, Pennsylvania, was eleventh, and Berkeley, West Virginia, twelfth. Of course, the traditional example of all who delve into the lore of the hillbilly farmer is home-cooked "mountain dew." It is indeed a labor product requiring elaborate processing and it is the prototype of all goods which represent a bulky raw material reduced to an essence worth the cost of transport.

REFERENCES

1. Bogue, Donald J., *State Economic Areas*, Bureau of the Census, Department of Commerce, Government Printing Office, Washington, D.C., 1951.
2. Hecht, Reuben W. and Glen T. Barton, *Gains in Productivity of Farm Labor*, U. S. Department of Agriculture, Government Printing Office, Washington, D.C., 1950.
3. Kercheval, Samuel, *A History of the Valley of Virginia*, fourth edition, Strasburg, Virginia, 1925.
4. Schwendeman, J. R., et al, *Land Areas of Kentucky and Their Potential For Use*, Frankfort, 1953.
5. Wilson, Leonard, Land Use Patterns of the Inner Bluegrass, *Economic Geography*, July 1941, Worcester, Mass.

land
use
in the
east-central
Appalachians

23

In southwest Virginia the contrasts between the kinds of land utilization in the ridges and valleys are closely related to the contrasts in topography. A generalized pattern of the landforms of this area is shown in Figure 23:1. The parent materials of soils on the ridges and hills are chiefly sandstones and shales, whereas most of the valleys are etched out of shales and soluble limestones. Soils of the valley lands are generally productive, although those derived from limestone are often shallow and those derived from shale sometimes drain poorly in the spring. The soils of the sandstone uplands are often of inferior quality.

Some counties in southwest Virginia lie entirely or almost entirely within upland or valley provinces. The difference between the landforms of uplands and lowlands is so distinct that these features are commonly used as county boundaries. It is therefore possible to obtain census data about land use in typical hill or valley areas by choosing representative counties. In Table 23:1 Dickenson County has been chosen as representative of the Cumberland Plateau uplands. Its entire

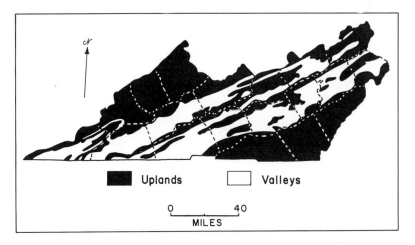

Figure 23:1.   Uplands and valleys of southwest Virginia.

area lies within that province.   By contrast Washington County is chiefly limestone lowland interrupted by occasional sandstone ridges.   Let us consider the contrasts between these two counties in types of farms and the ways the agricultural land is used.

There is a strong dominance of part-time, residential, and subsistence farms in the sandstone-shale uplands of the Cumberland Plateau. Prominent decreases in the amount of cropland and the number of farms during the period 1950–1954 indicate that agricultural activity is in decline.   The larger number of homes with power-line electricity is a reflection of the change that has come to most of the east-central Appalachians with the Tennessee Valley Authority's developments.   The changes in the local way of life which have resulted from the introduction of electric power and new industry can scarcely be appreciated by the outsider.   Recreational facilities for swimming, fishing, boating, and vacation outings created by new reservoir areas have made the Appalachian people some of the most fortunate in the nation.   It is no wonder that country living on factory pay and the eight-hour day is preferred to old time hoe-and-horse agriculture on substandard soils.   What was once a poor farm is today choice residential property.

In the Ridge and Valley Province, particularly on the sandstone and shale ridges, farms of both the commercial and noncommercial types are increasing.   In the limestone valleys commercial agriculture is vigorously pursued by most landowners, even though many farm on a part-time basis.   Note the increase in tractors.   These are associated with the

Table 23:1. Types of Farms in Dickenson and
Washington Counties, Virginia
(Source: Reference 4)

	Dickenson County (Cumberland Plateau)		Washington County (Ridge and Valley Province)	
	1950	1954	1950	1954
Area of Counties (square miles)		214,400		370,560
Number of farms	1,851	1,682	3,814	4,317
Average size of farms (acres)	41.2	39.8	73.8	66.2
Farms under 10 acres	338	358	559	1,060
Farms over 260 acres	16	12	155	170
Farms with power-line electricity [1]	1,386	1,637	3,023	4,177
Farms with no tractor, horses, or mules	778	765	1,460	2,270
Farms having 1 or more tractors	5	10	506	1,019
Total cropland harvested (acres)	10,048	6,865	60,912	59,033
Number of commercial farms	100	146	2,351	2,566
Number of residential, subsistence, part-time, and other farms	1,751	1,536	1,463	1,751

[1] In 1930 52 farms in Dickenson and 896 farms in Washington had power-line
electricity.

most active types of commercial farming.   Because there are more towns
and cities in the Ridge and Valley Province, factory-job opportunities
are good and commuting distances are short.   Rural land nearly everywhere has a high residential value.   There is a local saying that, "You
may marry land or inherit it, but you can't buy it."   Nevertheless, there
are sales but prices are high.   Because of rising land values the consolidation of smaller properties into larger, more efficient modern farms is
not so rapid in southwest Virginia as in some other Appalachian districts.

To the mountaineer and to many outsiders there is no landscape more
beautiful than that of the eastern Appalachians.   Farm fragmentation for
the purpose of rural residence will doubtless continue with the progress
of industry and the increase in job opportunity.   As cities grow, attractive markets for agricultural specialties will expand.   An increasing
number of vigorous commercial farms will produce the dairy products,
eggs, poultry, beef, fruits, and vegetables that are in growing demand

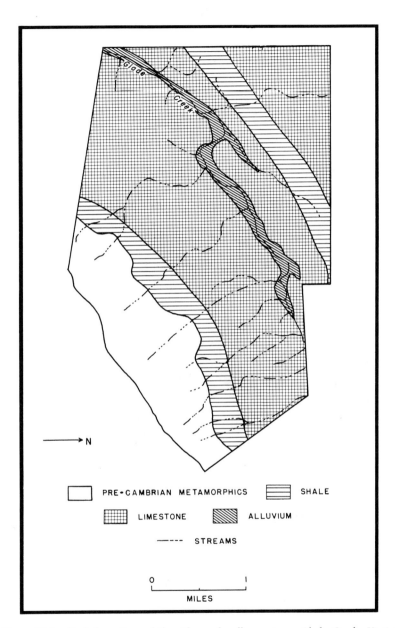

Figure 23:2. Rock formations of the ridge and valley region — Glade Creek, Virginia.

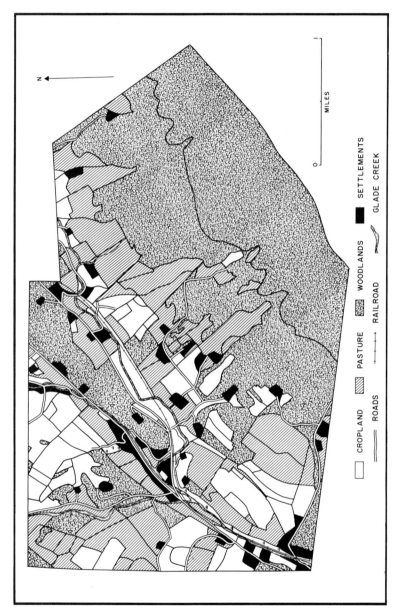

Figure 23:3. Land use in Glade Creek, Virginia.

CROPLAND   PASTURE   WOODLANDS   SETTLEMENTS

ROADS   RAILROAD   GLADE CREEK

MILES

N

at good prices. The total number of noncommercial farms will also continue to increase through fragmentation of larger properties. Their owners will be dependent upon urban employment.

As an example of how land utilization varies according to the nature of topography and soil we may consider Figures 23:2 and 23:3. These maps are of an area bisected by Glade Creek in Botetourt County, a few miles north of Roanoke, Virginia.

This is typical ridge and valley terrain. The sloping flank of the crystalline-rock ridge is almost entirely wooded. The shale area, outcropping between the hard metamorphics and the limestone, is sloping and eroded. There are only a few clearings of unimproved pasture and a small orchard. In contrast, the shale area which outcrops between the two limestone formations on the valley floor has an undulating surface and is just as intensively developed as the limestone on either side of it. The level limestone areas are intensively cultivated, whereas the limestone lands with considerable slope are in woods and bluegrass pasture. The amount of improved pasture, even in the valley lowlands, is small. This is typical of the Valley of Virginia where there is a lingering devotion to unfertilized native bluegrass sods rather than to fertilized grass-legume combinations.

A BEEF-POULTRY FARM IN THE SHENANDOAH VALLEY

Figure 23:4 is a land-use map of a well-managed and productive farm in the heart of the Shenandoah Valley in Rockingham County, Virginia. Its soils are derived chiefly from a shale outcrop with an undulating surface on what is more generally a rolling limestone plain. The farm itself consists of only 83 acres, which is small for a modern commercial farm. However, the owner of this property is representative of a growing number of industrious Appalachian farmers who are finding ways to compensate for having small acreages.

This combination livestock farm carries on its own pastures 30 head of Hereford brood cows and their calves from spring through fall. In winter the cattle are fed home-grown hay and corn silage. The calves are marketed as yearlings or younger and so are not fed any grain. The owner and his family raise 6000 turkeys annually in three batches of 2000 each. They care for 500 laying hens and raise 3000 broilers annually in two sets of 1500 each. All feed for the poultry is purchased.

The pastures are in excellent condition, and one of the fields designated as cropland is used as pasture each year. There are thus on the average 60 acres of rotation pasture available each year. While one pasture is being used the other four are resting. Since all are given

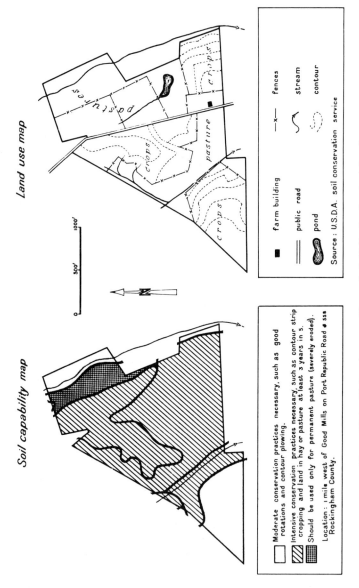

Figure 23:4. Eighty-three-acre Shenandoah Valley beef and poultry farm.

heavy top-dressings of cattle and poultry manure, they are highly productive. Preparations are underway to irrigate the pastures during drought periods with water from the two streams which flow through the property. The crop fields are on a three-year rotation of corn-wheat-clover and timothy hay. The wheat is the least profitable crop, although yields average 30 bushels per acre. It is essential as a nurse crop for the clover, and the straw from the wheat is needed to bed the cattle in winter. The grain itself is sold.

The poultry enterprise consumes most of the operator's time—and that is its purpose. If he had more land, he could expand the beef project, but land in the Shenandoah Valley is very expensive compared with its inherent productivity and market prices for beef. The distance from Washington, D.C., is not great, and many persons there, including government personnel, have acquired country properties as hobbies and for prestige entertainment. This trend has helped to bid up the value of land in some districts beyond its agricultural worth. The poultry require little land because they are confined to sheds, and poultry feed is supplied on credit by local dealers who contract with selected farmers in a way which protects the latter from financial loss. The arrangement is an ingenious one and is largely responsible for the very prominent growth of the poultry-feeding industry which has developed in Rockingham County.

Farmers of outstanding reputation for industry and careful management are favored by feed dealers. They are offered the opportunity to raise poultry on a cooperative basis, and poults, chicks, and feed are supplied on account. When the grown birds are ready for market the farmer sells them and keeps all returns above the charges against him. If, as sometimes happens, he receives less than they have cost, the feed dealer absorbs the loss. By raising the poultry in batches, less housing is required and the farmer is certain to make profits on most batches.

The poultry are insured against fire, windstorm, and theft but not against disease. The feed dealers thus take that risk, but they are careful to select farmers who will keep the flocks clean. The birds are always housed and are never in the open. The dealers also have technicians who make periodic visits to all farms under contract in order to check sanitation, and a veterinary is provided in case of trouble. The particular farm in Figure 23:4 used $39,000 in commercial feed in 1953 and is developing housing for enough birds to consume $100,000 in feed annually. This is intensive husbandry in any language, yet it is a one-family enterprise. It will be remembered that it was into the Shenandoah that Swiss and German Rhinelanders and the Pennsylvania Dutch introduced their system of livestock rearing and finishing in the eighteenth century. Their influence upon local thrift and good management is evident today.

THE NASHVILLE BASIN

The central portion of the Nashville Basin has a rolling surface of green pastures and cultivated fields interrupted by wooded knolls. It is one of the pleasantest, park-like countrysides in the United States. The charm of this landscape lies both in its natural beauty and in the evident good management of most of the farms. These farms are valued not only for their productivity but also for their aesthetic and social appeal. Rural estates in the central Nashville Basin are a cultural institution. Some owners are not dependent upon income from the land, but they are dependent upon the rural environment for an enjoyable way of life. The farm, or plantation as it may be called, is so much a part of family tradition and social custom that land is commonly entailed to assure a continuity from generation to generation of the amenities and pleasures which go with the use of it. The techniques of land management may change from time to time, but regard for country living remains constant.

In passing, it should be mentioned that there are a number of centers of rural elegance in the eastern United States. These are places where the ownership of country agricultural estates is a part of social tradition—an essential ingredient in the way of life. Among the most impressive of these districts are the Nashville basin, the Bluegrass of Kentucky, Loudoun County, Virginia, Montgomery County, Maryland, Chester and Bucks counties in Pennsylvania, Westchester County, New York, northern New Castle County, Delaware, Fairfield County, Connecticut, and Essex County, Massachusetts. Of course, there are many other places of similar character and beauty, but their development is on a somewhat smaller scale by fewer people.

It is customary to think of the American farm chiefly as a means of earning a livelihood, but, as our urban centers grow, there is a tendency, particularly in the East where metropolitan congestion is most aggravated, for the most beautiful rural areas to become estate country. The farm, thus enhanced, plays a prominent role in the social life of its proprietors whose principal business occupation is in the city. The study and practice of scientific agriculture is often a serious interest of the owners. It is quite likely that the finest countryside paralleling the nearly continuous band of cities from Boston, through New York and Philadelphia to Washington, may become estate country within the next century. The care which such properties receive and the respect for

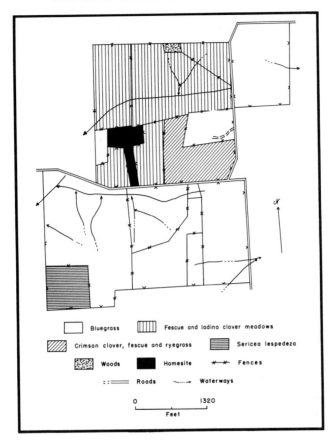

Figure 23:5.   A grassland farm of the Nashville basin.

preservation of the natural landscape which is common among their owners makes the prospect a pleasing one indeed.

On the rolling plains of the Nashville Basin the occasional deep soils are underlain with a soft limestone which is high in phosphate. Interrupting the undulating plain are numerous hills formed of cherty limestone. Their soils are thin. Over the millenia that the soft phosphatic limestone has been weathering much carbonate has been carried away in solution by drainage waters. Where there has been very little geologic erosion there have developed deep residual accumulations of calcium phosphate muds. These muds are actually utilized as raw material by the commercial fertilizer industry. To obtain them, the surface soil of a field or pasture may be bulldozed to the side, and the phosphatic substratum is removed to a depth of several feet by power shovels. Bulldozers then smooth over the excavations by recovering them with original topsoil so that the land becomes as productive as it was before the operation.

The Nashville Basin is traditionally a livestock area. It was there that the famed Tennessee walking horse was reared as the favored breed. From the time of earliest settlement the region has been a producer of beef, and that is still one of its major interests. Bluegrass and white Dutch clover, which were favorites in times past, are still in evidence, but these plants do not do well in midsummer or during droughts.

Figure 23:5 is of a 355-acre farm which is entirely pasture except for a small woodlot and the homesite. The use of the land is typical of true grassland farming as developed in parts of the southeastern states. The finest lowland areas, traversed by streams, are planted to fescue and ladino clover. Their production averages about 450 pounds of beef per acre annually. The upland pastures are bluegrass and sericea, and the excellent water facilities afforded by streams flowing through the pastures are an example of the Nashville Basin at its best. It was water, bluegrass, and soils high in phosphate which were the foundation of the region's early reputation as a livestock center. The phosphate passed from the soil into the animals' bones by way of the bluegrass.

About 100 fat calves and beeves are marketed annually on this farm. The cows calve in March. By August or September the young stock weigh between 400 and 500 pounds and some are sold. Those which are kept for feeding into fat steers and heifers graze through the winter and the following summer. They develop an excellent market finish on pasture alone. In addition to the cattle, this farm has a flock of 140 sheep and produces about that number of fat lambs annually. Wool from the ewes and rams is also marketed. There is not a row crop anywhere on the 355 acres.

A TOBACCO AND CATTLE FARM IN THE BLUEGRASS REGION OF KENTUCKY

Tobacco culture has been an important feature of agriculture in Kentucky from the time of its early settlement. The practice was introduced by Virginia planters, some of whom moved into Kentucky when their tidewater and piedmont properties declined in productivity because of continuous tobacco planting. Today the Bluegrass, Pennyroyal, and Jackson Purchase areas are the most prominent tobacco districts in Kentucky. (Figure A-12, Appendix.) The Bluegrass also has the finest development of grassland farming in the state. The soils of this region are of variable qualities, depending chiefly upon the nature of the rocks from which they were derived. The terrain is also a reflection of the underlying rock. Cherty limestone and shale give rise to shallow soils and to hilly, dissected land surfaces. The gently undulating plains of the area about Lexington are underlain with soft phosphatic limestones. The contrasts in topography and land quality are illustrated in Figure 22:1 which was prepared by Professor R. J. Schwendeman and others of the University of Kentucky.

Tobacco and grass-fed livestock make a fine combination of interests, especially for small farms. Most of the land of the rolling slopes is well suited to grass because the sod protects the soils from erosion. Tobacco offers the farm operator the best opportunity to convert available man-hours into a valuable crop while keeping cultivated acreage at a minimum. Manure from the cattle, concentrated on a few acres of tobacco, aids in maintaining good soil structure on the cultivated fields.

Figure 23:6 illustrates an ideal adjustment of land use to land capability on a 120-acre farm in Harrison County. The entire acreage of shallow soils is maintained in permanent sods of mixed grasses and legumes. The principal species are bluegrass, fescue, brome grass, ladino clover, alsike clover, and alfalfa. The grazing land, totaling 86 acres, is subdivided into rotational pastures, each of which has a fine water supply. Hay is required for a few weeks in mid-winter when the meadows make little growth, and 6 acres planted to permanent hay are set aside for this purpose. These six acres are the draws and flanks of natural drainage ways running westward between the two small areas of open-cultivated land. The hay fields thus serve a secondary purpose as sod channels for runoff waters.

The tobacco cropland is the chief source of income, for the returns from several acres of tobacco are greater than those from 92 acres of pasture and hay meadows. Without the tobacco, all of the land on the farm would have to be worked more intensively to be an economic unit. Intensive rotations on most of the land would result in severe erosion of the shallow soils found on all of the rolling slopes. The chief concern of the owner is to assure continued productivity and to prevent soil erosion on the few acres of gently undulating cropland. Terraces have been constructed to reduce runoff and to minimize the amount of soil removed.

There are only 14 acres of open-cultivated land. Four of these are nearly level and are planted to tobacco every year. The other 10 follow a two-year rotation of tobacco or corn followed by small grains. This is intensive cultivation, and soil erosion would be a hazard if it were not for the terraces and the great quantities of cattle manure

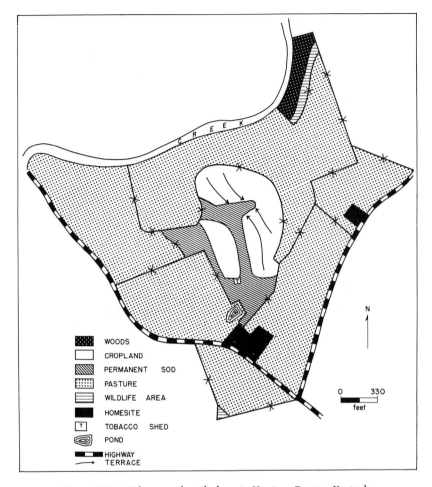

Figure 23:6.   Tobacco and cattle farm in Harrison County, Kentucky.

concentrated on the fields.   We have here an excellent example of how
a few acres of a valuable labor crop, integrated with a beef-cattle enterprise, can result in good land management.   The farm is too small to
provide full employment to its owner as a grassland-beef operation, but
the tobacco offers full employment and adequate income.   The integration of a few acres of labor crops with grassland meadows is an ideal
combination for the hill and valley country of the Appalachians.   Un-
fortunately, the national market for tobacco is not great enough to
permit a wider adoption of this system.

REFERENCES

1. Gottmann, Jean, *Virginia at Mid-Century,* Henry Holt & Co., Inc., 1955, New York.
2. Higbee, Edward, *The Present Condition of Agriculture in Virginia,* manuscript in the Library of the Old Dominion Foundation, New York, 1953.
3. Stose, George W., *Geologic Map of Virginia,* State Conservation and Development Commission, Richmond, 1928.
4. U. S. Bureau of the Census, *Census of Agriculture, 1955,* Government Printing Office, Washington, D.C.
5. Virginia Polytechnical Institute, *The Soils of Virginia,* Bulletin 203, March 1953.

the Cotton Belt

24

Cotton has become a specialty crop raised in a few favorable localities rather than a crop typical of so broad a region as an agricultural belt. What is designated as the Cotton Belt on the map of major types of farming (Figure 4:2) might be considered a climatic zone in which the growing season is suitable for cotton. Reference to Figure A-4 in the Appendix indicates the extent to which cotton culture is concentrated in the Mississippi Delta, East Texas, the irrigated areas of the Rio Grande Valley, the Texas High Plains, south-central Arizona, and the San Joaquin Valley. There is a saying in the South that, "Cotton is going west; cattle are coming east; the Negro is going north, and the Yankee is coming south." That is a pretty concise statement of some remarkable trends in southeastern agriculture. As for cotton, its western migration has been under way for over one hundred years.

The story of cotton in the South is one of great complexity. For a brief review of its beginnings and its development before the Civil War the reader is referred to Gray's classic study. (Reference 5.) From the standpoint of land-use geography there are several facts of major importance. The most productive soils of the southeastern states are in the Appalachian piedmont, in portions of the upper coastal plain, and in the alluvium-filled valleys of the lower coastal plain. The lower coastal plain southward of James River in Virginia is generally either marshy or sandy. Modern techniques are making some of these coastal marshes and sandy "flatwoods" productive. But in former days when intensive cultivation was largely dependent upon natural soil condition they were of little value. For the most part they were cattle range. The animals, which grazed unfenced, were rounded up from time to time for branding and slaughter by plantation owners and poor-white "crackers." (Reference 5; p. 484.)

The cultivated lands of the famed plantations of coastal Carolina and Georgia were confined chiefly to river-margin bottoms with rich alluvial soils. The sediment-built "Sea Islands" were also intensively used. Their location and a climate favorable for the growth of premium, long-staple Sea Island cotton made special cultural efforts feasible. Cattle were penned to provide manure. Marsh muds were utilized, and eventually South American guano was purchased to keep the soil productive. In agricultural techniques the Sea Island planters were considerably in advance of their contemporaries. Figure 24:1 of the Georgia coast in 1780 shows the drained rice fields of the Savannah and Ogeechee river bottoms as well as the alluvial Sea Islands from Amelia in the south to Great Tybee in the north. The larger inland portion of the lower coastal plain was not utilized agriculturally except as cattle range and for subsistence gardening.

George Washington in his diary described the environs of Savannah in 1791, eleven years later than the date of Figure 24:1.

The town on 3 sides is surrounded with cultivated Rice fields which have a rich and luxuriant appearance. On the 4th or back side it is a fine sand. Rice and tobacco (the last of which is greatly increasing) are the principal exports— Lumber and Indigo are also Exported but the latter is on the decline (supplanted) it is supposed by Hemp & Cotton. (Reference 3; p. 148.)

As to the extent of intensive cultivation, it is to be noted that the Piedmont and the adjoining upper coastal plain constituted the chief agricultural districts of Georgia and South Carolina in the early nineteenth century. At that time cotton had become the dominant money crop of the southeastern states. The Piedmont soils, derived from crystalline rocks, are commonly deep; in their virgin condition they were productive. The red clay loams were usually preferred to the grays and yellows in those days, just as they are now. Yields were usually better on them, and they held up longer under severe treatment. Not until

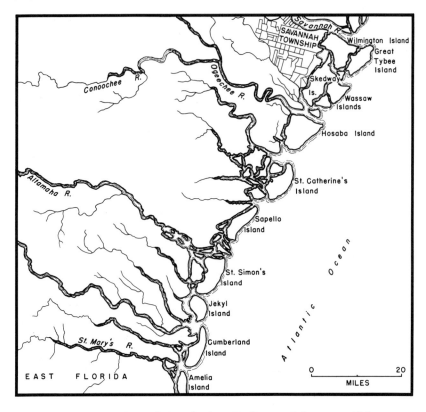

Figure 24:1. Georgia's Sea Islands, 1780. (Source: Reference; p. 71.)

constant cropping of cotton, tobacco, and corn led to excessive erosion and exhaustion of fertility was the greater part of the Piedmont considered anything but a choice agricultural area. The upper coastal plain had several fine districts of rich soils, particularly in South Carolina, western Georgia, south-central Alabama, and western Mississippi.

The student familiar with the geology of the Piedmont and the coastal plain is aware of the great variety of parent materials from which the soils of the southeastern states were derived. The area was not glaciated; thus the weathering processes of soil genesis have been going on for a very long time. Heavy leaching, to which all the soils have been subjected, has accentuated the importance of parent materials and natural vegetation in distinguishing productive from unproductive land. For instance, some of the finest cotton soils of the South were derived from the hardwood-covered shales and the limestone prairies of Alabama's

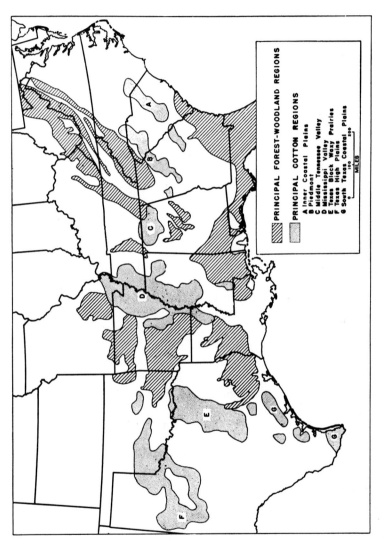

Figure 24·2.   Southeastern forest and cotton areas. (Source: Reference 6; p. 442.)

Table 24:1. Timber Stands, 1953
(Source: Reference 4; p. 40)

| Stand-Size Class | Total | | North | South | West and Coastal Alaska |
	Million Acres	Per- Cent	Million Acres	Million Acres	Million Acres
Sawtimber stands					
Old growth	50.0	10	negl.	negl.	50.0
Young growth	132.7	27	47.7	60.5	24.5
Total	182.7	37	47.7	60.5	74.5
Poletimber stands	169.5	35	65.5	78.4	25.6
Seedling and sapling stands	94.8	19	44.2	38.3	12.3
Nonstocked areas	41.6	9	16.6	16.1	8.9
All classes	488.6	100	174.0	193.3	121.3

Black Belt. The red Cecil clay loams of the Piedmont, which are derived from granite under mixed forest cover, were excellent for cotton until severely eroded. When limed, fertilized, and planted to grasses and legumes they are much desired for grassland farming.

Sands, sandstones, and silicious schists under pine and oak gave rise to soils that were quickly exhausted of natural fertility after a few years of cropping. The wealthier planters and more industrious homesteaders avoided these lands which were occupied by poor-whites who practiced a shifting system of gardening akin to that of Indians—clearing an area of its woody growth, planting subsistence crops for a few years, and then abandoning it. These piney-woods people lived almost as much by hunting, trapping, and scavenging as by their patch farming and open-range cattle herding. Today most of these districts with inferior soils are again wooded. However, under good silvacultural practices, the pine itself has become a profitable crop.

The areas designated as forest woodland in Figure 24:2 were on the average 75 per cent wooded in 1950. Exclusive of the dry plains of western Texas and Oklahoma, more than 55 per cent of the Southeast is forested.

About half of the nation's growth of sawtimber occurs in the South[*] which has only 40 per cent of the commercial forest land. Southern yellow pines account for 30 per cent of the growth of all sawtimber in

[*]The South, as classified by the Forest Service, includes Virginia, the Carolinas, Tennessee, Mississippi, Alabama, Georgia, Florida, Arkansas, Louisiana, and humid eastern Texas and Oklahoma.

the United States. Eastern softwood growth is 84 per cent southern yellow pine. This preponderance reflects the favorable conditions for pine over huge areas of the South. The future of forestry in this region would seem to be very good indeed.

Table 24:1 indicates the well-known fact that the West Coast has the greatest acreage of old-growth sawtimber. The South, however, leads in the amount of young growth and poletimber which must be looked upon to supply more of our lumber needs as the old growth is cut. That such a time is not far off may be surmised by the fact that twice as much timber is being cut on the West Coast as is being grown. In the South growth not only exceeds cutting but the amount of growth substantially exceeds that of both the West Coast and the North. The long-time trend, therefore, is toward southern dominance of the nation's saw-timber supply (Figure 24:3).

Along with improvement of the timber economy in the South, a new concept of forest management has developed. Although it is still common to see forest undergrowth deliberately burned to encourage grass for cattle, the practice is on the decline. Both timber and cattle are becoming too valuable to be treated in the old-fashioned manner of the

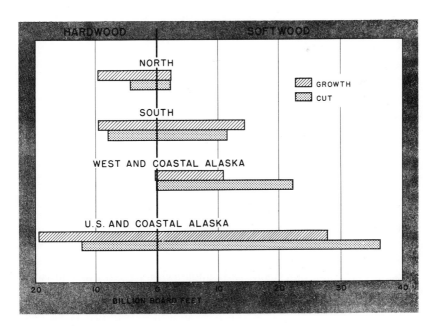

Figure 24:3. Comparison of net annual sawtimber growth and timber cut. (Source: Reference 4; p. 68.)

piney-woods crackers. Land best suited to timber is being increasingly reserved for that purpose. "Tree farm" is a designation familiar to the reader of roadside signs in the wooded regions of the South. Wherever the soil warrants more intensive use as grass-legume pasture it is being cleared of timber so that a better grade of cattle can be produced with better forage in shorter periods of time. Professor Merle Prunty, Jr., of the University of Georgia recently wrote,

There is extensive demand in the lower South for moderate to large tracts of land suitable for forests. This demand comes primarily from paper mills who wish to ensure their sources of supply; some mills are purchasing land as much as 150 miles from the mill site. Private individuals with capital to invest make up another purchasing group. This group is interested because (1) the return from reasonably managed pine forest averages at least 10 per cent on capital invested, (2) the income received may be treated as a long-term capital gain in income-tax returns, and (3) land in the South today is underpriced in comparison both with national average land prices and with its inherent production capacity. Even low-grade forest land constitutes an excellent inflationary hedge.

On the other hand, small farmers now tend to replace low-grade forest with more intensive forms of land use, especially improved pastures. . . . A slight decrease in forest acreage, especially about the periphery of the forest regions, is anticipated. (Reference 6; pp. 442–443.)

The major uses of land in nine states of the humid southeastern Cotton Belt are shown in Table 24:2. The preponderance of forest has already been emphasized. That the amounts of cropland and nonforested pasture are so small is not due to topography as is the case in the Appalachian uplands. There are other significant factors:

1. Poor sandy soils in the piney woods and flatwoods districts are better suited to forestry than to pastures. (However, there are significant exceptions to this generalization, particularly in Florida.)

2. The reclamation of coastal marsh lands is technically much easier than at any time in history, but there is an economic hazard in such investment unless the soils are the best and a valuable crop can be grown on the reclaimed land.

3. Much land already cleared is eroded and low in fertility. A large portion of this low-grade cropland has inherently productive soil. Many investors are finding that the reclamation of this type of land is a better financial proposition than is the clearing of forest. Most new clearings of woodlands are made to extend the boundaries of pastures or cultivated fields.

The same economic forces which have influenced the decline of field operations on small uneconomic farm units in the Appalachians and in New England have been at work in the Southeast. The results, however,

Table 24:2.   Major Uses of Land in Southeastern States—1954
(Source: Reference 8; pp. 61, 67)

(thousands of acres)

State	Cropland	Grassland Pasture and Grazing Land	Woodland Pastured	Woodland Not Pastured
Alabama	7,481	4,108	9,981	10,785
Arkansas	8,863	4,717	12,810	6,485
Florida	3,443	5,759	16,510	5,277
Georgia	9,009	3,258	10,211	13,456
Louisiana	5,494	4,680	11,754	4,152
Mississippi	7,805	4,995	10,734	5,706
North Carolina	7,264	2,236	3,170	15,980
South Carolina	4,891	1,469	3,074	8,820
Tennessee	9,096	4,903	3,865	8,436

have been somewhat different. The broadened opportunity for urban employment has led to drastic declines in farm tenancy. For obvious reasons the tenants have not remained on the land as part-time and residential farmers. They have moved with their families into the cities. The landowners have adjusted to this exodus in various ways: by mechanization and by conversion to tree farming, orcharding, or poultry husbandry. All of these developments have required capital, but that has become available through better prices and through credit. It was lack of capital and credit which helped thwart much agricultural progress in the southeastern states from the close of the Civil War until the late 1930's.

Until recently cotton in the Southeast has been overwhelmingly a tenant crop. Not only that, but the term "southern agriculture" itself was almost synonymous with the tenant-cropper system. Figure A-39 Appendix shows that only in the Mississippi "Delta" and on the coastal plain of the Carolinas is tenancy now heavily concentrated.

During the years between 1935 and 1954 the number of tenants in Mississippi declined from 225,000 to 100,000. In Alabama the number dropped from 176,000 to 61,000. Seventy-seven per cent of the farms in Georgia were tenant-operated in 1930, but by 1954 the figure was 35 per cent. Whereas tenants in Louisiana operated 66 per cent of the farms in 1930, they occupied 34 per cent in 1954. Generally, there were fewer, larger, more mechanized, and more productive farms. The total number of farms in the South declined 22 per cent between 1935 and 1950, but most of the land was consolidated into larger, more economical units.

The sharp reduction in tenancy has been so rapid in many places that the brick chimneys of dismantled rough board cabins still stand. Herefords and Brahmas graze on crimson clover and Bermuda grass over earth where not so long ago the shanties stood. The changes in southeastern agriculture are so fundamental and so dispersed that they reflect nothing less than a completely new assessment of how the land in these states may be used. Cotton culture, as generally practiced before World War II, represented a system of land utilization and social organization more akin to the times of the Pharaohs than to this age of science and skilled labor equipped with mechanized implements. All sections of the country have access to the results of scientific research conducted at their state and federal agricultural experiment stations, but in no other great region was the gap so broad between new and old systems of land use as in the Southeast. Thus, in no other region has the advantage of research been so spectacular.

The productive research of experiment stations, the strengthening of the national economy since the last depression, and the exodus of cheap but inefficient tenant labor have made the reorientation of southern agriculture possible. As previously mentioned, cotton is becoming a specialty crop in a few favored areas where mechanization is feasible and where there is less danger of soil erosion. These areas are shown in Figure 24:2. Once dominant in the Piedmont from North Carolina to Alabama, cotton is now important in but a narrow and still shrinking band (area B). It has practically disappeared from whole sections of the upper coastal plain, and in others it has declined drastically. The Black Belt of Alabama and Mississippi was one of the principal cotton districts a century ago. Today it is among the least important.

As large portions of the Piedmont and upper coastal plain became severely eroded under constant cotton and corn culture during the past century, the notion gained currency that southern soils were poor. Land abandonment, which was common, served to confirm that opinion. Actually poor management was the principal cause of soil exhaustion and erosion. Now formerly abandoned fields are being brought back into production chiefly as grass and legume meadows for beef and dairy cattle. The year-long grazing season and the abundant rainfall, characteristic of the Southeast, make it ideal pasture country.

Figure 24:4 shows the remarkable increase in beef cows which has taken place in the Southeast. The number of these animals is almost as large as in all of the mountain and Pacific states with their extensive ranges and productive irrigated valleys. And that increase took place in the brief period of seven years! It is a significant fact also that the 128 per cent increase in the Southeast is twice the national average.

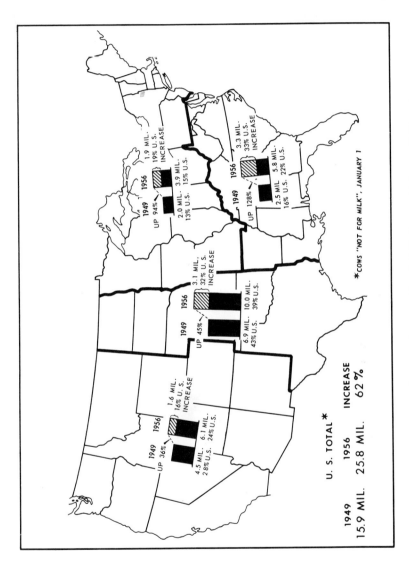

Figure 24:4. Beef cows on farms, 1949 and 1956. (Source: Reference 7; Cover.)

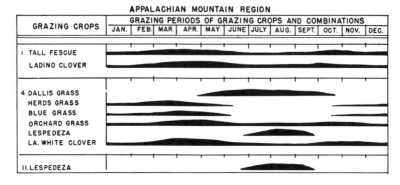

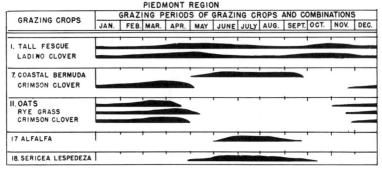

Figure 24:5.   Grazing schedules in three regions of Georgia. (Source: Reference 1; p. 47.)

The impressive national increase itself is due, in large measure, to the growth of the beef-cattle industry in the southeastern states.

Some of the basic reasons for the emergence of a significant southern beef-cattle industry have already been touched upon, but perhaps most important are the favorable conditions for grassland-livestock farming in that area, a long frost-free season, mild winters, and heavy annual rainfall. From 1 to 3 acres of the best meadows are capable of carrying a beef cow and her calf through the year; 20 acres are required in the Sand Hills of Nebraska. About 100 to 150 acres are required in the drier sections of the intermontane range country. The excellent grass, legume, and grass-legume meadow combinations which are possible from the Appalachian uplands to the coastal plain are illustrated in a chart prepared by the University of Georgia College of Agriculture, Figure 24:5.

In the Southeast, as in other sections of the humid eastern states, there is an important trend toward the use of supplementary irrigation. This is especially interesting because rainfall is generally adequate to bring crops to maturity. Short droughts, however, may be expected everywhere in the humid United States. Total crops are seldom lost, but yields are reduced, sometimes considerably. The function of supplementary irrigation is to carry crops through the occasional dry periods in a vigorous condition and to increase yields beyond what they would be if dependence were placed upon natural precipitation alone. Irrigation has been found useful to some farmers even in Georgia where the average annual rainfall ranges from 45 inches in the lower eastern piedmont and coastal plain to 76 inches in the northeastern Appalachian uplands. Table 24:3 shows the drought frequency by seasons at Savannah, Georgia, where the average annual precipitation is 45 inches. A drought is considered to exist when, for 14 days or more, there is not one quarter inch of rainfall in any one 24 hour period.

Table 24:3. Drought Frequency by Seasons, Savannah, Ga.
(Source: Reference 2; p. 5)

Season	Length	Years in 21	
Spring	2 weeks	21	every year
	4 weeks	12	3 every 5 years
	6 weeks	3	1 every 7 years
Summer	4 weeks	11	1 every 2 years
	4 weeks	3	1 every 7 years
	6 weeks	0	none
Fall	2 weeks	21	every year
	4 weeks	17	5 every 6 years
	6 weeks	7	1 every 3 years

Interest in irrigation has been spurred by technological developments which make the practice easy and economical. Lightweight, movable aluminum pipe, efficient pumps, and a growing realization that labor crops, such as tobacco, market vegetables, fruits, and nuts, are too valuable to trust to the vagaries of the weather have encouraged more irrigation.   Another important element in stimulating interest is the fact that stream, pond, and ground waters are widely available.   Some of the most intensively cultivated lands have always been the alluvial areas bordering streams.   Fields in such favorable locations are most easily irrigated.   There are many districts on the lower coastal plain where irrigation is feasible on lands which must also be drained during certain periods of the year when rainfall is excessive.

The combination of sandy topsoils which dry quickly and clay subsoils which impede drainage is a common one in Florida.   In months of heavy precipitation the rain, failing to drain through the subsurface clay, may accumulate until it rises to the surface of the sand above.   By the use of open ditches and tile drains, however, this surplus water can be re- moved.   Then during drier months, the mechanical drainage operations can be suspended by lowering control gates at the outlets.   By means of these control gates the water table can be kept at a level suitable for plant roots.   This system of controlled water management, balancing precipitation and drainage waters in order to avoid both waterlogging and drought, calls for expert engineering.   When supplemented, as it sometimes is, with irrigation the farmer need never be concerned about the moisture condition of his soil.

The irrigation of pastures is becoming rather common.   This is be- cause the better-quality, improved pastures represent considerable capital investment.   It is often cheaper to irrigate these lands than to add additional acreage which would be dependent upon natural precipi- tation.   Heavy fertilization, supplementary water, rotational grazing, and year-long pasturage, which is possible from lowland Tennessee southward, make an ideal combination for intensive livestock hus- bandry.   The following quotation from the Georgia Agricultural Ex- tension Service is an indication of contemporary thinking.

Studies being made at the present time in connection with the larger river development projects in the State indicate that irrigation is being given major consideration as an important contribution to the economic justification of the projects.   Preliminary irrigation data compiled for one of these large river basin projects reveals that the increased value of diversified crops due to irrigation would amount to $25,000,000 annually on about 464,000 acres of land.   Low-cost electrical energy, produced by power plants on the project, would be utilized to operate the irrigation pumps for the community projects.

Pasture irrigation is drawing the interest of the livestock people, particularly dairymen, and demonstration projects and experimental work is under way. Irrigation of permanent pastures is resulting in increases in nutritive value of forage as well as in yields.   Protein, phosphorous, lime and vitamin content of the forage is increased due to irrigation when pastures are supplied with ample fertilizer elements.   Dairymen often refer to the fall months when long dry periods retard growth of pastures and consequently cause milk production to fall off.

REFERENCES

1. Alexander, E. D., J. B. Preston, and J. R. Johnson, *Pastures for Georgia*, University of Georgia College of Agriculture, Athens, 1952.
2. Bennett, Roger Q., *Irrigate For More Profits*, Georgia Agricultural Extension Service, Athens, 1950.
3. Brown, Ralph H., *Historical Geography of the United States*, Harcourt Brace & Company, New York, 1948.
4. Crafts, Edward C., *Timber Resources Review*, Chapter 1, preliminary draft, Forest Service, Government Printing Office, Washington, D.C., 1955.
5. Gray, Lewis Cecil and Esther Katherine Thompson, *History of Agriculture in the Southern United States to 1860*, Carnegie Institution of Washington, 1933.
6. Prunty, Merle, Jr., *Land Occupance in the Southeast: Landmarks and Forecast*, The Geographical Review, New York, July 1952.
7. U.S. Department of Agriculture, *The Livestock and Meat Situation*, Agricultural Marketing Service, Washington, D.C., May 9, 1956.
8. Wooten, Hugh H. and James R. Anderson, *Major Uses of Land in the United States —1954*, U.S. Department of Agriculture, Government Printing Office, Washington, D.C., 1957.

some
land-use
systems
in the
humid
South

25

The agricultural character of the South is in flux. It is still easy to find examples of land use which in the past caused soil exhaustion and farm abandonment over wide areas. As these methods are continued, more land will be injured and abandoned with each passing season. Fortunately, however, it is just as easy to find examples of soil conservation which are redeeming the southern landscape and making it highly productive. Fields so gullied that they were abandoned to weeds and brush have come back to a highly useful state, thanks to the bulldozer, commercial fertilizer, and a new attitude of mind. As the land heals, the whole southern economy, both rural and urban, is entering a period of vigorous growth and progress.

Nowhere else, except possibly in certain newly opened irrigated districts of the western states, is the enthusiasm of whole communities of farmers so contagious as in parts of the Southeast. The basic reason for this enthusiasm is the knowledge that there are new ways of farming and that they are profitable. From the Virginia Piedmont, through the Black

Belt of Alabama, to the Texas Gulf Coast and Black Waxy Prairie enough modern grassland farming is being practiced to acquaint the observant landowner with its attractive possibilities. The fact that there is so vast a field for improvement, based on modern methods developed by the agricultural experiment stations, generates new hope and determination. The spirit of confidence in their new agriculture is accelerating the rate of land renovation by southern farmers.

Whenever the trend toward grassland farming in the southern states is mentioned the example of the Black Belt is seldom overlooked. This is the zone of lime-chalk prairie loam which swings like a crescent moon from Montgomery across central Alabama into northeastern Mississippi. During the early nineteenth century it attracted wealthy and aristocratic planter families who were forced by exhausted soils to leave the Carolinas, Georgia, and Virginia. People of all classes came, but by 1840 most of the better prairie lands had been acquired by great proprietors, whose holdings, often comprising thousands of acres, were brought into cultivation with scores of slaves. It is said of Alabama that in ante bellum days more slaves were held in the Black Belt than in all the remainder of the state. Today the century-old mansions in cities such as Columbus and Montgomery are almost the only remaining testimony to the period before 1860 when these lands were new and their cotton the finest and most profitable in the South.

The Black Belt is now one of the primary cattle districts of the South. This is illustrated in Figure 25:1. Most of the counties with more than 25 thousand head of cattle are in or adjacent to the Black Belt, which is also the district with the largest amount of improved pasture in Alabama. Between 1930 and 1950 cotton acreage was reduced from 108,100 to 34,800 in Dallas County in the heart of the Black Belt, and the number of its Negro farmers declined from 6,405 to 3,693 during the same period. The great majority of those who left the land were tenants who have since found employment in the cities. The cropland once sown to cotton is now in improved grass-legume meadows.

On a visit to a Black Belt plantation near Selma, Alabama, some remarkable transformations were observed. In 1940 this property of 3600 acres had living on it 51 Negro tenant families totaling 235 persons. At that time 500 acres were in cotton, 615 in corn, and 100 in soybeans, oats, and peanuts. Except for 18 acres of kudzu, there were no improved meadows. Thirteen years later this same plantation had not a single acre of cotton, and only three Negro families remained. Cattle and fine pastures had entirely replaced croppers, cotton, and corn. Three hundred acres of oats had been planted for grain and grazing. Two thousand acres of improved meadow lands were partially sown to crim-

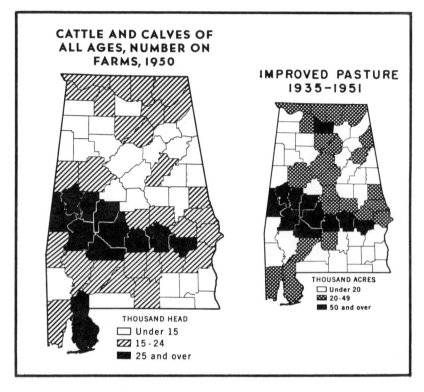

Figure 25:1.   Cattle and improved pasture in Alabama. (Source: Reference 1.)

son clover, Bermuda grass, and sericea lespedeza, of which 175 acres were under irrigation, although the monthly rainfall seldom drops below 2 inches. This is not the most remarkable example of the new *ranches* that not so long ago were *plantations*. Many properties of 5000 to 10,000 acres in extent have undergone a similar evolution, and comparable changes have taken place on smaller properties.

That this area, once a primary cotton district of the South, should have become one of the nation's richest cattle sections in so short a time is remarkable. Several factors brought the rapid change. As early as 1915 the boll weevil checked enthusiasm for cotton. In 1914 the community of Uniontown, Alabama, sold 22,000 bales; in 1915 it sold 1500. That was a year of disaster and the beginning of the exodus of the starved-out Negro tenants. In 1917 the war so increased the value of cotton that it hung on. With insecticides and fertilizers many owners and tenants fumbled along with the crop for another twenty years, although some switched to cattle. Now conversion to livestock-grassland farming is almost complete. There are just enough large cotton plantations left to make the change seem credible to the outsider.

Figure 25:2 is a 540-acre unit of a larger operation. It is a former cotton plantation which has been absorbed by a cattle ranch and is completely given over to improved permanent meadows and to woodland. The latter is protected from grazing to increase the growth rate and quality of the timber. The soil of this property was severely

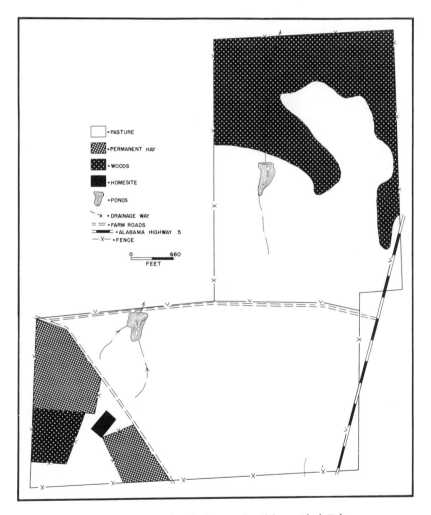

Figure 25:2. Beef-cattle farm in the Alabama Black Belt.

eroded and its fertility was exhausted in 1945. At that time it was sold to its present owner for rehabilitation and conversion into a cattle ranch. The 402 acres of permanent pasture are divided into two parts for the purpose of rotational grazing, and each range has its own combination stock and fish pond. These ponds were constructed with bulldozers and are filled with runoff water during rains. Ponds such as these are becoming one of the most conspicuous features of the southeastern landscape. They are vital to livestock farming and they are of great recreational value. Much as fishing is enjoyed elsewhere in the country, that enthusiasm amounts to a passion in the South where the season lasts the year around. Continuous grazing is possible. There are 36 acres of legume meadows from which hay is cut for use during short droughts. This ranch unit supports 120 beef cows and their calves.

The land-use pattern of a 1490-acre, tenant-operated plantation is shown in Figure 25:3. This is a type of land use and farm organization which has practically disappeared from the Black Belt. The woods are on lands used for cotton many years ago. These fields became eroded under cultivation and their fertility was exhausted when they were abandoned to volunteer growth of cedar, pine, and miscellaneous hardwoods. The pastures are all volunteer growth, chiefly Johnson grass, which is a tough, stoloniferous species and a serious pest in clean-cultivated fields because it is so difficult to eradicate. Johnson grass is hardy and resistant to grazing. On limed and fertilized ground it makes good pasturage when interplanted with legumes. The pastures on this plantation are more recently retired cotton fields which serve the mules kept for working the cultivated fields. There are 21 tenant houses with half-acre plots allotted as garden space to the tenant families. The 450 acres of cropland are divided among the tenants and devoted almost entirely to cotton and corn. Corn is the basic food of the tenants and the principal concentrate feed for their mules. Heavy applications of fertilizer are required to keep the cropland in usable condition, but its productivity is low, chiefly because of lack of humus, gradual erosion, and obsolete cultural methods. Perhaps by the time this account appears in print this relic of the old-plantation South will have been converted to a cattle ranch with fine grass and legume meadows.

The fact that large landholdings predominated in the Black Belt was an important reason for the rapid conversion from cotton to pasture. Before the change occurred it was believed by some that such plantation farms would be the last bulwark of the tenant-cropper system. Others contended that bigness in itself would hasten this alteration. Analyzing the situation with some hindsight, it seems that the small

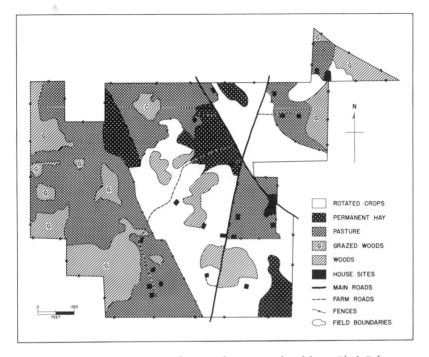

Figure 25:3.   Tenant-operated cotton plantation in the Alabama Black Belt.

operators were obliged by the very smallness of their farms and the immediate need of revenue, to continue row-cropping.   The shift to cattle
imposes a few lean years of low returns until the herd is built up and
pastures are established.   The consolidation of small farms into large
units is a difficult and prolonged affair.   Evolution of this kind on a
community scale does not occur rapidly because many people must
decide to sell to the few who may be willing to buy.   Consequently,
changes which came so quickly to the Black Belt will require relatively
more time elsewhere even though the soil in some other areas may
be superior.

A PIEDMONT COTTON FARM

The first permanent settlements in the piedmont of South Carolina
were made in the period from 1740 to 1760.   The first cotton gin was
not erected until 1795, but by 1808 a few of the old settlers had noted
that the soil was washing away much more rapidly than in former times
when subsistence agriculture was the principal interest of the culti-

vators. In 1818 William R. Davie, president of the South Carolina Agriculture Society, discussed the Piedmont in an address before the membership:

Large quantities of land have been cleared within the last twenty years, and a new tax . . . imposed on the strength of the soil, compeled to bear alternate crops of corn and cotton, or successive crops of the latter. This system, if it may be so called, of perpetual exhaustion, has impoverished our lands to an alarming degree, and, if pursued for half a century more, would make this interesting portion of the state a perfect desert — exhibiting a naked barren surface, spotted here and there by a few patches of broomstraw, or starved shrubbery, and ruined from future recovery by deep washed gullies, the permanent and accusing witnesses of our apathy and indolence. (Reference 2; pp. 2–3.)

The surface relief of the Piedmont is gently undulating to steeply rolling. There is almost no level land except on the narrow alluvial plains along river margins. During the first years of the cotton and tobacco era, it was the custom to cultivate the crops in straight rows regardless of slope. Erosion became serious, and experiments with cultivation began. Thomas Jefferson and his son-in-law T. M. Randolph endorsed contour plowing as a result of their experience at Monticello in the Virginia piedmont. The idea was first tried in South Carolina sometime between 1815 and 1820 and was called horizontal plowing. However, the shallow furrows were unable to hold back the heavier rains, and gullies developed. Later, hillside ditching was tried.

The typical hillside ditch was a primitive terrace. It was constructed obliquely downward with a bank paralleling the lower side to prevent overflow. At the lower end it usually emptied into a convenient natural draw, creek, or wooded area at the edge of the field. The grades of hillside ditches ranged from 8 to 35 inches per 100 linear feet and were usually laid off with a level. By 1860 this practice was fairly widespread in the Piedmont. Despite such efforts at erosion control, the successive planting of clean-cultivated row crops led to soil exhaustion and much abandonment of land. (Reference 2.)

Figure 25:4 is the land-use map of a 75-acre cotton farm on the South Carolina piedmont in Spartanburg County. An aerial photograph of Spartanburg County would show it to be one of the most thoroughly terraced areas in the United States. Through the years many improvements have been made in the techinques of construction and maintenance of terraces. All of the cropland on this farm, a total of 35 acres, is contour-terraced. In addition, erosion-resisting cover crops and green-manure crops are planted. Corn is interplanted with cowpeas, and small grains are seeded with lespedeza. Such a cropping system tends to maintain the humus content of the soil and

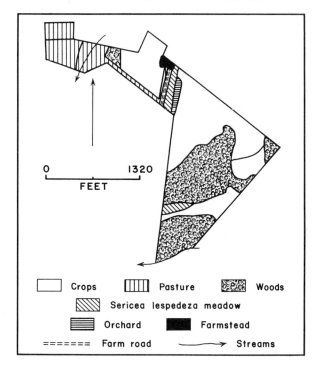

Figure 25:4.   A cotton farm in the South Carolina piedmont.

to reduce erosion losses during the winter as well as during the summer months.   On a farm as small as this a labor crop such as cotton is essential in order to offer opportunity for full employment to its owner. The cattle, hogs, and poultry raised are sufficient only for the needs of the family.   The woods, protected from grazing, can be selectively cut from time to time to add slightly to income, but cotton is the basic crop.

The Piedmont is still predominantly an area of small farms, although during recent years consolidation has been going on.   Many small units have been converted into larger ones suitable for grassland-livestock farming.   This type of conversion is well advanced in northern Virginia where the large Washington-Arlington-Alexandria milk market makes dairying attractive.   Beef cattle are raised as a hobby and for commercial purposes.   In South Carolina there has been a strong trend from cotton to peaches, which also require much labor per acre.   Peach orchards are suited to small farms.   According to the 1950 Census of Agriculture, Spartanburg County had become the leading peach-producing county. These trends toward grassland-livestock farming and perennial tree culture are wise from the standpoint of good soil management in this province of rolling surface relief.

A DELTA COTTON PLANTATION

Mississippi is the most important cotton state east of Texas. In large measure it owes its strong position to the "Delta" which is a fertile, nearly level, alluvial plain lying between the Yazoo and Mississippi rivers. Peripheral extensions of similar soils stretch into adjoining Louisiana, Arkansas, and Tennessee. Today the heart of the Cotton South lies between Memphis and Vicksburg. The alluvial soils of this district, and the almost level topography are excellent advantages for farmers engaged in intensive row-crop cultivation. The dangers of erosion are minimal. Much of the area is so flat that drainage is necessary; a reflection of the abundance of ground water which can be drawn upon for irrigation during short periods of drought. From the standpoint of physical assets, the Delta is one of the finest agricultural provinces in the United States. Nearly level topography, a wide variety of soils, a long frost-free growing season, and an abundant annual rainfall, which can be supplemented by irrigation, are an impressive array of assets.

In the Delta one now witnesses one of the most remarkable transitions in social custom, agricultural techniques, and land use observable anywhere in America. In the same fields where a Negro drives a $10,000 mechanical cotton picker other rows are harvested by hand in the age-old manner. Because of the fine quality of its better soils and nearly level surface, erosion is not an important problem. Maintenance of humus, good soil structure, and fertility command attention, but these are problems common to all agriculturists. Because there are important differences in the suitability of various soils there is no need to take land out of cotton to establish grassland-livestock farming. The great variety of soil classes from clays to sandy loams has resulted from the way in which the Mississippi River and its tributary sloughs have deposited sediments since the time the river system itself was established.

The well-drained sandy loams are suited to cotton culture and are commonly reserved for this crop. Some lands with compact subsoils are developed for rice. The reclamation of river bottoms for this crop is particularly outstanding in Arkansas. The silty loams which are not quite so good for cotton are well suited to grassland-livestock farming, although they generally require ditch drains. Thousands of

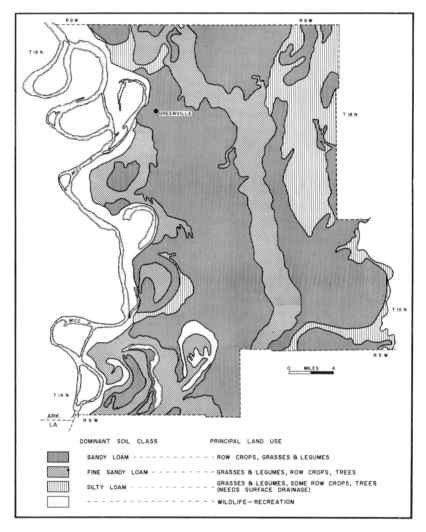

Figure 25:5.   Generalized land uses and soil textures in Washington County, Mississippi. (Source: U.S.D.A.)

acres of stiff "buckshot" clays are being cleared of river-bottom timber, drained, limed, fertilized, and planted to grasses and legumes. Because cotton was for so long the almost exclusive interest of many planters in the Delta the potentialities of the region were not fully appreciated until recently.   Cotton will very likely remain a major crop, for yields of 1.5 to 2 bales per acre are common.   This compares

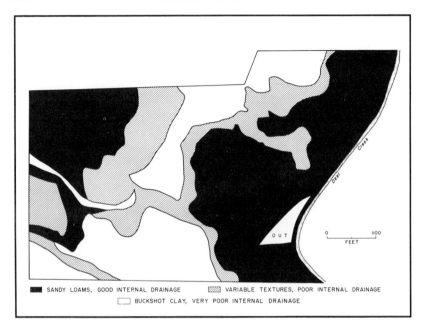

SANDY LOAMS, GOOD INTERNAL DRAINAGE   VARIABLE TEXTURES, POOR INTERNAL DRAINAGE

BUCKSHOT CLAY, VERY POOR INTERNAL DRAINAGE

Figure 25:6.   Land capabilities on a Delta cotton-beef plantation. (Source: U.S.D.A.)

favorably with the irrigated areas of the West.   Mechanization is advanced, and dependence upon tenant croppers is declining rapidly. Large land holdings are common, as they are in most other prominent plantation areas of the South.   This makes conversion to efficient modern mechanized methods easier and quicker than in areas where land is held in small parcels which do not warrant heavy investment in machinery.

Figure 25:5 is a generalized land-capability map of Washington County, Mississippi, in the heart of the Delta.   The pattern itself is a reflection of dominant soil characteristics which are themselves a reflection of fluvial action in the past.   Blank spaces are the immediate border swamps of present active channels.   The silty loams (and sometimes clay) are lowlands in need of drainage.   They are the buckshot lands or old overflow areas.   The fine sandy loams are old river channels and natural levees.   Cotton culture is concentrated on the sandy loams which are the best drained.   This map, being a generalized inventory, does not portray the great variation in soil texture and drainage conditions which appear on soil maps of individual farms made in the field on the basis of detailed examination.

Figure 25:6 is the land-capability map of a 718-acre plantation near Greenville, Mississippi. It is a highly developed condition. There are three major land types on this plantation and all are typical of the Delta. The dark areas are nearly level, sandy loams with good internal drainage. Row crops, such as cotton and corn, may be planted annually on these areas if winter legumes are grown as cover and green-manure crops. The principal soil-management problem is maintenance of humus and good soil structure. Legume-grass meadow may be established for a year or two on these excellent lands when they appear to suffer from continuous clean cultivation.

The shaded areas on the capability map are nearly level but with poor internal drainage. The soil textures range from sandy loams to clay loams. Cotton may be grown on these lands if alternated with grass-legume meadows two to three years out of six. They make fine permanent pasture ground and are advantageously used for that purpose, unless required for cotton and corn. The white areas on the capability map are flat, heavy clays which require artificial drainage. They are suitable for meadow and rice but are poor for corn and cotton.

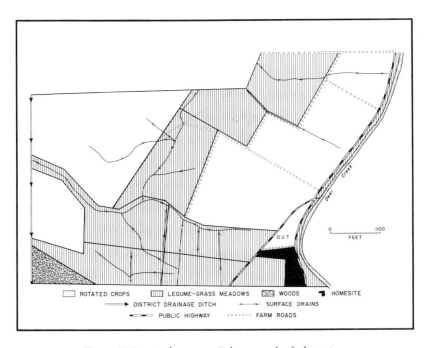

Figure 25:7.   Land use on a Delta cotton-beef plantation.

Figure 25:7 shows how the land on this plantation is used. There are 310 acres of improved grass-legume pastures divided into units to make rotational grazing possible. Since the grazing season extends the year around, several grass-legume mixtures are planted so that there may be good forage both in winter and summer. Some hay is cut to supplement the winter feed supply, and red clover and ryegrass are a summer pasture and hay combination. Dallis grass and lespedeza are also used for summer grazing. Ladino clover and fescue are planted for winter grazing. A herd of 165 Black Angus brood cows and their calves can be maintained by this excellent grassland program.

Impressive as the livestock enterprise is, it is secondary to intensive cotton production. Of the 380 acres of row-crop land 350 are annually planted to cotton; the normal yield is nearly a bale and a half of lint per acre. Fifteen acres are sown to soybeans and 15 to corn. When all of the land in the Mississippi River bottoms from Cairo, Illinois, to Baton Rouge are developed and utilized to their full capabilities, as they are on this farm, there can be little doubt that the region will be one of the richest agricultural provinces in the nation and one of the least susceptible to erosion.

A COTTON FARM ON THE BLACK WAXY PRAIRIE OF TEXAS

The Black Waxy Prairie of Texas is the transition zone between the humid southeastern United States and the dry Southwest. The gray-black rendzina soils of this area, similar to those of the Alabama-Mississippi Black Belt, are likewise derived from limestone and would be equally productive if rainfall were higher. Erratic precipitation averages 30 to 36 inches annually, but severe droughts are common. Considering the high rate of evaporation in this warm region, the rainfall is insufficient for high yields. The old problem of drought which is so common in the West and rare in the East must here be dealt with. The eastern margin of the Black Waxy Prairie is the western fringe of the Old South. The cattle range lies on its western border. There the soils are thin, and the "white rock" often appears on the surface. The cotton which is raised on the western high plains of Texas and Oklahoma is either irrigated or, like wheat, planted in a manner typical of that region of sparse and erratic rainfall. Fallowing is common and losses due to drought must be expected.

Being a fringe area, the Black Waxy Prairie has features peculiar to itself as well as evidence of both western and eastern influence. The native grasses included such bluestems as the tall "turkey-foot" which was dominant on the lands of Iowa. This has been all but

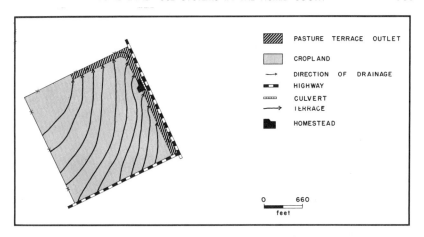

PASTURE TERRACE OUTLET

CROPLAND

→ DIRECTION OF DRAINAGE

HIGHWAY

CULVERT

TERRACE

HOMESTEAD

0   660

feet

Figure 25:8.   Terraced cropland in Lancaster County, Texas.

eliminated by cultivation and overgrazing. Now the usual seeded pastures are Bermuda grass which is adapted to the Southeast and buffalo grass which is a dry-plains dominant. Cotton until recent years was the primary cash crop. Wheat, more typical of the North and West than of the South, does as well as cotton and even better under good management. Winter wheat is favored by cool growing weather in late winter and early spring, whereas cotton, a summer crop, is often caught by mid-season drought. As in other sections of the more humid South, cattle are moving into this territory in greater numbers as stockmen reduce their interests in the dry mesquite lands to the westward.

Because the soil is thin, often less than a foot above the limestone and seldom more than 5 feet, erosion may easily destroy the usefulness of the land for cultivation. Terracing is widely practiced. In fact, this is one of the notable features of the landscape which, although appearing flat to the eye, is actually slightly sloped. Not only terracing but also the use of humus restorers, such as grasses and legumes, are essential to increase the permeability of the soil which bakes and cracks easily when low in organic materials.

Figure 25:8 is an 80-acre unit of a 300-acre operation. Originally this was a single cotton farm, but like many others in the area it is now considered too small to support a family or to employ its labor efficiently, and like many of these small units it has been absorbed in a consolidation. All the land is terraced to reduce runoff so that more water will penetrate into the ground. What does leave the cultivated fields empties onto a permanently sodded pasture. The rotation followed is designed to maintain soil humus. Cotton-grain sorghum-vetch or clover is the basic cropping system. It would not be practical if the other units worked with this farm did not have extensive pastures and some additional cropland which is worked in the same way. The grain sorghums are fed to the cattle but the vetch and clover are often left to mature. Their seed is harvested as a cash crop and the green matter is plowed under. The legumes can also be harvested for hay if necessary.

We have completed our survey of the major agricultural belts of the humid East and we have returned to the borders of the dry plains. However, there are in the East a number of important agricultural districts which deserve our attention, even though they are not large enough to be considered agricultural belts. We shall turn now to consider some of the more important specialty-crop districts which are an important feature of the farm picture in the eastern states.

REFERENCES

1. Alabama Agricultural Experiment Station, *Alabama Agriculture*, Auburn, 1953.
2. U.S. Department of Agriculture. *The Story of Soil Conservation in the South Carolina Piedmont, 1800–1860*, Government Printing office, Washington, D.C., 1940.
3. Gray, Lewis Cecil and Esther Katherine Thompson, *History of Agriculture in the Southern United States to 1860*, Carnegie Institution of Washington, Washington, D.C., 1933.

specialty-crop areas in the humid East

26

As California leads the arid West in the production of specialty crops, Florida holds those honors in the East. In both areas it is a long frost-free growing season that makes possible the raising of an imposing list of specialities and off-season staples. Of course, there are many farmers in Florida, as in California, who prefer to cultivate the conventional and to abstain from the unique which requires heavy investment and is particularly subject to rather sharp price fluctuations. Except for the Keys, no part of Florida is truly tropical, but there is a narrow band along the southern coast of the peninsula which experiences frost only occasionally. Numerous tropical and subtropical plants tolerate frosts for brief periods, and some of these, including papayas, pineapples, mangoes, avocados, and guavas, are grown commercially. Florida is the nation's leading producer of citrus fruits. It has important plantings of sugar cane and, according to the Florida Department of Agriculture, could produce all of the cane sugar required by the United States if it were not restricted to a quota by international agreement. Florida is

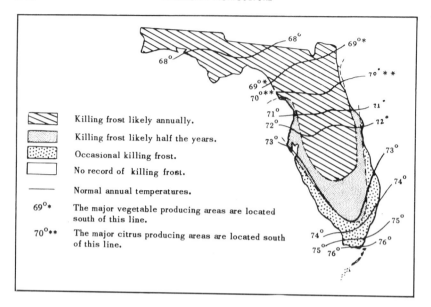

Figure 26:1. Frost-hazard zones and normal annual temperatures. (Source: Reference 8; p. 9.)

not the Producer of the amazing variety of special crops that makes California so exceptional, but the state has only begun to develop its latent potentialities. Although comparisons between these two states are interesting, there are also certain significant contrasts between them. California is both desert and humid, with an agriculture very much dependent upon irrigation and associated drainage. Florida is so humid that drainage is a paramount consideration. However, supplementary irrigation during temporary droughts is becoming common. California has the highest mountains and the lowest valleys, with many variations of terrain in between which help to foster a multitude of microclimates. Florida is fundamentally flat with limited areas of undulating topography, and microclimatic variety due to terrain is comparatively slight though very important, as we shall note in connection with citrus culture. The soils of California are among the state's primary assets. Until recently the soils of Florida were considered a prime handicap. Both states have a considerable latitudinal range, but that of California is greater. Hurricanes, common to Florida and to all the Atlantic-Gulf coast, are unknown in California. The important differences between these states might suggest that their agricultural interests would also differ more widely than they do. Actually their mild, brief winters outweigh all other considerations.   Thus they have much in common, including some competition with one another.

Peninsular Florida, jutting out into the sea, has an atmosphere similar to that over ocean islands.   The tang of salt air asserts itself far inland. Even when one loses the taste of it one continues to be reminded of Florida's intimacy with the sea by the sand encountered almost everywhere.   It is in pockets; in one's hair and shoes.   It is in one's bed and tub.   Without the feel of sand it would not be Florida.   Of course, those Florida farmers who have muck, peat, and heavy loams would not concur in calling their state an agricultural sandbox.   Yet, no one could be more aware than they that, except for the organic soils of the Everglades, good soils are uncommon.

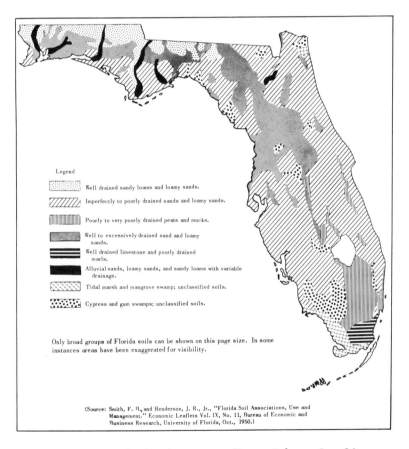

Figure 26:2.   Florida soil associations. (Source: Reference 8; p. 3.)

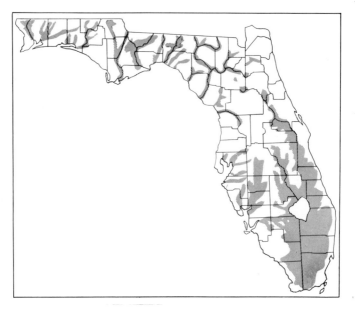

Figure 26:3.   General areas subject to flood damage. (Source: Reference 8; p. 13.)

Modern technological progress in soil management and water engineering has greatly influenced Florida's agricultural activity.   No longer
are many sandy areas dismissed.   Farmers have learned how to supply
the nutrient materials in which the soils are naturally deficient.   Fertilizers are used in vast quantities, including those with the trace elements:
boron, manganese, copper, cobalt, iron, and zinc.   One of the major dis-
advantages of sand is its poor water-holding capacity, but Florida often
has more than enough water.   Hydraulic engineers have developed systems of combined drainage and irrigation which remove water in times
of excess and return it in times of temporary drought.   The task of
draining the most productive lands in Florida is somewhat analogous to
the problem of supplying irrigation water to the best agricultural districts of California.   Both require expensive and skillful engineering.
Without modern hydraulic techniques, neither California nor Florida
would have achieved agricultural prominence.

Lake Okeechobee is the largest fresh-water body in the nation entirely
within the borders of a single state.   It is very shallow and is more like
an enormous pond within a swamp than a lake.   Drainage from south-
central Florida enters Lake Okeechobee via the Kissimmee River, and in
times past the lake has overflowed.   In 1928 a hurricane-driven wave,

sweeping over the southern shores, killed about 2400 people. Drainage from Lake Okeechobee into the Everglades to the south contributes heavily to swamp conditions. The period of flood is being reduced by the construction of dams on the Kissimmee River, levees around Lake Okeechobee, and a series of floodway canals draining into the ocean. At the same time the northern Everglades are being drained for agricultural development. Because there are times when droughts occur, crops in the northern Everglades, as elsewhere in Florida, may require irrigation. Consequently, water conservancy districts have been formed in

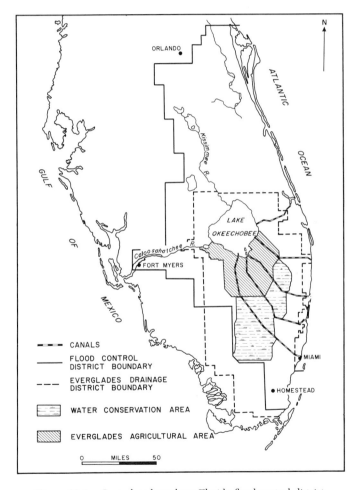

Figure 26:4.   Central and southern Florida flood-control district.

the Everglade swamps south and southeast of the agricultural areas. Levees are being built around the swamps of the conservancy districts so that the water level of the swamps may be raised with drainage runoff from the north. Thus in times of heavy rainfall water is admitted via the canals into the swamps of the conservancy districts. In times of drought the stored waters may be pumped from the swamps of the conservancy districts to irrigate the agricultural areas or they may be released to recharge ground-water levels of coastal cities and resorts. The combined drainage and irrigation engineering being conducted in southern Florida is the most elaborate in the state, but the same principle is being widely applied elsewhere on a smaller scale. Coupled with proper fertilization and crop rotation, these water-control methods are making intensive cultivation possible on both sand and organic soils which once were thought to have little agricultural value. Sugar cane, rice, kenaf, ramie, truck crops, and improved pasture are all successful.

CITRUS PRODUCTION IN FLORIDA

Citrus production has held a prominent place in Florida's agriculture for many years. The orange was introduced by the Spaniards and propagated by Indians for their own use. Some of the first commercial groves in nineteenth-century Florida were the result of budding superior strains on the pruned stock of earlier Indian plantings. Today there are approximately a half-million acres of citrus in Florida. The crops tolerate light frosts, but severe damage may occur when temperatures drop to the lower 20's. Even 25°F at blossom time may be devastating. Cold weather in Florida is caused by excessive radiation of heat from the ground on clear, dry, and calm winter nights and by the invasion of cold waves from the North. Local citrus growers still refer to the disastrous winter of 1894–1895 as the time of the "Big Freeze" when most groves in the northern section of the state were destroyed or injured. Since that time the industry has shifted southward and is now concentrated approximately at the geographical center of the peninsula. The best citrus is produced where there is some cold weather because the fruit benefits by the lower temperatures in color, percentage of solids, and in sweetness. To maintain quality and to take advantage of terrain the growers of central Florida risk occasional frost. There are a number of methods of frost control but they are costly.

The following data are taken from observations made during the winter of 1954–1955 in a Polk County orange grove. They read like a hospital chart with temperature recordings and the companion reactions of the patient.

Table 26:1.   Relation of Temperatures to Frost Damage of Citrus
(Source: Reference 3; p. 4d)

Station	Date	Minimum Temperature	Duration in Hours and Tenths of Hours At and Below								
			27°	26°	25°	24°	23°	22°	21°	20°	19°
2827–D	12/11	25.0	4.7	3.5	1.0						
	12/16	26.1	1.8	0.6							
	12/21	23.4	5.4	4.4	4.1	2.8	1.0				
	12/22	25.4	2.0	1.5	0.3						
	1/6	(Observation)	Considerable number of specks found in outside fruit. Only very few in sheltered fruit.								
	1/14	19.2	4.1	4.0	3.9	3.3	2.8	2.4	2.0	1.2	0.3
	1/27	(Observation)	100 per cent defoliation on trees up to 5 inches in diameter. 50 per cent to 70 per cent on more mature trees. All fruit sustained freeze damage to a greater or lesser degree.								
	1/30	23.7	2.0	1.8	1.4	0.6					
	2/13	22.2	3.4	2.7	2.5	1.9	1.2	0.2			
	2/24	(Observation)	Bark split on limbs up to three-quarters of an inch in diameter. Twigs all killed. Many young trees killed to the ground.								

The damage noted late in February was the cumulative effect of the previous cold spells.

The most widely used method of combatting frost is by burning oil in high-stack heaters. These have a three-foot louvred stack for more complete combustion of gases, a tight-fitting cover, and a draft adjustable to three or more positions for low, moderate, or high heat. They burn about a gallon of fuel an hour at moderate setting, enough to last until morning on all except the coldest nights. The heaters are usually lighted when the temperature in the groves reaches about 26 degrees and are regulated to bring the temperature up to about 28 or 29 degrees and hold it there. Usually only half of the heaters are lighted. This leaves the other half in reserve in case of severe cold or for the following night. The effectiveness and cost of operating heaters may be illustrated by a report of the Federal-State Frost Warning Service of an experiment conducted in 1947 in a 400-acre Polk County grove.

In this grove two nights of full firing and one night of scattered firing were required to protect it from frost. The only damage sustained was around the edges on the southern sides and then only in spots. Pots had not been placed on the south side of the grove and late on the morning of February 6 the light winds experienced came from the south and damaged leaves and twigs on exposed edges. Pots were ignited in every other row during the worst periods of this freeze and the other half were left as reserve in case conditions became more severe or for use on the next night on which freezing conditions could be expected. On each night of total firing it took from fifty to fifty-eight men about one hour to get all the pots in operation and another thirty to forty-five minutes to check and adjust the pots so that they were burning with about five inch openings.

Temperatures recorded just outside the grove on the morning of February 6 were as low as 18.5 degrees and on the morning of February 11 were as low as 21 degrees. Other groves sustaining such temperatures were severely damaged, experiencing split bark on limbs and some trunks as well as complete defoliation and total loss of fruit. The figures below are typical of firing costs in this section of the State. These are actual figures taken from the books of the manager of the grove.

Date	Total Hours of Firing	Number of Men	Labor Cost	Gallons of Oil Used	Cost of Oil	Total Cost
Feb. 6	10	58	$580	55,000	$4010.60	$4590.60
Feb. 11	10	58	$500	55,000	$4010.60	$4510.60
						$9101.20

With 400 acres and 20 hours of firing the cost per acre per hour is $1.14. (Source: Reference 7.)

Citrus requires drained soil as well as protection from damaging frosts. In central Florida there are a number of areas which have many ponds and lakes separated by low rolling hills with sandy topsoils. The topography and sandy surface soils assure adequate drainage. Also important is the good air drainage above the ground that is afforded by the hilly relief. Cold air, being heavier than warm air, tends to settle in low areas at the base of the rolling hills. Citrus planted on the slopes and shoulders of these hills is protected from frost to some extent on cold nights. The Federal-State Frost Warning Service and the Florida Forest Service have made temperature readings at Avon Park since 1935. Located at Avon Park is "a rather high hill." Its crest is 30 feet above the level of a low frost pocket 150 yards away. On the crest of the hill and in the frost-pocket depression thermometers are set 4.5 feet above the ground. Records show that the temperature at the frost-pocket station has been as much as 18 degrees lower than the temperature at the hilltop station when simultaneous readings have been made. (Reference 4; p. 6.)

In central Florida the lakes and ponds are an added protection against frosts; air currents blowing off the water are warmer than the overland air which loses its heat readily through radiation on clear nights. The double protection of air drainage afforded on the slopes and the warming

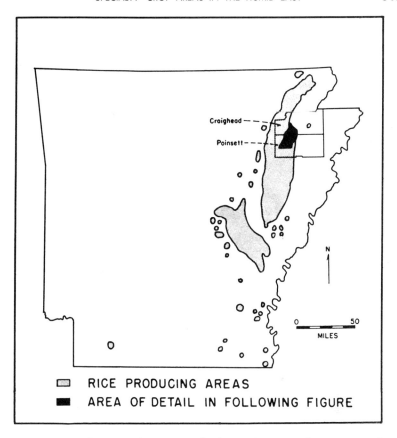

Figure 26:5.   The rice-producing areas of Arkansas. (Source: Reference 5; p. 10.)

effects of surrounding water bodies is of great value to the growers.   Such sites have a high commercial value not normal for sandy hills in most other parts of the world.

Two important specialty crops of the South are rice and peanuts. They are not likely to compete with one another for available land because rice is best grown where flood irrigation is practicable and where the subsoil is clay and will not drain easily.   Peanuts are most successfully produced on very well drained, light, sandy loam soils.   Both crops require warm growing weather and much rainfall or irrigation. Suitable climatic and soil conditions for both crops are common on the Gulf-Atlantic coastal plain.   Rice production is prominent in Texas and Louisiana and on the alluvial plain of the Mississippi River in Arkansas.   The Central Valley of California, particularly near Sacramento, is also an important rice district (Figures A-10 and A-11, Appendix).

The rapid expansion of rice production in northeastern Arkansas has been one of the important agricultural developments in that state. This expansion has been made possible by the clearing of forest from swampy river bottoms and by the construction of drainage and irrigation systems by which water levels may be controlled. Before World War I Arkansas rice was grown on land which had been river-bottom prairie. Such prairie land was very limited. Much more extensive were the wooded bottoms, but they were then thought to be inferior. However, there has been impressive progress in the conversion of the wooded lowlands into excellent rice plantations. Figure 26:5 shows the rice-producing areas of Arkansas with the Weiner district of Craighead and Poinsett counties blocked out in black. Figure 26:6 is a detailed map of land-clearing operations which were undertaken between 1937 and 1949 in the Weiner district. The primary purpose of this clearing has been to put the land in condition for rice cultivation.

A major reason for this rapid progress is the development of cheap mechanized timber-removal methods. By diking and by establishing proper drainage canals on the wooded bottoms before the timber is cut it is possible to provide dry and firm ground for mechanized operations. Mechanical tree saws mounted on rubber-tired wheels are in common use, although hand methods are also employed. Between 1947 and 1949 the Arkansas Agricultural Experiment Station made field studies of the costs of tree removal on potential rice lands. In its report the Experiment Station concluded that,

> On farms where detailed records of clearing costs were kept, complete clearing by hand averaged $63.37 per acre. Where clearings were cut with a self-propelled tree saw and piled with a bulldozer, the average cost per acre was $53.58. (Source: Reference 5.)

New lands are also coming into rice production in one of the oldest settled sections of the Gulf states. In the early eighteenth century, while English colonists were pinned behind the Appalachians by hostile Indians and French, the latter created along the Mississippi River a well-charted land of fur-trading posts. A flourishing community of rice farms in the bayou country at the river's mouth helped produce a needed food supply. French West Indian sugar plantations were also stocked with rice from paddies northwest of New Orleans. Almost a century later, at the time French rule was extinguished through Jefferson's purchase of the Louisiana Territory, levees had been constructed on both sides of the Mississippi River for fifty miles above New Orleans. Be-

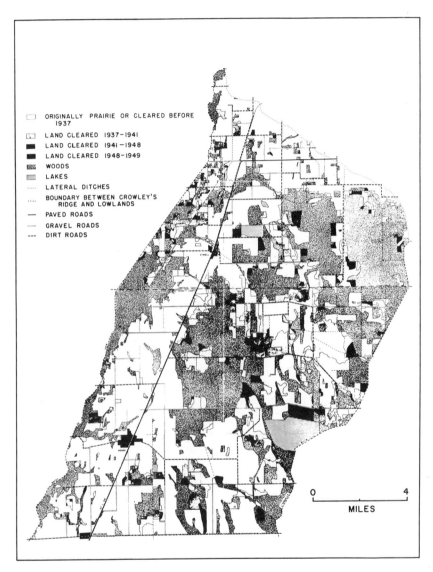

Figure 26:6. Land clearing in the Weiner district, Arkansas, 1937–1949. (Source: Reference 5; p. 10.)

hind the levees were irrigated fields to which water was conveyed through gates.

The agronomics of land utilization in the swampy, clay soils of the Gulf fringe, while sometimes complicated, are relatively simple compared with the associated tasks of drainage and irrigation. Both of these techniques are needed for successful rice culture. For almost three centuries the very enormity of any undertaking that would cut drainage channels through hundreds of square miles of the lushest and most tangled marshland in the United States stymied invasion except along the fringes. Before the advent of modern draglines it seemed that the interior would remain forever the feeding grounds of migratory waterfowl. Now these machines are opening ditches for drainage along the Gulf coast to create new rice farms.

Few methods of crop cultivation have undergone so drastic a change as those of rice production. Literally they have progressed from the horse to the airplane in a short span of years. With no other crop is the airplane so intimately associated as an agricultural implement. The farmers of Louisiana's coast, with only a slight degree of exaggeration, say that it does everything but harvest the grain. It is their seeder, their fertilizer spreader, and their pesticide dispenser. By spraying weed killers, it is used as a substitute for the cultivator. Now desiccants are being applied by plane to assure uniform ripening of the grain which is a major problem in rice culture. Birds are a particular hazard to rice because there are so many of them living in the adjacent bayou areas. The airplane is used to buzz the fields during the ripening season. Scarcely a rice farm is more than a few miles from a farm service airstrip. Commercial planes for hire by rice growers are regularly available by telephone. Supplies are shipped to the air strips and the pilots apply them according to instructions given by the plantation owners.

Figure 26:7 is the plan of a recent private reclamation project which drained 1000 acres of marsh on the Louisiana Gulf coast near Jennings. Here 370 acres are set aside for rice cultivation, and much of the remainder is used as pasture. A dragline was employed to construct a dike completely around the reclaimed area. The dragline, in building the dike in front of itself, used the flat crest of the dike as a road on which to travel; otherwise it would have sunk into the marsh. As a result of scooping up marsh clay to build the dike, a moat or canal was created around the inner side between the dike and the reclaimed land. This canal, and an additional spur, serves to withdraw water to a point where a pump lifts it over the dike into a drainage canal that empties into a bayou.

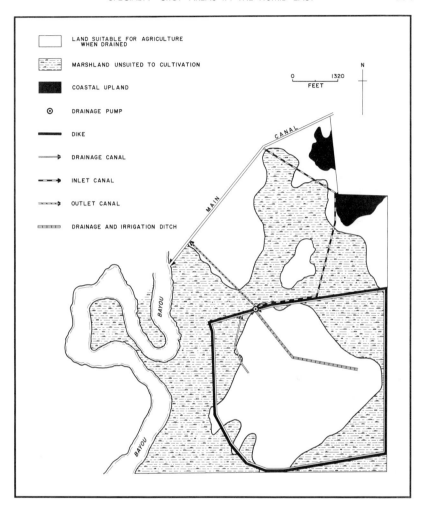

LAND SUITABLE FOR AGRICULTURE
WHEN DRAINED

MARSHLAND UNSUITED TO CULTIVATION

COASTAL UPLAND

DRAINAGE PUMP

DIKE

DRAINAGE CANAL

INLET CANAL

OUTLET CANAL

DRAINAGE AND IRRIGATION DITCH

N

0   1320
      FEET

CANAL

MAIN

BAYOU

BAYOU

Figure 26:7.   Gulf-coast rice plantation in Louisiana.

Through the mild winter season the rice field remains drained. A cover crop may be grown for winter pasturage and green manure to keep the soil in good condition. The Louisiana State University Rice Experiment Station recommends a rotation of two years of rice and three years of improved pasture to keep the land productive. The land is plowed in April or May. Water from the bayou is then applied to a depth of about 4.5 inches, and an airplane is employed to broadcast the rice seed in the water. After germination, when the seedlings are about one half inch long, the water is withdrawn by pumping. When the plants are 6 to 8 inches tall the land is again flooded to a depth of about 4.5 inches and remains submerged during the growing season. Water is withdrawn ten days to two weeks before harvest to allow the ground to dry out so that self-propelled combines can operate. Rice lands are submerged during the growing season mainly to control weeds and grasses and to meet the high moisture needs of the crop. Rice can tolerate flooding, but its competitors generally cannot.

A VIRGINIA PEANUT FARM

Peanuts are grown in a number of localities on the coastal plain from Virginia to Texas. The crop is quite satisfactory for small farms because it is another labor crop and, like tobacco, its culture is restricted to those farms which have federal acreage allotments. Such allotments add materially to the value of the farms which possess them, since a small amount of tillable land will often enable a man to be fully employed. The prices of peanuts reflect the labor expended in producing them. This crop will grow on a wide variety of soils including clays, but to get the peanuts out of the ground successfully light sandy loams are best. Compact soils tend to hold on to the pods when the vines are lifted; thus a large portion of the crop may be left buried in the ground. Well-drained land is essential; otherwise the plant does not develop properly, and the fine stems, by which the pods are attached, may rot.

Light sandy soils are essential if a good set of pods is to be obtained. Peanut flowers emerge at the joint where the leaves are attached to the stems. As soon as pollination takes place the flower fades; then the seed stem called "peg" elongates and goes into the soil, where the pod develops. For good yields it is essential that the crop be grown on loose soil into which the pegs can enter easily. A warm growing season and an annual rainfall of 42 to 54 inches is normal in the best peanut areas of the coastal plain. Figure A-11 in the Appendix shows that commercial peanut culture is most highly developed in southeastern Alabama, southwestern Georgia, southeastern Virginia, and the adjoining area of North Carolina. Soils and climate are particularly favorable in these districts.

Under the best conditions a portion of the peanut crop is unavoidably left in the ground, and its recovery by hand or mechanical devices is impractical. Consequently, it is common for peanut growers to combine their operations with hog raising because hogs will root for the buried pods after the harvest and make an almost complete recovery of what

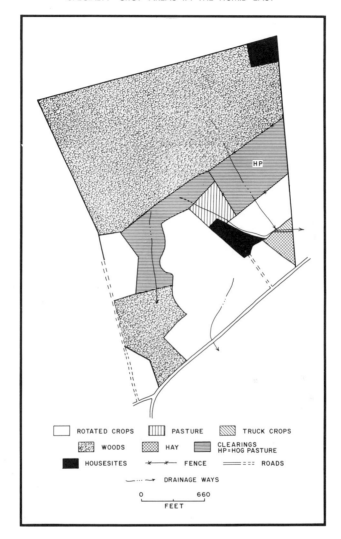

Figure 26:8.   One-hundred-eighteen-acre peanut-hog farm in Virginia.

otherwise might be wasted.   Because peanuts are high in both oil and protein they are an excellent feed for swine.   Peanuts are sensitive to weed competition, and the best way to overcome this problem is to rotate them with clean-cultivated crops such as corn and soybeans.   Crimson clover, a winter-legume cover crop, is excellent for smothering weeds and for maintaining mellowness of the soil.   All these crops fit well

Figure 26:9. Farm drainage on the southeastern coastal plain, 1947–1953. (Source: Reference 1; p. 61.)

into a hog-peanut program. Corn is used as a finishing feed for the hogs in the final weeks before they go to market. The clover, used as pasture, makes excellent cheap feed for the pigs.

Figure 26:8 is the land-use plan of a 118-acre hog-peanut farm in the Smithfield area of Virginia, so well known both for its hams and its peanuts. It is farms like these which are the basis of that reputation. One of the striking features of the way the land is used on this farm is the large proportion of woodland. This is typical of the area in which much of the wooded acreage is poorly drained. With the aid of bulldozers, draglines, and community drainage agreements, these woodlands are being progressively converted to cropland where the soils are satisfactory.   Eight acres of this farm were recently reclaimed in this manner, and more are scheduled for reclamation in the future.

It would be very difficult to make a good living on 52 acres of cultivated land in this day of modern mechanized operations if it were not for the fact that much labor must be expended in producing the peanut crop.   It is this employment rather than the size of the farm which makes it a very desirable economic unit maintained in the neatest and most efficient manner.   The progress being made in land reclamation by drainage in southeastern Virginia and in the Carolinas is bringing into production some level, sandy loams which will stand the most intensive cropping to corn, soybeans, peanuts, and tobacco without serious hazard of erosion.   The fact that leguminous cover makes good growth in winter means that humus can be maintained while intensive row-cropping is carried on every summer.   In the future the Atlantic coastal plain from southern Delaware to Florida will play a much more important role in American agriculture than it has in the past.

REFERENCES

1. Anderson, James R., *Land Use and Development, Southeastern Coastal Plain*, U.S. Department of Agriculture, Government Printing Office, Washington, D.C., 1956.
2. Beattie, W. R. and J. H., *Peanut Growing*, U. S. Department of Agriculture, Government Printing Office, Washington, D.C., 1943.
3. Federal-State Frost Warning Service, *Notes on Critical Temperatures of Citrus*, Ridge District, Florida, 1955 (mimeographed).
4. Federal-State Frost Warning Service, *Temperature Inversion Experiments*, Lakeland, Florida, 1953 (mimeographed).
5. Jenks, George F., and Robert W. Harrison, *Methods and Costs of Clearing Land in Northeast Arkansas*, Arkansas Agricultural Experiment Station, Fayetteville, 1950.
6. Manheim, Uriel L., *The Florida Everglades—Their Farming Prospects*, University of Miami, Coral Gables, 1954.
7. Norman, O. N., *Determination of Firing Costs*, Federal-State Frost Warning Service, Ridge District, Florida (mimeographed).
8. Reuss, L. A., *Florida's Land Resources and Land Use*, University of Florida, Gainesville, 1954.

some
specialty crop
areas
—continued

27

The number of specialty crops is so large that selection of those discussed in these concluding chapters is highly arbitrary. However, the choices have been influenced by the amount of acreage employed and by rather special environmental prerequisites. Tobacco deserves attention on both counts. From the standpoint of the agricultural economy it is the most important crop in North Carolina—such names as Winston-Salem, Durham, and Raleigh are familiar to every smoker. In Kentucky, Connecticut, South Carolina, Virginia, and Maryland tobacco is a major crop (Figure A-12, Appendix).

Usually the most important quality of tobacco is its aroma, but this is not always so. For instance, Connecticut shade-grown, cigar-wrapper types are valued for their texture and color. Color and aroma are both important in the bright, flue-cured leaves for cigarettes. Most strains are developed by geneticists not only for special uses but also for best quality obtainable on specific soils. Perhaps the market value of no other crop is so easily influenced by soil character. This is because

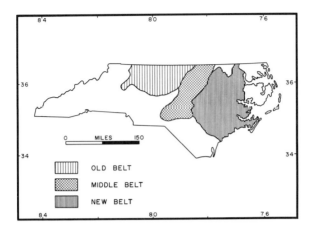

Figure 27:1.   Tobacco regions of northeastern North Carolina. (Source: Reference 2.)

aroma, color, texture, and burning quality are altered by slight variations in soil, and these subtle features are often more important than maximum yield in determining value.

In northern North Carolina three tobacco belts are located side by side. They are called the Old Belt, Middle Belt, and New Belt. These names correspond respectively to three physiographic provinces: the piedmont, the fall zone, and the coastal plain. The soils of these three physiographic provinces also differ.

In the days when natural soil fertility was of major importance and when bright color was not a prime characteristic of cigarette tobaccos the Old Belt or piedmont district of North Carolina was the principal growing area. Old Belt tobaccos are generally heavier in body and darker in color. New Belt tobaccos are lighter in both body and color. In their natural condition the best tobacco soils of the New Belt are infertile. In a sense they are almost neutral media. The grower on the coastal plain now wants this kind of chemically inactive soil so that the special blends of fertilizers used will affect the tobacco with results that are less influenced by side-reactions. What may be considered a poor soil for most crops may be regarded as excellent for tobacco in North Carolina. As we noted in Chapter 26, this is not true for the Burley types grown in the Bluegrass area of Kentucky where the soils are rich silt loams derived from limestone.

It is sometimes remarked that the fine shade-grown tobaccos of Connecticut are grown on sands. It is true that the best shade-tobacco farms are located on deltas built into what was once a glacial lake.

These deltas are composed chiefly of sand and gravel, but of great importance is the fact that the best tobaccos come from areas on these deltas where the topsoils are derived from a superficial layer of aeolean silts or loess. Some have loess mixed with subsoil sands as the result of deep plowing. Only the deeper subsoils are truly sandy.

Figure 27:2 is the land-use map of a 160-acre tobacco, vegetable, and fescue-seed farm in Sampson County on the coastal plain of North Carolina. The terrain is nearly level. Subterranean tile lines are located in several fields to improve drainage. The sandy loam soils are easily susceptible to desiccation during brief but common droughts. The crops raised on this farm are much too valuable to trust to the vagaries of the weather; consequently, a pond has been constructed by damming a drainage channel. This pond holds enough water to irrigate the tobacco and vegetable crops; usually there is also sufficient water to irrigate the fescue which is grown for seed. Possibilities of constructing such irrigation reservoirs on the coastal plain exist on many farms; this is one reason that the coastal plain will doubtless become a more important agricultural district in the future than it has been in the past. The combination of level terrain, abundant water supplies, a long growing season, and soils which will respond to proper fertilization are all splendid assets. Statistics show that 28.6 per cent of all the fertilizers consumed in the United States in 1950–1951 were used in Florida, Georgia, the Carolinas, and Virginia.

To raise good plants the soil must be well supplied with nutrients. Probably lack of phosphorus will be our chief fertilizer problem in the future. The free atmosphere above us is chiefly nitrogen, and only a moderate expenditure is required to convert it from an inert gas to a useful plant nutrient. In addition to a number of rich accumulations of potassium salts, much of the earth's rock crust contains significant quantities of this critical element. Granite dust from quarries in Massachusetts has already been used successfully as a potassium fertilizer in Connecticut Valley tobacco fields. But the world's supply of phosphorus, so essential to plant and animal life, is comparatively low. We in the United States are in no immediate danger of a phosphorus deficit, but there is a positive limit to commercial sources. A 100-bushel crop of corn requires 55 pounds of phosphoric acid; yet most soils contain far smaller amounts in forms that are available to cultivated plants. This available portion is not all phosphorus in the soil. Much more is chemically bound in mineral molecules from which it is only slowly and partially released. Much commercial phosphate fertilizer applied to the soil is rendered unavailable to plants by the mineral soil's own affinity for the element.

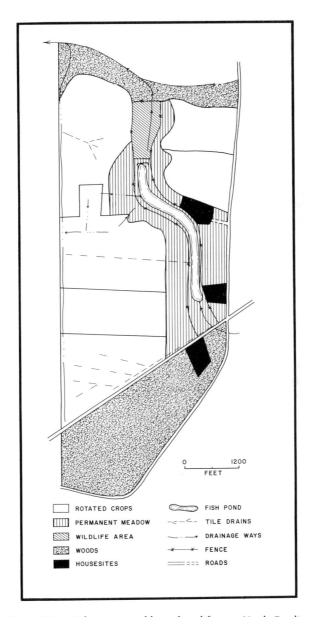

Figure 27:2.   Tobacco, vegetable, and seed farm in North Carolina.

In the scientific literature on fertilizers and soil management there is a wealth of information on the behavior of phosphorus. A series of papers by Dean Dale H. Sieling and his associates at the Massachusetts Agricultural Experiment Station are particularly informative as to the availability of phosphorus in soil. They emphasize the importance of organic matter as the agent which promotes availability of this element. (Reference 1; p. 5.) Any system of agriculture which helps to extend the usefulness of phosphorous supplies already in the soil is one which will lessen pressure upon limited commercial reserves.

A DELMARVA VEGETABLE FARM

The production of market vegetables is said by some growers to be a form of gambling rather than a type of farming. This is a way of stating that the market is the most important factor in the business. Although this is somewhat true of every commodity, fresh vegetables or truck are particularly vulnerable to immediate market conditions because they are not stored for long—usually not at all. Each acre represents a very high expenditure for labor and fertilizer; so that actually what is being cultivated is an investment even though it is called a crop. The story is told in a town on the Delmarva Peninsula that in one boom year when crops "hit" the market right, a certain farmer challenged the local Cadillac dealer to flip a coin for "double or nothing" on a flashy new model. The next year the market collapsed and the farmer went broke.

The southern tip of the Delmarva Peninsula, sometimes called Virginia's Eastern Shore, is one of the most important vegetable crop centers on the Atlantic seaboard. There the tempo of the truck market is such that all men cannot take it. It divides them, as they say, into two classes: the "plungers" and the "stayers." The plungers are the gamblers. They buy land or rent it at high prices, and they don't hedge themselves by preseason contracts with dealers. Such contracts assure the grower the minimum price, but they also tie him up so that if the market should be high he cannot take advantage of it. The stayers are the conservatives; the ones with long memories and some with land titles in their families dating back to the King's Grants. They are the ones who rent lands to the plungers or play it safe by contracting their crops to dealers at low but guaranteed prices. They never have bonanza years, but neither do they lose their farms as long as they remain cautious.

Nearly every city of any size has market gardeners on its periphery who supply perishables in season; but, as every housewife knows, some fresh vegetables are on the counters of grocery stores and supermarkets every day of the year. To supply these truck crops in a steady flow there must be crops to harvest somewhere at all times.   Figure A-9 in the Appendix shows the distribution of commercial vegetable farming.   Certain areas stand out prominently and it will be noted that with few exceptions the most important ones are either near the sea or on the shores of the Great Lakes.   Other features of the distribution pattern are the areas of concentrated production extending from subtropical Florida to the Canadian border.   These two factors of location and spread are both intimately tied in with the gambling aspects of vegetable farming.

We may use the example of green beans to illustrate the tight schedule by which a vegetable crop comes on the market.   The green-bean season begins with the harvest in southern Florida in February or early March. By the middle of March central Florida and the Rio Grande Valley of Texas are already in competition, and by the first of May there are harvests in California and along the Gulf coast.   As more localities contribute to the supply, prices may decline.   The first growers to harvest are generally, but not always, the ones who receive the best prices. From the end of May to early July so many areas are producing green beans that proximity to the biggest markets is more of an advantage than timing.   It is then that the growers of New Jersey, Long Island, and the Lake Ontario area compete with one another for the nearby metropolitan markets.   After the middle of July the growing season is generally too warm for successful production, except at high altitudes in the West, along the shore of Lake Ontario, or near the coasts of Maine, Oregon, and Washington.

Such a schedule as that outlined is a general one which is certain to vary with changes in the weather.   Because temperature variation is reduced near oceans and lake shores these locations are preferred by the growers of many specialty crops.   Also, the sea tends to warm the air over coastal lands during the early spring months and thus hastens the season.   In summer the sea and the Great Lakes tend to cool the air along their shores, thus extending the season where high temperatures might otherwise do damage.   It will be noted that the most important centers of production in the humid East are

1. Peninsular Florida which is bounded by the Gulf and the Atlantic.
2. The Delmarva Peninsula, bounded by Delaware Bay, the Atlantic, and Chesapeake Bay.
3. Southern New Jersey, bounded by the Atlantic and Delaware Bay.
4. Long Island in the Atlantic.
5. The shore of Lake Ontario.

The terrain of these areas is level to gently rolling.   This permits intensive cultivation with little prospect of soil erosion.   Of particular

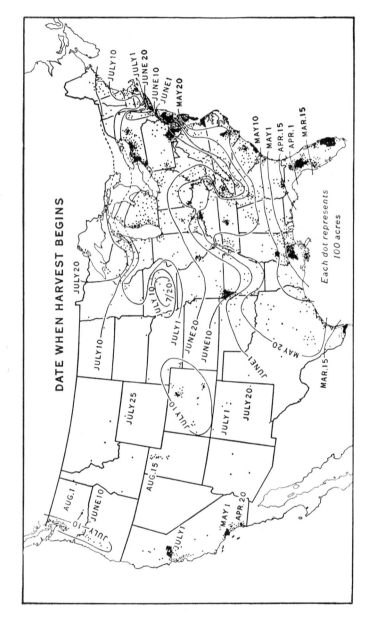

Figure 27:3.   Fresh green beans — date when harvest begins. (Source: U.S.D.A.)

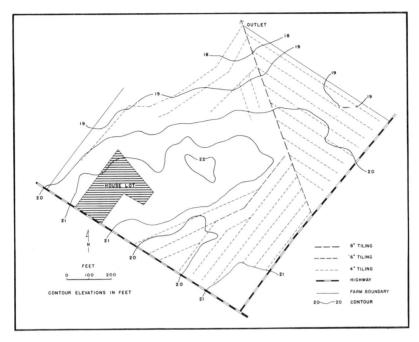

Figure 27:4.   Drainage systems on an Eastern Shore truck farm in Virginia.

advantage is the sandy loam texture of coastal plain soils from Long Island southward.   These light-textured soils drain more easily and warm more quickly in the early spring than heavier textured soils which are common farther inland.   The matter of getting a crop to market just a few days early may mean the difference between a substantial profit and a small one.   The farm with the best-drained soil, nearest the sea, at the right latitude, may be worth two or three times as much per acre as another farm only a few miles or a few degrees distant but not so well situated.

As we know, drainage is one of the common problems on the coastal plain.   Figure 27:4 shows the design of a tile drainage system on a truck farm in Accomack County, Virginia, which is on the Delmarva Peninsula, or "Eastern Shore."   The one-foot contour lines reveal the nearly level character of this land, and the figures on the contour lines indicate the slight elevation above sea level.   In Accomack County, as elsewhere on the coastal plain, the possibilities for irrigation are often excellent.   Rainfall is approximately 43 inches annually, and there are many fresh-water swamps and brackish estuaries.   By placing dams across the estuaries the tides can be repulsed and the waters kept fresh. Some swamps may be converted into reservoirs by damming the streams which drain them. Supplementary irrigation is now becoming common on the Eastern Shore, just as it is in Florida, the Carolinas, in New Jersey, and on Long Island. In fact, irrigation is rapidly becoming essential to vegetable farming everywhere because the investment risk is too great to trust to natural rainfall. Some farmers are discovering that they may bring crops to market a week or two ahead of normal schedule by planting early in spring before the danger of frost is past. By using sprinkler irrigation systems on frosty nights they keep the plants from being nipped.

POTATO CULTURE

In terms of volume the potato is the most important of the vegetable crops. It is a desirable labor crop where the growing season is short and cool. Also it is about the only one which grows well under those conditions and is also in strong demand. The potato has excellent keeping qualities if protected from heat, frost, and dampness—and this type of storage can be easily and cheaply provided on growers' farms by building simple masonry buildings in the ground. The soil serves as excellent insulation against heat and frost. Of course, the location of such storage structures should be on high, dry ground. The potato is a boon to farmers along our northern border and in high altitude areas of the West. California, South Texas, and Florida produce late- and early-season potatoes by taking advantage of cool growing weather in the South while the ground is still frozen in the major production areas of the North and high-altitude West.

The potato is important in the agriculture of Maine, Idaho, Colorado, and the Red River Valley of Minnesota–North Dakota. There is a general interest in the crop in all of the northern Great Lakes states, but on the whole the bulk of the nation's supply is produced in a few areas of intensive concentration as shown in Figure A–14 of the Appendix. Long Island's prominence is due not only to its proximity to the New York market but also to the fact that the harvest comes at an opportune time when new potatoes from the South have been sold and harvests in the major northern areas have not begun.

The potato, native to the South American Andes, is one of very few food plants which can be grown far above the timber line where days are cool and nights are cold. So intimate is the potato with a cold climate in the Andes of Peru, Ecuador, and Bolivia that one

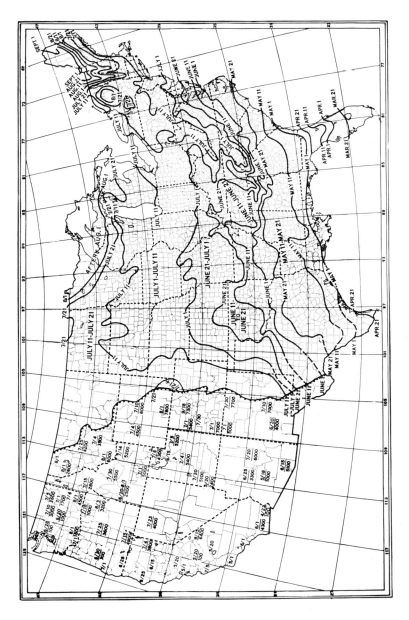

Figure 27:5.   Potatoes — date when digging begins. (Source: Reference 3; p. 83.)

of the Indian methods of preserving it in those countries is with frost. When the potatoes are dug on the high intermountain basins, or alti-planos, they are carried farther up the slopes above the frost line where they are diced and exposed to freezing and drying winds. The combined treatment completely desiccates the potato so that it may be stored almost indefinitely.

Aroostook County, Maine, is the potato capital of the United States. Usually Aroostook produces two to three times more potatoes than any other county in the country. There, the average frost-free season begins in the last week of May and ends by the third week of September. At Van Buren, in northern Aroostook County, the frost-free season begins about the first of June and ends in the middle of September. The average temperature for July is 65 degrees. Few of the major crops, except small grains, peas, and hay, will mature during such a short and cool growing season. It is no wonder that they are the crops generally grown in rotation with potatoes in the North and in the high-altitude West.

FRUIT CULTURE

There was a time when nearly every farm had its own kitchen orchard and berry patch from which fruits were gathered for family use without much thought of market sales. In years when the harvest was plentiful the surpluses were sold, but that purpose was secondary. Since the maintenance of these orchards and gardens was a sideline operation which received attention only when major activities of the farm were already attended to, the produce was seldom of uniform grade or quality. It satisfied dietary needs, but often it was not up to better standards of appearance. Commercial horticulturists, facing this amateur competition, concentrated upon producing fruits of superior quality in order to gain a market advantage. As the United States became more urban during this century and the methods of preserving fresh fruits by refrigeration were improved, only the best grades merited the expensive handling charges of shipping to distant cities, of cold storage, and the special packaging which makes the modern fruit department of retail stores so attractive to the customer. The fruits, nuts, and grapes on today's market are the product of one of the most exacting and highly refined agricultural operations.

We have noted in an earlier chapter that California leads the nation in the value of its agricultural production not because the area of its cropland is larger but because expensive specialty items are

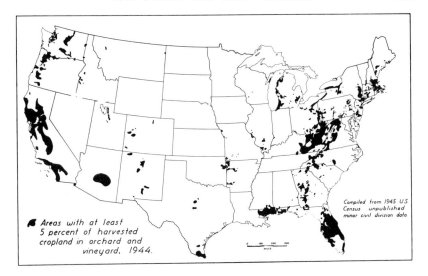

Areas with at least
5 percent of harvested
cropland in orchard and
vineyard, 1944.

Compiled from 1945 U.S.
Census unpublished
minor civil division data.

Figure 27:6. Orchard and vineyard in relation to cropland harvested. (Source: Reference 4; p. 192.)

the sole interest of so many farmers.   Fruits and nuts are prominent among these specialties.   Figure 27:6 is a generalized map of the nation's fruit production which was prepared by Professor Clarence Olmstead of the University of Wisconsin.   The prominence   of California and Florida is not surprising.   Concentrated production along the eastern shore of Lake Michigan and the southern shores of Lakes Erie and Ontario is related in part to the influence of those bodies of water in moderating winter, spring, and summer temperatures.   Some advantageous features of climate, terrain, and soil can be attributed to every area on the map, but the prominence of the Appalachian Plateau of West Virginia and eastern Kentucky is an anomaly.   Apples account for this prominence, yet this horticultural industry is not particularly outstanding except in the northeastern extremity of West Virginia and in adjoining Virginia and Maryland.

For an explanation we may reconsider our previous discussion of West Virginia and eastern Kentucky.   In this broader area the total amount of cropland is very small, and commercial agriculture is overshadowed by residential and part-time farming.   What would be considered a modest acreage of fruit in most other sections of the humid East thus becomes statistically conspicuous here.   The physical conditions of climate, soils, and terrain in the coves and valleys of this section of the

Appalachian Plateau are often good for apple orcharding, and the total acreage devoted to this crop may increase enough to make it an important area of production.

The principal advantages enjoyed by fruit growers of the mountain states and of the Pacific coast are climatic. Warm winters in the Southwest permit citrus culture. It will be noted that all the fruit-growing areas of the Pacific Northwest and mountain states are in valleys where they are protected from the coldest continental winds by high mountain ranges. Also, in most instances, water is available for irrigation, the best possible assurance against low yields and poor quality due to drought.

Mild winters along the Gulf coast of Louisiana, Mississippi, and Alabama permit the growing of tung nuts and the native pecan. The upper coastal plain of Georgia is the outstanding area of pecan production. The Piedmont from Georgia through the Carolinas into Virginia and Maryland is one of the major peach and apple districts of the eastern states. The Piedmont slopes eastward and is protected from the coldest continental winds by the Appalachian Plateau and the Blue Ridge Mountains. Protection from freezing winds is most essential in the early spring when the sap starts to flow and buds begin to develop.

Apples, peaches, pears, plums, cherries, and grapes are prominent on the shores of the southern Great Lakes. There, winter temperatures are several degrees higher than on the shores to the west and north. Also important, spring temperatures remain cold, thus retarding the development of leaf and floral buds until danger of frost is reduced. Well-drained soils derived from lacustrine deposits and glacial till are characteristic of these areas and are highly regarded by horticulturists. Midsummer temperatures are cooler than they are inland, which is an advantage to the grower of the best grades of deciduous fruits, and large urban markets are within short shipping distances of the Great Lakes orchards and vineyards. Advantages similar to these are also enjoyed by the apple growers who dominate the horticultural scene in southeastern New England. There the sea moderates winter temperatures to some extent. The spring season comes late when the danger of frost is reduced, and summers are cool. The hilly terrain assures good air and water drainage.

A CRANBERRY BOG IN MASSACHUSETTS

Although most fruits require well-drained soils at all times, the cranberry is a conspicuous exception. One might call cranberries the rice crop of the fruit industry because of tolerance to flooding. In fact, flooding is a deliberate practice on the part of most producers, just as it is among the best rice growers.   The primary advantages of controlled inundation are protection of the fruit against frost before harvest, protection of the plants against winter-killing, weed suppression, and assurance of an adequate moisture supply.   The cranberry is a ground-hugging perennial which grows in a thick mat when well established. In its wild state it is found on the margins of seasonal swamps which overflow, inundating the cranberries, particularly in the late fall, winter, and early spring.   Because cranberries are raised in low-lying bogs, heavy frosts are experienced earlier in the autumn than on the higher, surrounding land.   The type of location which most fruit growers carefully avoid is deliberately sought by the cranberry producer.

Major cranberry areas are located in southeastern Massachusetts, southern New Jersey, and in west-central Wisconsin.   In each of these areas the countryside is dotted with ponds and marshes which are the consequence of impeded natural drainage.   The preparation of a bog for commercial production is a costly operation.   Ponds existing at a higher elevation than the bog must be dammed and the dam provided with a water-control gate.   Canals are dug from the dam to the bog, and the bog itself must be leveled so that it may be flooded to uniform depth. Open ditches are dug around the fields and lateral ditches are dug across them at frequent intervals.   These ditches serve to bring water in and to drain it away when either operation is desirable.   Of course, the bog itself must be at a level above an outlet channel which will carry away the water quickly when a decision is made to drain.

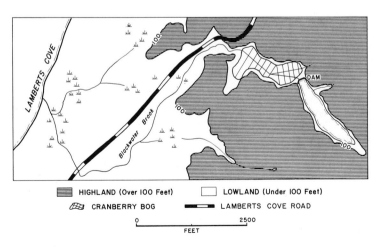

Figure 27:7.   Cranberry bog on Martha's Vineyard.

Figure 27:7 is the plan of a cranberry bog on the island of Martha's Vineyard, Massachusetts. It is to be noted that the bog has a pond from which water may be drawn at will by gravity. Subsequently the water may be drained into a natural watercourse. Before the land was prepared in this fashion the pond, bog, and outlet were parts of a single natural watercourse. The land forms of this area of Martha's Vineyard are chiefly composed of glacial moraine. The time since glacial retreat has been so brief that the natural drainage system in lowland areas is immature and therefore sluggish. This is an advantage in developing a cranberry bog because a pond may be established and controlled by building a low dam. The bog here was originally a marsh with much the same dimensions as the present cultivated land. The outlet is essentially as it was before development. During the winter water is turned in on the bog to the depth of a foot or more. The surface of this water freezes and serves as an insulator to protect the cranberries from more severe cold.

During the summer growing season water is not used unless irrigation is desirable. In the fall the fruit harvest extends over a period of several weeks and there is danger that frost will destroy some of the crop before it is picked. On still, cold nights when a hard frost is possible the grower must patrol the area with a thermometer and be ready to open flood gates in case the temperature drops to a critical point. By covering the plants with water the fruit is saved, but several days may pass after the flood is drained away before the ground becomes dry and firm so that harvesters may work again.

REFERENCES

1. Dalton, Joseph D., Glenn C. Russell, and Dale H. Sieling, Effect of Organic Matter on Phosphate Availability, *Soil Science*, March 1952.
2. Gage, Charles E., *American Tobacco Types, Uses, and Markets*, U.S. Department of Agriculture, Government Printing Office, Washington, D.C., 1942.
3. Hainesworth, Reginald G., *Seedtime and Harvest Today*, U.S. Department of Agriculture, Government Printing Office, Washington, D.C.
4. Olmstead, Clarence W., American Orchard and Vineyard Regions, *Economic Geography*, July 1956.
5. Sieling, Dale H., Organic Matter—The Key to Phosphate Availability, *What's New In Crops & Soils*, Madison, Wisconsin, October 1953.

appendix

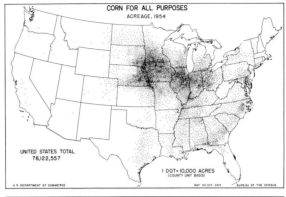

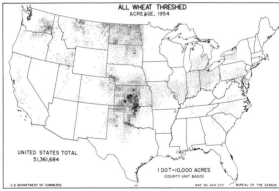

Figure A–1.   Corn for all purposes.
Figure A–2.   All wheat threshed.
Figure A–3.   Oats threshed.

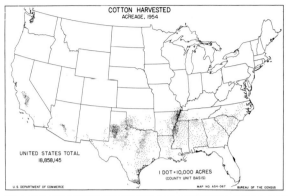

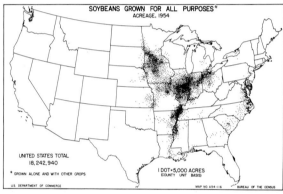

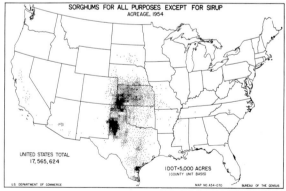

Figure A–4.   Cotton harvested.
Figure A–5.   Soybeans grown for all purposes.
Figure A–6.   Sorghums for all purposes except sirup.

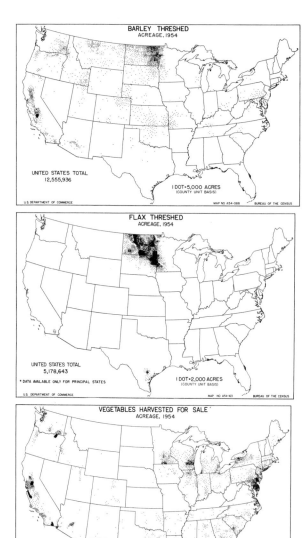

Figure A–7.   Barley threshed.
Figure A–8.   Flax threshed.
Figure A–9.   Vegetables harvested for sale.

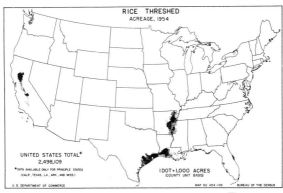

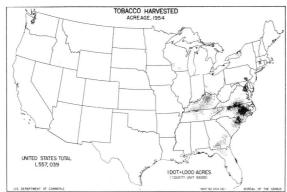

Figure A–10.   Rice threshed.
Figure A–11.   Peanuts grown for all purposes.
Figure A–12.   Tobacco harvested.

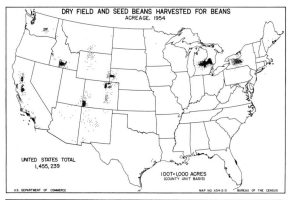

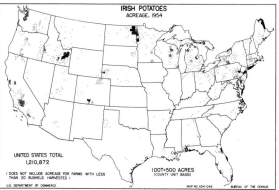

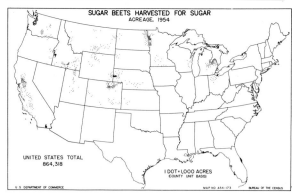

Figure A–13. Dry-field and seed beans harvested for beans.
Figure A–14. Irish potatoes.
Figure A–15. Sugar beets harvested for sugar.

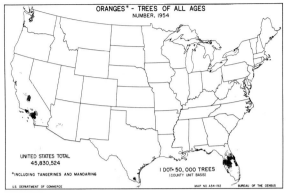

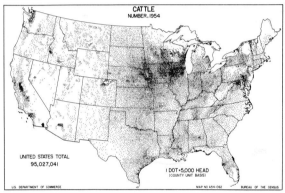

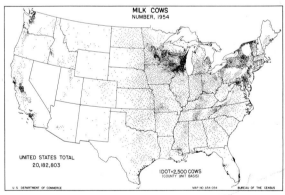

Figure A–16.   Oranges—trees of all ages.
Figure A–17.   Cattle.
Figure A–18.   Milk cows.

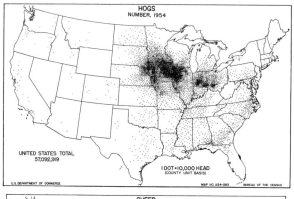

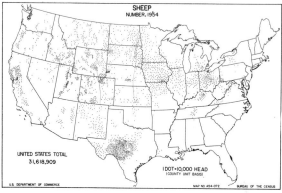

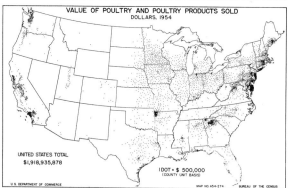

Figure A–19.   Hogs.
Figure A–20.   Sheep.
Figure A–21.   Value of poultry and poultry products sold.

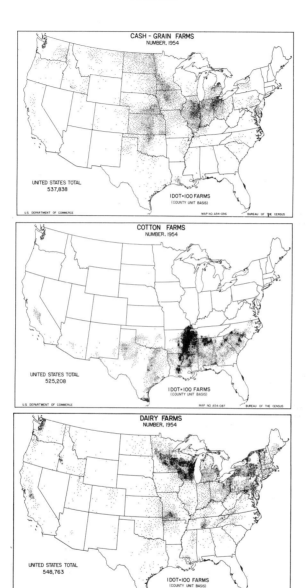

Figure A–22.   Cash-grain farms.
Figure A–23.   Cotton farms.
Figure A–24.   Dairy farms.

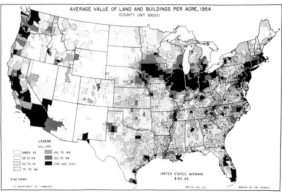

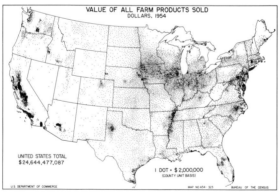

Figure A–25.   Poultry farms.
Figure A–26.   Average value of land and buildings per acre.
Figure A–27.   Value of all farm products sold.

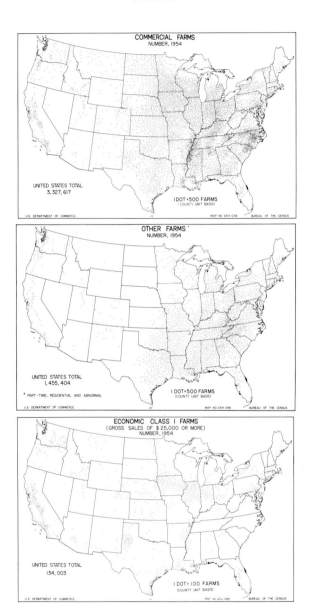

Figure A–28.   Commercial farms.
Figure A–29.   Other farms.
Figure A–30.   Economic Class I farms.

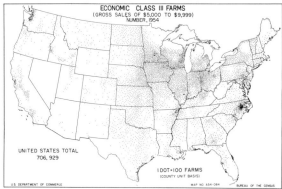

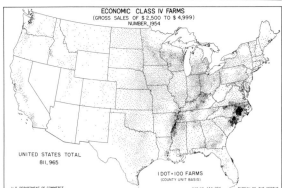

Figure A–31.   Economic Class II farms.
Figure A–32.   Economic Class III farms.
Figure A–33.   Economic Class IV farms.

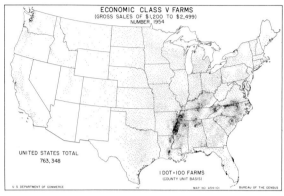

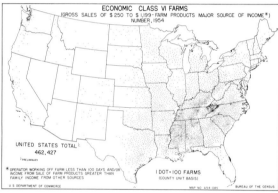

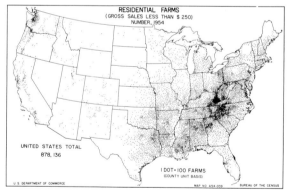

Figure A–34.   Economic Class V farms.
Figure A–35.   Economic Class VI farms.
Figure A–36.   Residential farms.

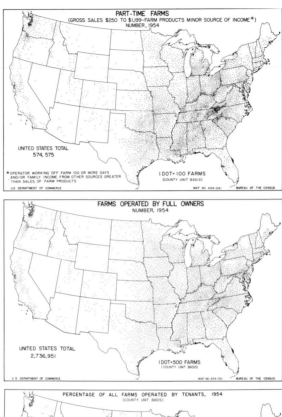

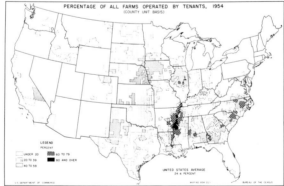

Figure A–37.   Part-time farms.
Figure A–38.   Farms operated by full owners.
Figure A–39.   Percentage of all farms operated by tenants.

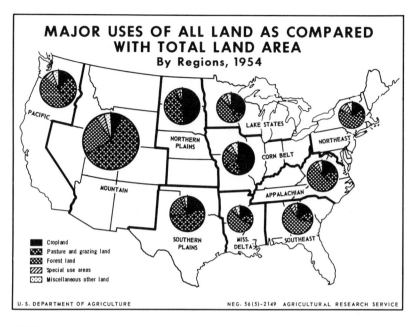

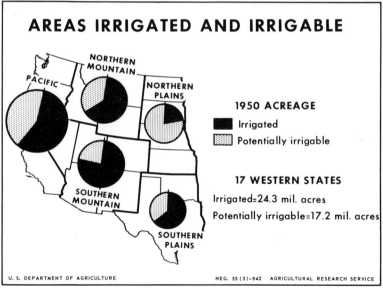

Figure A–40.   Major uses of all land as compared with total land area.
Figure A–41.   Areas irrigated and irrigable.

index